Wallis, Robert

Time, fourth di-
mension of the
mind

DATE DUE

TIME: Fourth Dimension of the Mind

Also by Robert Wallis

Recherches sur les albumines du serum sanguin
au cours des cirrhoses du foie

Passions et maladies

TIME:
Fourth Dimension
of the Mind

Robert Wallis

Translated by Betty B. and Denis B. Montgomery

Preface by Marshall McLuhan
Epilogue by Olivier Costa de Beauregard

Harcourt, Brace and World, Inc.   New York

First edition

Library of Congress Catalog Card Number: 68-12603

Printed in the United States of America

Originally published in France under the title
Le Temps, Quatrième Dimension de l'Esprit

This Book Is Dedicated to the Men of All Times

To those who have preceded us: in gratitude for the knowledge they have brought us.

To those who accompany us: for the assurance of their criticism.

To those who shall follow us: in the hope of helping them a little, by projecting a greater light from the mind onto the world of facts.

Preface

This is probably not a book for the electrical engineer. It is very much a bridge between *The Two Cultures* deplored by C. P. Snow. Dr. Wallis takes us on a journey through the modern looking glass. Lewis Carroll took Alice on her trip a century ago, recognizing that we had come to the end of the age of Euclidean space. Our visual sense alone provides experience of a space or time that is continuous and connected. Our other senses tell us nothing of such attributes. Electric phenomena are beyond the level of visualization and are naturally discontinuous and unconnected. The electric environment of global information has afforded us a mosaic of many times and many spaces ever since the telegraph began to shape the pattern of the newspaper. It is worth much meditation that the news stories of the telegraph press are unified by a date line rather than by a story line. The discontinuity among the news items themselves creates a mosaic rather than a pictorial effect. The mosaic brings about deep involvement on the part of the reader who is obliged to create his own connections. The same result occurs in the electronic environment in general. It is a world of intervals rather than of connections, of intervals rather than of lineality. Lineality and visual connections, Euclidean space in a word, had been born centuries before of the interface between the phonetic alphabet and the ancient tribal and auditory culture. The visual values resulting from this interface have been designated as "civilization" for more than 2,000 years. Yet today the electronic mosaic of unvisualizable properties has begun to transform our traditional visual values. We have even begun to have a new conception of Nature altogether.

Dr. Wallis is aware of these things, though he may appear to underestimate the effects of electronic information in transforming our images of ourselves and of our world. When the satellites encircled the earth, the old world of Nature went inside a man-made environment and began to be transformed into a work of art that was capable of being programmed in new ways.

Many reversals have occurred as a result of the new information environment. Culture has become our business. The knowledge industries have become by far the largest. On perhaps an even greater scale has been our effort to westernize the Orient by exposing it to our old technologies. Meantime we appear to be orientalizing ourselves by our new electronic forms. The "inner trip" by LSD is as nothing compared to the inner trip and the psychedelic effects introduced by the omnipresence of electronic circuitry. The child seated in front of TV is undergoing a perpetual X-ray which leads him to expect depth and involvement in every situation. He is naturally disappointed to encounter a visually organized schoolroom and curriculum where the instruction follows a pattern of classified data which demands detachment rather than involvement.

There has been a good deal of observation concerning these matters but it has been confined mostly to the artist of the age. So-called "abstract" art simply consists in pulling out the visual connections between surfaces and planes. The same procedure is followed in the music of Schoenberg, in the poetry of Rimbaud, as well as in *The Waste Land* and in *Finnegans Wake*. Even the movie as produced by Fellini and Bergman now dispenses with the story line. Perhaps more significant, however, was the discovery by Edgar Allan Poe in his detective stories that, in order to involve the reader as co-author and participant, it was necessary to break up the story line. Since Oswald Spengler there has been the work of Wyndham Lewis, which has considered the re-emergence of the primitive and tribal consciousness in the Western world. The work of Edward Hall (*The Silent Language* and *The Hidden Dimension*) has drawn attention to the feature of imperceptibility that attaches to the new environments created by new technologies. The new environments seem to act as rear-view mirrors in which we perceive the old environments. (Robert Ardrey's *Territorial Imperative*, like Dr. Wallis' book, points out how events shape their own times and spaces.) This has long been an awareness of the Oriental world, especially in the Vedantic philosophy. Heidegger and Sartre have tried to assimilate this philosophy to our Western thought without understanding the technological pressures that are "turning us on" Orientally.

A recent issue of *Esquire* featured "The New American Woman, Finished at 21." One could add, "Grown up at 10—Finished at 21." That is the world of speed-up, of instant coffee and instant culture. Time becomes the most real of all dimensions now. The *now* includes all other times and cultures. History ends in an eternal present. Speed reading, for example, is only one indicator of the new recognition that we live in a world of speed writing and information. Speed reading does not try to keep the data moving on a single plane or in one direction. It simply reveals the thought form as an abstract icon. In any kind of work whatever, the thought form recurs and repeats. That is why, paradoxically, speed reading is deeper than ordinary reading. It is like a direct interface or dialogue. It is thus easier to retain as well. The question of values in such matters is irrelevant. The experiences are new and unique and not to be compared or contrasted with the older experiences. It would, of course, be absurd to allow the new experiences to abolish the possibility of the older ones. Liberal, literate Western man, not understanding those processes, has tended to allow each new environment of technology to wipe out the earlier ones. It is not necessary to act in this way.

In his recent book, *The Effective Executive*, Peter F. Drucker stresses the time dimension as a hidden environment affecting all the new knowledge industries. This work makes an ideal introduction and complement to this book by Dr. Wallis.

Marshall McLuhan

August 29, 1967

Introduction

Time is perhaps the thing in all the world of which the most use is made and of which the least is known. This is due, no doubt, to the fact that it can be experienced without apparent discontinuity, hence without being noticed. How does one recognize subjectively an element which is apparently fixed, in spite of motion or novelty? How does one recognize the changing of something continually renewed, especially if the vital movement of becoming accompanies this changing? How, in a word, does one disengage psychological time if the self is engaged in the duration? Saint Augustine put it very well in his *Confessions:* "What is time? If no one asks me the question, I know; if I must explain to someone who asks me, I do not know." (*Quid est tempus? Si nemo a me quaerat, scio, si quaerenti explicare velim, nescio.*)

What Saint Augustine felt intuitively, that is implicitly and *internally,* he could not explain or *externalize* through language. At the start of this account we shall share this ignorance, and not until the end of the book will we attempt to find an answer.

Along the way, we must seek, without mysticism or prejudice, to discover analytically what is contained in the word "time." But, without playing on words, we can say that the term has become so "comprehensive," and includes so many diverse things that it has become "incomprehensible." An added difficulty: the terms which seek to grasp time, to define it, are expressed in the language of space.

This confusion of language is very often justified: thus the child acquires the notion of time by means of that of space and along with the notion of space; inversely, in the course of old age or of certain psychoses, the alterations in the memory can undo the notions of time and space together. In short, from the psychological point of view, in general, the notions of time and space are formed and undone together. Not always, however, and the particular cases furnished by the dissociation of mental illness will retain our attention in temporal alienations.

Likewise, this confusion of language may seem justified, even prophetic, for the physicists interested in macrophysics, since it already contains the "impression," if not the expression, of the special relativity of "space-time" revealed by Minkowski-Einstein. Time—fourth dimension of space.[1]

Nevertheless, without entering into the details of the discussions which will be recalled in the course of this book, this identity of language no longer seems justified when, with Planck, Bohr, Schrödinger, one approaches the study of microscopic times, on the subatomic scale, with their quantum discontinuity. Heisenberg, one of the first to remark on this, described a certain indeterminacy in the possible measure of individual times, which, following the electron mechanism, should have been replaced with statistical and probable times. Louis de Broglie did not fail to notice this difficulty, which tended to impress physics with a fixed point of view "from which becoming," that is time, "had been excluded." Nor was it too much for his genius to reconcile the phenomena of classical wave mechanics with particle physics, relativity, and quantum physics.

What of the physiologists and physicians? Most of them, with a few rare exceptions, were not preoccupied, or even occupied, with these questions. And yet the philosophers, above all Bergson, had sounded the alarm signal insistently, and repeatedly. (Cf. *Essai sur les données immédiates de la conscience, Matière et Memoire, L'evolution créatrice, La pensée et le mouvant.*) Among the physicians,

---

[1] Let us note that the term dimension, a spatial term, can lead to confusion, and often does. In the inspired mind of Einstein, time constituted no more from the physical point of view, as from the mathematical, than a fourth function of space.

Jean Delay is one of those who responded to the alarm signal; his broad literary and philosophical background, allied with his great clinical insight as a psychiatrist, enabled him to grasp the crucial importance of the notion of time, as his works attest: *Les dissolutions de la mémoire, Les dérèglements de l'humeur, Les maladies de la mémoire.*

More recently, it is the distinction of a great French physicist, O. Costa de Beauregard, to have made in two fundamental books— *La notion de temps, équivalence avec l'espace, Le second principe de la science du temps*—the synthesis between Bergsonian philosophy and the physics of Einstein, Louis de Broglie, and Brillouin. His creative work has been to show where, from the point of view of temporal physics, the junction should be made between objective and subjective phenomena, thanks to an extremely precise study of the intimate mechanism of exchange between information $\rightleftarrows$ negentropy. It is from this physical study that he differentiates between matter and mind and treats the problem of determinism.[2]

Between the cerebral material time and the mental psychological time which springs from it, a greater distinction should be established. The electrical, or electrochemical, mechanism of the central nervous system in general, of the brain in particular, need no longer be demonstrated. The recent works of T. H. Bullock, E. Z. Furshpan, D. D. Potter, and above all John Carew Eccles' fine book on the physiology of the synapses (1964) contribute to clearing up the problem. This electrical mechanism common to the brain and to electronic computers also justifies the study of the cybernetic comparison of their functions in general, and of the performance of the temporal function in particular.

True, from the epistemological standpoint, *comparaison n'est pas raison,* but here it will be much more a matter of a comparison between an initial problem and a final result. The electrical processes of demonstration are comparable. Between perception by the sense organs, information, symbolic coding of the image (internal language, idea), memory, association of ideas, will, initiative to action,

---

[2] I had almost finished the research involved in the present work—it was three-fourths written—when I became acquainted with the recent work of this physicist. May he find here the expression of my gratitude for the light that he brought me, and which has allowed me to make one more step in physiopathological research and in the interpretation of the temporal function in man.

xiii

and action on the one hand, and on the other, instruction, programming, coding, registering, association of circuits, communication of the order, and execution of the action, there are more than similarities of language; there are similarities, even identities of process, if not of action.

Should we be astounded? No, not insofar as electronic computers (digital or analog) have been built by man and programmed by him. Yes, insofar as man has finally built, for the first time in his history, an instrument which is capable of simulating most of his functional behavior once the problem is correctly posed. Thus for the first time, the possibility is glimpsed of studying together complex functions performed simultaneously without ruining the observation at the start by a dissociation and division which suppress the phenomenon studied. For the first time, the extraordinary complex which constitutes the biological cerebral "computer" (W. Ross Ashby) has created a complicated instrument, less perfect than itself but on its own level, which permits it *to be the observer when it itself is under observation.*

From similarity, one may never conclude identity, and one must guard against this. It is a false question to wonder whether machines are intelligent or capable of learning from experience in view of a determined goal. They are certainly intelligent, capable of learning from experience and of attaining a preplanned goal if they have been exactly conditioned to this end. That the pupil (machine) can surpass the teacher (man) in the rapidity of action proves nothing if not that we shall at last be able to study authentically the temporal function *as* the independent variable in the operation of behavior.

Cybernetic evaluation has its limits, curiously dependent on its greatest advantage. This probably consists in the fact that the function can be studied apart from the structure, once the effects to be produced or reproduced become possible. To cite only one example (to which we shall return in Chapter 15), it matters little if, in the study of the mechanism of the "memory," the information already "received" is marked by an electromagnetic hysteresis in a core of ferrite, or if the information is already "perceived" by a "trace" which modifies the electrochemical permeability of a living synaptic membrane; what counts is that these differences of substance (anatomic) apart, the electrical function can operate and end in analogous results, in spite of disparate mechanisms. But this is to say that one must never conclude an identity of substance from a functional similitude.

This is also to say that in the study of functional behavior, when the cybernetic result is negative, one must sometimes accord it greater value than if it were positive, and often accept the fact that the functional mechanism investigated was not possible, before hastening to say that the problem was badly posed.

And this leads us to conclude this introduction with the greatest benefit which electronic computers have had for the mental development of man. They have forced him to develop his thought and his language: his thought in forcing him in his intellectual "computation" to differentiate between false problems and real ones, without seeking to solve them, and on the contrary, to arrange the terms of the real ones in a hierarchy in time, for it is on that condition only that the sequence of the terms implies the fact that to pose a problem correctly is often to solve it; his language, because, from the cybernetic standpoint, it appears that *words are essentially nothing but a temporal integration of past experiences,* and hence language constitutes the *code of the ideas* capable of being exteriorized in a new heuristic action, whether they serve or not to program an electronic computer to increase knowledge. In every way man, to remain and become still more the *deus ex machina,* will have to affirm himself in his active quality as a thinking man.

R. W.

New York. September, 1967

Contents

Tables

The Tables will also be found following page 247.

TIME: Fourth Dimension of the Mind

Chapter 1

The Method of Research in the Investigation and the Exposition of the Problem of Time

One of the first difficulties comes from the fact that most men do not consider time as a problem. They act as if it had been given to them, as if it were completely acquired and always expendable. In other words, a precise formula sums up the two terms of the above sentence: Men take time for granted.

No doubt they notice its limitation when they experience a lack of it. They forget to think about time, in the same way they forget to think about the air they breathe. As soon as air begins to run short, their need for it makes them immediately conscious of the lack. But in both cases—lack of air or lack of time—this will be a superficial and false way to become aware of the cause. Thus, paradoxically, it will be a quantitative point of view, a measure of air or a measure of time which will bring about the real or qualitative problem dealing with the nature of air or with the nature of time.

Right at the start, we can press this comparison a bit further. The composition of air on the outside of a man (a mixture of oxygen and nitrogen) does not explain his respiration, a complex, inside phenomenon which he cannot be aware of under normal circumstances. At most, he will have an idea of it if he has studied the complex physical, chemical and physiological mechanisms. This is not the place to enter into the details of the respiratory cycle, other than to say that oxygen is absorbed by the pulmonary capillaries,

3

becomes attached to the hemoglobin of the red cells, is transferred for the oxidation of tissues, and eliminated in the form of carbonic anhydride. Thus, the hemoglobin is restored and the respiratory cycle starts again, its equilibrium controlled by complicated circulatory and nervous factors. This describes the respiratory phenomenon in a very simplistic fashion; we could explain the role of the arterial gaseous tensions, the reasons for the phenomenon of reversibility, the enzymatic phenomena, the physical-chemical phenomena of permeability of membranes and their electronic equilibrating mechanisms. Nevertheless, beyond all these extraordinary mechanisms, the man who is breathing has no awareness of their complexities. He ignores them even if he knows about them, or thinks he knows!

In the same way, as regards time, man is aware of a certain exterior duration to which he adjusts in his daily life, but he has no original consciousness of his interior time, his psychological time, and does not think very much about it.

The second difficulty: While most men confess their ignorance about a mathematics, physics, or chemistry problem when they are not mathematicians, physicists, or chemists, they appoint themselves experts as soon as a problem is brought up touching on either nature or medicine.

Third difficulty: The human mind functions in such a way that it tends to consider only immobility: the sense organs only accept movement in space as part of the information process, and, indeed, in order to accept it the natural tendency of the brain is to join successive immobilities which can only strain the interpretation of nature of an eventual duration theoretically superimposed upon this spatial mobility as habitual description imagines it.

As we proceed we shall meet with many other difficulties. Those just enumerated show that it is difficult for a man to be an impartial observer of time when he himself is involved in a direct or indirect way, whether he recognizes it or not. But to recognize this is already an important step. To know that he is a partial observer, because he is at the same time judge and jury, is better than to believe that he is an impartial experimenter in an instigated observation, where man is involved. This being so, it is better to admit at the beginning of this account that man will always have, whether by education or by intuition, a certain preconceived idea,

4

which I do not pretend to avoid when approaching the solution of such problems.

But as a great experimenter, Claude Bernard,[1] remarked, this does not constitute an insurmountable obstacle and can even represent a favorable element, if this preconceived idea remains "always interrogative"—that is, relatively objective—and refuses to turn into a fixed subjective idea. For observation as for experimentation, he says, "Preconceived ideas are necessary, indispensable: one builds no foundation without them; it is only necessary to know how to abandon them when they no longer make sense. At that point, if one retained them, they would cease being preconceived ideas and become fixed ideas, and would constitute a veritable infirmity of the mind." And he concludes scathingly, "Men with inflexible ideas only inquire for form's sake, they have asked and answered their question in advance."

Let me reassure the reader that this is what I have refused to do from one end of this work to the other. I have, on the contrary, attempted to maintain an objective, questioning attitude. And having nothing to prove and everything to seek, I have gradually reached results so unexpected that they finally destroyed the preconceived ideas which had served me as a point of departure, or a point of inquiry.

No doubt it would have been easy for me, in writing this book, to abandon retrospectively the preconceived ideas which were afterwards revealed to be false. But in the search for truth one must discard his pride and have the courage to make mistakes as well as to question himself: the mechanism of thought which is exercised in research has as much value, if not more, as the final result. When man is at one and the same time (whether he wishes it or not) *the observer* and *the observed,* these goings and comings from one object to another constitute an integral part of the experimental process, verifiable by others.

Studying the temporal function in man, I have had not only to compare it with and to oppose it to the temporal notion of the classical or relativity physicists but to confront it with the sort of time encountered in subatomic quantum physics. Since the brain is

---

[1] Claude Bernard, *Leçons sur la physiologie et la pathologie du système nerveux* (Paris, Baillières, 1868).

made of matter, I have had to study its behavior with regard to the information and communication which it received from the outside world before being able to perceive the active manner in which this very functioning, by its very "length," conditioned what happened inside, its interior time, now detached from any exterior context, even if the latter had been what provoked it initially and originated the process.

This is to say that the reader who is expecting a deductive exposition with logical axioms would do better to stop here. For complex mechanisms, often disparate in spite of certain appearances in common, such an exposition would be wrong and, in fact, a work of the imagination. I have preferred simply to pass from one subject to another, without reference to any anticipation of a basic common denominator which I could not yet perceive in the development. So I have often had to put the cart before the horse to show a comparison, test a fact of experience or of observation by a sort of counterproof, always avoiding generalization, which is as dangerous from the experimental viewpoint as it is seductive from the philosophic.

In particular, on several occasions I have had recourse, perhaps in a premature way, to a "cybernetic reasoning" before explaining it in detail and in its entirety. If I have taken this liberty, it is because I have acquired the conviction, not destroyed this time by the observation of the facts, that to study every complex function, man has found in the general electronic computer an instrument sufficiently faithful, in spite of its complexity, that responds in a pertinent manner to the parallel complexity of the human brain. Conceived, constructed, interrogated by man, the general (both digital and analog) electronic computer is, in effect, and for the first time, capable of answering man "no" as well as "yes," and with relevance.

Now, let us anticipate another point to the degree that it touches on the very method of research. Programming a computer has taught us that, even outside mathematics, to state a problem well is often to solve it; in any case, it is to see whether the approach to the question is possible or not, in view of a solution. For electronic computers have taught us that in the study of a complex function, it is often the *action of a mechanism* through which we continue to gain new knowledge about the *mechanism of an action*.

For the first time in the history of mankind, we possess an in-

6

strument of such plasticity that we will be able to study *outside the human brain* a phenomenal complex in its *simultaneous functional entirety*, without destroying it at the outset by a dissociation which immediately alters its eventual behavior. In the study of the functions of living systems, and even of functions as complex as that of the brain itself, the electronic computer will therefore be able to serve as a dual control between the observer and the observed man himself in his vital dynamic functions, which, without any alteration in health or jeopardy to its functional equilibrium, this computer will be able to simulate—in short, to study a living system in its internal variations, but from the outside. If up to now the psychologist has been concerned with behavior and only indirectly with the structures capable of producing it, if the anatomist and the physiologist have been concerned with the structures and have wondered what functions they were supposed to serve, it may well be that now it is the engineer who may be able to construct the difficult bridge connecting structure with function in biological systems.

If from the beginning of this study, it is allowable to view this extraordinary result with humility, it is because it is a question of much more than a comparison between these electronic models and the human brain. The latter, in its general function as well as with regard to the mechanism of its internal time function, behaves in fact like a living electronic or electrochemical computer, all the more remarkable by its concentration, its effectiveness, its perfection.

Chapter 2

Initial Confusion of the Limits of the Problem by Reason of the "Multiplicity of Times"

It is regrettable that I am forced to write this chapter. In spite of the highlights that quotations from Bergson, Einstein, and Piaget will cast upon it, it will give the appearance of a confusion which is repugnant to me, but which, however, has to be described if one wishes to take into account the ignorance that rules the mind when it comes to time! There are two essential reasons for this: temporal descriptions are made in terms of space; the exterior times of the physicists are not systematically dissociated from the interior cerebral times. Double misunderstanding and double confusion of language: the result is that some very good minds are led to "reason" exactly on the basis of false postulates. There is a constant tendency to confuse in the same sentence or the same study, the subjective temporal sensation and the objective evaluation of exterior duration. Under the pretext of a common measure, many have attempted to identify phenomena of a different nature.

People have a tendency to confuse a distance traversed, a geographical interval, with a flow of duration which is not inherent to it—which cannot be cut or interrupted without ceasing to exist by very definition. As an example, an artificial barrier can turn the course, but not the flow of a river; if it ceased to flow, it would no longer be a river, but a lake, a reservoir. So it is with time,

8

which nothing stops; if it ceased to flow, it would no longer be time, but a dream . . . or a nightmare.

This difficulty was apparent to Henri Bergson. Studying the structure of human understanding, "it appeared to us," he writes in *Matière et Mémoire*,[1] "that one of its functions was to *mask duration,* whether in movement or in change." A little further on he says, "Our action is conveniently practiced only on fixed points, it is therefore fixity which an intelligence seeks; it wonders where the body in motion is, where the body in motion will be, where the body in motion goes." So that, "Our intelligence supposes after the event that the movement was applied to itself in space (as if the movement could coincide with immobility!). . . . But the instants of time and the positions of the body in motion are only instantaneous positions taken by our understanding about the continuity of movement and of duration!"

The habitual confusion between space and time, their automatic association, could not be better described. Acceptable in language as in practical life, as well as in our measures in macroscopic physics, this confusion must be denied and dissociated if the essence of psychological time and the consequences that derive from it are being scientifically considered.

Everyone thinks he knows what time is: it is "taken up," it is "found," it is "wasted," it is "passed," or it "passes." And one doesn't know what it is, even whether it exists, as soon as one tries to define it.

To define time in terms of a duration accomplished constitutes a vicious circle; that is, to explain it by time which has flowed, amounts to saying that it is a flow. But is this not very incomplete and little more than a hypothetical characteristic?

More often, one seeks to define it in terms of speed, that is in limiting time to space traversed; but there too the problem is put off without being solved, for to imply a time in an interval of space is only to apply a certain characteristic to a moving body and to confuse this time with space traversed. This is a mistake of confusing a measure with an essence.

Nevertheless, since antiquity there has been a tendency to regulate the time of men approximately by the courses of the stars:

---

[1] Paris, Félix Alcan, 1896; *Matter and Memory* (New York, Humanities Press, 1962).

9

one year is the revolution of the earth about the sun (in fact: 365 days, 5 hours, 48 minutes, 45.51 seconds); one day is 24 hours, the time of the rotation of the earth on its axis to the point where the sun passes the same meridian again (in fact, the sidereal day is 23 hours, 56 minutes). As everyone knows, the hour is divided arbitrarily into 60 minutes, the minute into 60 seconds. Very artificial divisions obviously, and the most precise measurements established by our chronometers will do nothing (we shall see this in detail in Chapter 17) except put the problem off without really solving it.

Newton's great merit was that he recognized this artifice and this ignorance and denounced them officially. To avoid confusion, he wisely decided to set up this ignorance as a postulate before making a working hypothesis, *limiting* time and space for the purposes of his research and declaring them *absolute:* "Absolute time, true and mathematical, of itself and by its own nature, flows evenly, independently of anything whatsoever outside, and is now called duration." The definition of these terms resembles his definition of absolute space as always similar to itself and immutable. We shall see later on to what point this limitation and this imposed precision were fruitful, but we shall see that Newton had to invent differential and integral calculus to capitalize on the variations of the temporal function.

The philosophers have sought to define time as a physical quantity and a basic concept, without believing in the reality of its existence. A mental, subjective concept which can be defined, they say, by the fact that an event is distinguished from before and after its occurrence. . . . This is that which measures or situates at least an aspect of duration: that "something" during which the change takes place. Hence, we can foresee, by looking at the world of facts with the aid of our simple senses or with the instruments that extend and perfect them, that a multiplicity of times must exist. To cite but a few of these: the time of the stars; the time of men—(a) exterior (as we have seen it regulated traditionally according to the stars), and (b) interior, psychological—the time of the animals; the time of the plants; the time of minerals; the time of chemical reactions; the time of wave propagation; the time of atoms; the time of electrons, of neutrons, of positrons, etc.

One could multiply these examples. But what is their common denominator? What is the essence of the word "time" in all these denominations sanctioned by usage?

It is always a concept that tends to evaluate change, if not to measure the accomplishment of an energetic reaction, in connecting it with a material object which is situated and moves in space and is compared to a displacement in space. Whatever the camouflage, it is under this cloak of space that our notions of time are disguised, and the physical and mathematical disguises are neither the least convincing nor the least specious.

To say, for example, that an electric charge $q = it$ (that is, the factor of an intensity i times the symbol "time" t) permits us to reduce, to measure and define this time as $t = i/q$. But this is still a space traversed; for example, that of the revolution of the dynamo when we are dealing with an electric motor. It is still a matter, therefore, of reification: having created the name or the symbol, we believe we have discovered the thing.

But in mathematics, at least, one does not prejudge, and whatever the "temporary" symbolism lent to time, it is treated sometimes as a variable, sometimes as a constant. So the hypocrisy of "taking it for granted" is suppressed, its original dynamic individuality is restored. If it is associated with space (as Minkowski and Einstein did in the concept of "space-time"), this is done openly and is not surreptitious. If it is dissociated somewhat from matter, it is taken as wave frequencies but it is never lost sight of. Whatever the system of reference, light or wave, the phantom becomes or remains a dynamic reality. Time is integrated in all the equations of conservation or transformation of matter or of energy, a quantity as inherent in the evolution of matter as in the conservation of this energy—a quantity so constant that it is elevated in modern physics to the height of an essential quality. The time that we "lost" in space is "recovered" in the atom and the electron.

Einstein's photon—whether or not it is propagated on de Broglie's wave or whether it jumps invisibly from orbit to orbit about the radius of Bohr's atom, with the uncertainty and discontinuity according to the statistics of Heisenberg—has nothing to do with the time pertaining to matter. At this level more than at any other, matter and energy, particles and waves, are confused; spaces of innumerable dimensions (surpassing our imagination as well as our understanding). These times are no more than electromagnetic; consuming energy or consummating time, at that level it is all the same. Would this be, in a multiple and yet infinitely small space, the general justification outside the atom for the assimilation of time and space? Bohr and Heisenberg, to whom we shall return, *have insisted on the fact that these extrapolations were not permitted.*

This is merely for the simple reason that the natural sciences in general and physics in particular *do not describe nature in itself, but the relations between man and nature.* The world of the atoms has its own laws, different from ours, even if we are composed of atoms. The time of the atoms, the time of the electrons, of men and of the stars are *different.* There does not exist, in spite of Newton, an absolute time, but only relative times: probable times, possible times, times variable according to the systems of reference. With the latter fixed, it becomes possible to conceive of times comparable to an energetic flow relatively fixed and continuous—something which is fundamental for research. Among these, one of the most constant in the invariance of its rhythm is that of the disintegration of radioactive substances. The measure of the residual radioactivity permits us, therefore, to appraise in a fashion more precise than any other, the age of the radioactive substance, from its origin up to the time of the evaluation, and to predict with accuracy the length of the later life of the specimen. Without discontinuity and without stopping the process, we can fix the past, present, and future of the radioactive specimen and envisage its duration, which nothing stops and which is determined by nuclear disintegration, as we shall see, in an exponential manner.

But if the life span and the age of a radioactive substance can be accurately appraised by an intrinsic, nuclear system of reference to a fixed evolution, it is difficult, on the other hand, to find for living beings a system of reference that would be intrinsic to them. The biological age of a plant, of an animal, or of a man has nothing to do with the number of times that the earth has turned about the sun. This is an exterior simplistic system of reference which is continued more by the survival of astrology than by astronomy! It would be worth more in evaluating the biological age of a man, to count the number of heartbeats: on the order of 100,000 per 24 hours (the usual measure for the length of a day), that is on the order of 2,555,000,000 for a statistically average life of seventy years. Or it might be measured, as Lecomte du Nouy [1] desired, by the speed of cicatrization of a wound, which varies in inverse proportion to the square root of age.

---

[1] Lecomte du Nouy, *Le temps et la vie* (Paris, Gallimard, 1936).

It will be more interesting to consider, as we shall do in a later chapter, on the one hand the relations between the times of the cellular exchanges and the propagation of nervous excitation which depend upon them, and on the other the electromagnetic times, to the extent that life itself is really an electromagnetic phenomenon. But henceforth we may wonder whether the nerve cells of our brain invented time after perceiving space and motion through our sense organs, or, on the contrary, whether the brain itself and its behavior might not be a creation of space and time, received from the outside and then secondarily internalized in the same way one can put information into the larger memory "storage" of an electronic computer.

This memory would therefore be at the very basis of man's temporal function. For if the succession of events is irreversible, only the memory can give to thought the means of making the round trip, through the image of the goal attained or of the route traversed, towards the point of origin or of departure. Without memory there would be no reversibility, no going and coming in the history of a phenomenon, but only a simple going, and then not real time but only a present, timeless in its artificial immobility and its exclusive isolation.

With Henri Bergson, we can therefore wonder whether it is true that *"Time is creation or it is nothing at all."* For this creation memory is indispensable. To the contrary, when there is a dissolution of the memory, either by intoxication or by disease or by physiological disappearance during sleep, then consciousness, memory, notion of time are destroyed together.

All these phenomena, which I have enumerated in this chapter in order to point out the diversity of times, will be studied separately and in detail later on, to compare them or contrast them with psychological times. But now I must digress and specify how this association of the temporal function with space originates in the depths of childhood. Jean Piaget,[1] following the suggestion of Einstein himself, has studied the development of the notion of time in the child and has demonstrated, in a quasi-experimental manner, that during the first five to seven years of life the notion of time is not yet in operation; it is at the *perceptual* stage of temporal or-

---

[1] Jean Piaget, *Le développement de la notion de temps chez l'enfant* (Paris, Presses Universitaires de France, 1946).

13

ganization, sensory and motor, with the impossibility of separating time from spatial structures. This constitutes at the beginning a time without speed, without possible simultaneity except in the rare case of coincidence or overtaking.

In the second stage, the child around eight to ten years old becomes capable of *retrospection:* he has learned to liberate himself from the present, to return to the past, and to reascend or redescend the course of time, beyond the real train of events. Later, as an adolescent, he will become at last capable of introspection and will be able to appreciate, with his "interior time," exterior time thrown back to the past or projected forward into the future; to appreciate as well the inverse relationships of time and of velocity.

Duration becomes then the distance traversed relative to the speed, or the work accomplished relative to the power, to the action, or to the activity. Time has become qualitatively operatory: a relation between velocity and movement, between activity and work. The temporal notion is now established as a function of its content. This is henceforth a construction after experiencing an opposition to the perceptual time of the beginning, which unfortunately relied upon observations often false or falsified.

For the child, an hour of play is shorter than an hour of work, because time passes "faster"; when he begins to grow up, an hour of play is longer than an hour of work, because he does many more things. Finally, when he recalls the events, the memories are not authentically evoked, but it is a genuine account, according to Pierre Janet,[1] which the child invents and invokes, often confusing succession with causality. Alas! this error does not remain the privilege of the child, and a good many adults have the tendency to elevate the sequence of phenomena to the height of consequence, wrongly identifying this sequence as a cause and effect relationship when there is no more than a relationship of precession.

In short, the growing child has in general a *perceptual* notion of time, the adult a *conceptual* notion, since he has been able to accept not only the irreversibility of events but also, thanks to his memory, the reversibility of his thought in the course of time. Is this to say that the adult commits no other errors? The first is in forgetting that the concept of time is a subjective concept, that time,

---

[1] Pierre Janet, *L'évolution de la mémoire et la notion de temps* (Paris, A. Chanine, 1928).

14

as it is ordinarily described, is a human invention. The history of the science abounds in examples which illustrate the annoying consequences of this forgetfulness: the invention of absolute time by the great Newton, the invention of a nonexistent ether to propagate the luminous waves of time through space. . . . In the eighteenth and nineteenth centuries numerous mistakes of this sort were made by the greatest physicists. And this is explained: *one error entails another but two errors never produce the truth.* One had to await the twentieth century and the coming of Einstein to restore to the idea of time its functional truth, that is, its relativity in connection with the system of reference of the observer. What is more, Einstein mathematically includes the time variable in a close connection with the observed phenomenon: time regarded as a quantity becomes through Einstein a specific essence, that is, a quality.

How different then becomes each specific time! The time of men or their appraisal has little to do with the time of the stars, the time of the atoms, the time of the electrons, the time of the speed of the propagation of light. This last appeared to Einstein as constant, whatever its source, and as incapable of being exceeded in the observation of natural phenomena, becoming for this very reason an important basis for comparison and reference. If the speed of the propagation of light really *is* constant—and on the whole this seems to have been affirmed after Einstein—the incomplete experimental verifications of the past (Michelson, Lorentz) like the new facts foreseen by Einstein and verified after him all tend to confirm it. It would then be more efficient for the understanding of the universe as well as for the clarification of the minds of men, no longer to take the time of the revolution of the stars as the unit of time, but the time of the very propagation of light: 186,-000 miles per second.

At this stage, propagation and velocity and the concept of time can at last be legitimately described and unified as defining the unit of transmission of matter or of energy—propagation of matter, consumption of energy, conservation of the one and of the other in a time now *received* by experience and no longer *given* by theory. The fluidity of time can now be legitimately described and *measured,* and no longer suspected, or invented. Eternity at last means something, since it is this conservation of time attached to mass or to energy.

Time would then be part of a momentum. To define it, or to

15

define the force in an extensive fashion by the term "eternity," means nothing, for this is only an attempt to infer that this force has neither beginning nor end, and hence would not be a force; because if this were true, it would not have the specific characteristics of a force and hence would not exist. This would confirm the abovementioned view of Bergson's, "Time is creation or it is nothing at all." To this purely negative definition must be opposed, as was done by the theologians even before the philosophers, the positive "resurrection" of the present, whether it is an electron or a man which serves as a point of application or as a support for this force.

To this at first mystical consideration, the positive reality must be added by analytically considering how the notion of time is born and is created in the child, is developed in the adult, and is finally modified in the old or in the ill. The study has been masterfully made by Jean Piaget,[1] and having verified his results, we can espouse his conclusions. Subjectively, the notion of time is essentially tied to the memory and, to a certain extent, parallel to its acuity. When the conscious memory disappears, the notion of time disappears with it, as in sleep. To the unconscious—which, to be sure, also has a memory—present, past, and future are all one. The infections or intoxications (drunkenness) which attenuate the memory simultaneously alter the sense of time.

This means that the succession of phenomena is *irreversible*. On the other hand, the mechanism of thought is *reversible*, capable of running over the road in both directions, from the present to the past and *vice versa*, often even passing its point of departure and thus projecting itself into a future which it has already created by anticipation.

The result of this is that the notion of time, considered subjectively, is essentially operatory, not intuitive. Experimentally, this operation is necessarily tied to the notion of space, especially to space traversed, now called "duration," this notion being secondarily associated with the idea of speed, whenever intelligence develops with experience. For the child, to grow older is to grow bigger; when he has ceased to grow bigger, the child, now a man, realizes that between exterior time and interior time "felt" and understandable to him in terms of duration, there exists a connection

---

[1] Jean Piaget, *op. cit.*

16

which is not necessarily tied to a space traversed but to a task either accomplished or to be accomplished—in short, to activity.

If duration is considered as work, time would be energy, energy applied to a material object which, if it is living, is only an ephemeral substratum. Then if the liberated energy goes beyond this temporary support in order to continue on more permanent supports, we have put our finger on the spot where the concept of the eternal soul, surviving the body, is born: this would be only another name for the conservation of energy.

But let us return to some considerations which are more subjective, to the "emotional times": it is convenient to state that the quantity of time saved or gone through may be compensated, even overcompensated for by the quality of the time—that is, the particular quality which the activity adds to the action. Thus in love, whatever tends to frustrate the desire of the subject for the beloved object—separation, absence, waiting, silence—tends to make time seem prolonged, which is added agony. The length of the time seems multiplied by what is dividing the lovers. Conversely, the pleasure of company, of contact, of communication, speeds up duration: time flies. At the peak of communion in the fulfillment of the act of love, time loses its own: the instant touches eternity, man feels in heaven or as a god, loses his head and his consciousness—time no longer exists. Appearance to be sure, and yet if the act of creation takes place, a new material support can be given to the energy of time. Thus nature has arranged things well to turn illusion into reality, past man's knowing. When the act of love has been consummated, time again seems significant and takes back its reality; the notion of before and after reappears, the duration of the energetic explosion is erased from the memory; it was only an instant torn from the curve of exterior duration. A subjective instant if it is one; the Countess de Noailles can say that "there always comes a *moment* when one loves and when one suffers according to oneself, and not according to the object which is worthy or unworthy of it." I would gladly complete the thought with a line from one of her own verses, "I am dead already, since I am bound to die." But that would be to give to the subjective notion of time a pessimistic anticipation which the reality of life undertakes to contradict.

If, in fact, it is true that one year for a child of *four* years rep-

17

resents an enormous stretch of time, because it is as long as a quarter of his life, and that one year for a man of seventy passes as rapidly as one-seventieth of his existence, this appearance of the course of time gradually accelerated with the passage of the years is largely counterbalanced by the quality of this time. Whereas in children, just as in young animals, the interests or sensations are limited to the point that they can devote considerable time to sleeping (and one can augment sleep time experimentally by reducing sensations, for example by sealing the ears with paraffin). The contrary is true for the elderly adult, grown old in the course of things, whose interests will have been refined and multiplied: to the exterior life of sensations an interior life of feelings has been added, an interior and engrossing reflection has made room for the preoccupation of pure contemplation. The child tends to receive everything from the outside, including love; the man who is growing old tends to give from inside himself, including love. His notion of time has not necessarily lost by the change. He is no longer the impatient slave of a time which he thinks lost, but the patient master of a time which he knows is precious, because it is limited for him, though still unlimited for the others—the young.

Is youth enviable? Perhaps, since it is envied. But this envy comes only from the fact that older people have a mistaken tendency to neglect their present and to relive with regret their own past: thus, from there, identifying with the youth of the moment and with their privileges is only a short step. In taking that step, alas, they cease to enjoy the privileges conferred on them by age. Their regrets become justified—not, as they claim, because of time past—but because of time present, which they lose by not making use of it.

But these are subjective considerations. Let us return to the time which, artificial or not, apparent or not, has not ceased to flow: like the river which seems sometimes immobile, but does not cease to flow towards the sea where the water will evaporate, become clouds, fall again as rain—and which will nourish the spring, which will become again a river, so that there is a cycle, a perpetual flow in perpetual motion bringing up a perpetual return. But this classical image is *comparison* not *reason;* it is false in this context, or, anyway, sterile. As we shall see, it does not help us to understand duration with regard to time.

Bergson saw correctly that it is not with our intelligence that we

18

shall be able to appreciate the true nature of duration. For our intelligence tends essentially to start with the stationary and to try to construct movement from a number of those stationary movements placed side by side. But even an infinity of these would never correctly constitute movement. It was, however, on this principle that Auguste Lumière invented the motion picture: remembering that the retina of the eye could physiologically perceive light sensations lasting, at most, for one-tenth of a second, he had the brilliant idea of unrolling motionless (still) pictures on film at the speed of one-twentieth of a second, which gave an illusion of movement. But no matter how fast the film, *i.e.*, a series of still pictures, was unrolled, *this succession, however rapid, could never achieve either the real continuity of movement or of duration, but only its fake and imperfect image.* The intelligence proceeds in the same fashion when it "spatializes" time, for the intelligence is in thrall to the outside world, to the imperfection and limits of our senses, which condition the function of this very intelligence in its reflexes, as well as in its reflections. On the other hand, the intuition is free from this thralldom: the intuition is pure spirit, movement of spirit, interior duration, a force inside us always ready to adapt itself, even to identify itself with a force which moves outside, an immediate and continuous consciousness ready to coincide with the movement outside, to dissolve into it, to perceive it as the selfsame reality. Now it is the immobility which turns out to be the possible exception, the paradoxical snapshot torn from nature's essential mobility, appearance abstracted by the inference of the mind in order precisely to establish a phenomenal mobility.

Thus perceived by the intuition, duration would be the strongly felt parallelism between a material change outside and the spiritual movement inside which adapts itself to it, often to the point of expecting that change and even of going further. To await this moment is to live it; to pass it by is to tend to make it eternal, to make it divine, to sublimate it. Why this double tendency? If this is only living, it is necessary to act, to feel that one is alive; to cling to the movement of time is to hope to pass oneself by, to linger beyond the term. Man is curiously unafraid of death, but dreads not being assured of immortality. All religions seek to adapt themselves by their consoling dogmas to this paradoxical double tendency.

To assure life in the hereafter, the Egyptians embalmed their

19

dead, gave them reserves of provisions, money, and clothing, and built them pyramids against oblivion. And yet, symbolically, next to the pyramids they built sphinxes, symbols of the doubt and the mystery of man tortured by the problem of spiritual survival. A salutary doubt: if it does not reassure about death, it makes us value living; and surpassing man's understanding, the idea of doubt integrates precisely into this movement and this change which are the continuity of time, duration itself. This is probably why the Egyptian sages carved hieroglyphs on the pyramids depicting the movement of the stars, which nothing stops, and Osiris, the sun god, and Isis, goddess of the night—as if an unerring succession of day and night could guarantee days continuing for those alive in the world as well as days reserved to the dead, in an "eternity" of continuity. Furthermore, in an attempt to account for such occurrences, modern mathematicians have tried symbolically to express more than the frozen facts of a disconnected present, but also what these facts contain today of momentum and potential future. Thus they are able, since Newton, *to substitute for static mathematics a dynamic mathematics, differential, integral, capable of being inserted in the movement of things and in the evolution of time, capable of embracing the scope* (or curve) no longer from the outside in a numerically fixed result but *from the inside,* following its tendency towards change, representing mobility in all its possible magnitudes, infinitely small, infinitely great, in any case infinite—that is, eternal in the proper sense of the term, on the scale of man.

Whatever the discontinuity of exterior physical phenomena, would human thought propagated beyond the individual then perhaps constitute the only term of continuity in this world? We shall study the objective facts in detail and see that it only appears that way.

Chapter 3

Internal Temporal Function and the Brain Considered as a Natural Electronic Computer

What is existence? The word comes from the Latin, *ex*, out, and *sistere*, to be, to stand out. In other words, to continue to be in space and time. Existence implies reality, which in turn implies the notion of space and of time. We have already seen how these notions take hold successively in the child. This turns out to be a confirmation of the old adage that "nothing exists in the intellect which did not exist in the senses beforehand." (*Nihil est in intellectu nisi prius erat in sensu.*)

If this is true, it is not the mind that originally conceives space and time: *space and time fashion and condition the mind*—through sight, hearing, touch, and muscular movement. Originally, space is merely the distance interposed between a desire revealed by the sense of sight and the muscular movement necessary to attain it; time would be nothing more than the duration of the intensity of a desire before it is satisfied by contact, oral or otherwise, but in general at first oral, at least in the child, which leads to the intrusion of two other senses—taste and smell.

In short, at first time is seen as waiting. Later, the intellect would merely come back to this original conception of space and time. This explains the words of Saint Augustine already cited: *"Quid est tempus? Si nemo a me quaerat, scio, si quaerenti explicare velim, nescio."* This affirmation implies that our notion of time (like our

21

notion of space traversed, always linked to time by childhood experience) is alive and internal, as if "secondarily" instinctive, but that when we are asked to specify it, it is difficult for us to furnish a coherent explanation of this automatic, obvious experience.

There is a clear notion of before and after; more vague is the notion of the apparent continuity which separates or unites them. From the perceptual, one must pass to the conceptual, from the particular sensation to the more general feeling, which is more difficult to define even though perhaps easier to perceive. Even the verb "to be" in the past tense "was," reveals the indispensable presence of the memory to announce time to ourselves as well as to others.

In the same *Confessions*, Saint Augustine, to indicate with as much humility as pride his impotence in explaining what he felt, remarked: "Too lofty, too powerful for ourselves, we go beyond the narrow boundaries of our knowledge, and yet we are not outside ourselves." Is this to say that the temporal might be contained within us, and born of spirituality? But we have seen that spirituality is born on the outside of a person, fashioned by his sense organs. Thus the circle is closed: what was taken or learned from the outside is given back and *this time projected from the inside onto the outside,* in appraising, if not the facts, at least their relation. And this initial notion of observer and observed contains the seed of an appreciation of Einsteinian relativity. It is because we misunderstood it in its absolute simplicity for too long that we had to await the twentieth century to recognize it.

Newton, the great innovator, had simplified the question and, to answer to the needs of the physicist as well as of the astronomer and of the average man, had postulated an absolute time and space, existing independently of any outside influence, sufficient indeed for everyday life and for the practical utilization of the phenomena of time, space, and velocity on a macroscopic scale. But whether time is regarded as relative or absolute, the question remains: is it linked to the existence of man?

Might time be revealed to man—by his consciousness and memory—just as a radio wave is revealed only through the presence of a detector circuit, or a color revealed by the interpretation of the retina? Without these revealing devices, time, sound, or color would exist more or less as a photographic print on an undeveloped plate, the chemophysical or biological reaction constituting the indispensable medium for imprinting on a phenomenon its appearance of existence. The question of the reality of these electromagnetic phenomena, outside of man, will be studied later. But without anticipating that argument, I suggest that recording by means of an instrument built by man to keep time, to take pictures, or to preserve phenomena magnetically on tape, proves nothing and merely puts the problem, like the interpretation, aside.

The question remains the same: Are time and space an invention of man? Or indeed, on the other hand, might the conditioning of the human mind by the sense organs, perfected and sharpened by some physical apparatus for investigation and recording, be an artifact, that is, a product fabricated in space and time by man? In short, like an electronic computer educated and "programmed" from outside, might the human mind not be, from this point of view, only the receptacle of a memory constructed from outside? The fact that this memory, so conceived and constructed, can become in turn constructive and intelligent is not a contrary argument.

In fact, although the mind is generally considered as conceiving space and time, I along with Samuel Alexander [1,2] would tend to conclude that it is the contrary which is originally and historically true, to believe that *it is time which fashions the memory, more than the memory fashions time;* that in a general way *the outside world conditions the mind,* more than that the latter intrudes on matter or space.

However it may be, it is not illogical to suppose, given what we know of the progressive formation of the notion of space and time in the child as Piaget has described it, that the human brain is progressively *programmed from outside* through the medium of the sense organs in general and of vision in particular, like an electronic computer. This seems to be more than just an idle comparison, given what we know today about the electric functioning of the brain cells and about the intimate electrochemical mechanism of neuronic propagation.

For a long time, indeed, it has been known that in the substance

---

[1] Samuel Alexander, *Space, Time and Deity,* "The Gifford Lectures at Glasgow for 1916–18" (London, Macmillan and Co., 1920).

[2] Harry Ruja, "Samuel Alexander's Concept of Space Time," *Philosophy of Science,* Vol. 2, No. 2 (Baltimore, April, 1935).

of the cerebral cortex, like that of the thalamus and of the gray matter at the base of the brain, currents are constantly developing throughout the life of a human or an animal, varying in intensity from 5 millivolts to 100 millivolts, but in general oscillating around 50 millivolts. These currents are presently recorded by electroencephalograms: the majority of normal waves, alpha waves, are of a frequency of about 10 per second, the beta waves over 15 per second, the theta waves below 5 per second. Current observation also indicates that these waves diminish in frequency and amplitude when there is nervous tension or light-induced excitation; they are modified and augmented in certain phases of sleep,[1] by epilepsy or by brain tumors, which they help to individualize and eventually locate; finally, they disappear completely when an individual dies.

We also know that these waves, which are emitted by the nerve cells, are analogous to waves of modulated frequency, which shelter them from certain parasitic variations, and that the brain cells, like their afferent nerves leading from the sense organs, behave (depending on the circumstances) like semiconducting transistors, or like braking or amplifying tunnel diodes. This accounts, electronically, for the thresholds of sensitivity below which no response is registered and for the "all-or-none" principle according to which this threshold is reached and surpassed or, on the contrary, not reached.

A topographical study of the seat of these phenomena has proved to be rather deceptive, except as concerns certain very localized sensorimotor zones, pre- and post-Rolandic. For the rest, traumatic and surgical study has clearly shown that a considerable number of zones of brain matter could be destroyed without a comparable disappearance of the memory or of the notion of time. It seems as though *chronological* and functional *engrams* have a greater value and diffusion and are not restricted to precise topographical localizations, which means that function counts more than anatomical situation.

This diffusion can be explained by the anatomical or functional interrelations of the electric circuits of the brain, which nevertheless are disorganized, if not partially destroyed, by therapeutic electric shocks, with power alternating between 60 and 120 milliamperes, without any loss of brain substance.

So far as the afferent nerves of the brain are concerned, Sir John

---

[1] Nathaniel Kleitman, *Sleep and Wakefulness* (Chicago, University of Chicago Press, 1939, 2nd ed., 1964).

24

Eccles,[1] Andrew Huxley,[2] and Alan Hodgkin[3] have shown and measured the electrochemical mechanism of nerve conduction born of the cerebral processes. The Nobel Prize of 1963 was awarded to them for the precision of their work. In short, it turns out that the nerve cell at rest, the axon, contains an excess of potassium ions, while the membrane contains an excess of sodium ions. For this reason and others (the electric potential of the membranes), the axoplasm possesses a charge of -70 millivolts with respect to the membrane. When a nervous influx takes place, the permeability of the membrane changes, allowing a large number of sodium ions to invade the axoplasm. The difference in potential changes from the original -70 millivolts to $+35$ millivolts. *Thus, instead of a simple depolarization* as was formerly thought, there takes place, at the moment of cerebral excitation, *a veritable reversal of the potential* which *creates* a *current* that propagates the initial electric impulse along the nerve.

Pursuing the study of this phenomenon, Hodgkin and Huxley verified that, after a millisecond's delay, a repolarization of the nerve fiber occurred, the potassium ions passing back outside the membrane. This *restitutio ad integrum* is a complex process: the equilibrium of the nerve fiber remains vitiated by the loss of potassium and the gain of sodium until a "pumping" process intervenes and, through the medium of adenosine triphosphate, attracts the potassium to the inside of the axoplasm and drives the sodium from it. At that moment only is the cycle completed and the nerve cells once more ready for the new impulse, and for the propagation of a new current.

If I have deliberately expatiated on the description of the intimate mechanism of these phenomena, it is to underline clearly that to say the functioning of the nervous system is *electrochemical* is no longer a vague assertion but a *definite fact, which can be measured in an experiment*. It accounts for a good many phenomena observed in the past but which, until now, were unexplained.

---

[1] John Carew Eccles, *The Physiology of the Synapses* (New York, Academic Press, 1964).

[2] A. F. Huxley and A. L. Hodgkin, "A Quantitative Description of Membrane Current and Its Application to Conduction and Excitation in Nerve," *S. Phys.* 117 (London, 1952).

[3] A. L. Hodgkin, "Ionic Movements and Electrical Activity in Giant Nerve Fibres," *Proceedings Royal Society,* B. 148 (London, 1958).

Among these phenomena, one should cite the mechanism of the action of anaesthetics in general and, in particular, electrical anaesthesia; the mechanism by which homeopathic doses of physiological substances, such as acetylcholine or adrenalin (we shall return, in very detailed fashion to these phenomena in Chapter 18) do their work; and finally, the workings—which cannot be explained other than as an "electrical paralysis"—of exotoxic substances such as cyanide of potassium, whose action blocks with its tetravalent ions the electrical permeability of the membranes of the nerve cells and suddenly interrupts the whole vital process by cutting, in the proper meaning of the term, the nervous electric circuit.

However this may be, there is more here than necessary to suggest that the nervous system, in fact, behaves like, and may be imitated by, an electronic computer in its four stages:

First, reception by the sense organs;

Second, memorization by the nerve cells;

Third, elaboration and programming by the selectivity of the brain circuits;

Fourth and last, externalization to the motor muscles of the tongue and larynx for speech, of the limbs for motion.

That being so, it is not illogical to suppose that to go further in the study of these phenomena in general and of the time factor in particular, the copying of the electrochemical nature of these cerebral phenomena in an electronic computer would be indicated. We shall find in it more than a static comparison, hoping to create in this way a dynamic model actuated by the same electrical incitations, whose functioning we can study and vary experimentally.

It may be immediately objected that if there is a similarity in the nature of a "cerebral computer" and an electronic or mechanical computer, there is not necessarily a similarity of essence, and that the latter will never be alive. Accordingly, before going any further, I am compelled to note that the chemical phenomena noted in biology do not exist in electronic computers. But one reply would be that chemical phenomena are reducible to physical-electrical phenomena, and that perhaps one day, in a more selective, more perfected computer, we shall be able to simulate them, that is to say, at least to account for them.

In theory, to imitate the brain with an electronic computer, two solutions are possible.

1. Either one will make use of a general electronic computer, at

the same time both binary (because of the "all-or-none" principle) and analog, which one will program to limit its responses to those which are similar to the human brain;

2. Or one will build a specialized electronic computer, presenting all the essential characteristics of the brain that are known, creating a sort of "model" in order to *imitate* the brain and study its behavior.

Theoretically, the second solution seems the more favorable; we shall see that it is so in practice as well. But for historical reasons, I shall study the first solution first.

The great mathematician, John von Neumann, in his lectures at Yale in 1957 (published after his death in 1958 under the title *The Computer and the Brain*,[1]) compared the functioning of a giant computer with multiple electronic tubes to that of the human brain. At that time, albeit recent, microelectronics had not yet made the progress realized today with integrated microcircuits, transistors, and diodes. It was then a matter of a computer with many thousands of tubes with three electrodes each, whose huge volume von Neumann compared with the restrictive volume of the brain (of the order of one liter). Consequently, he said, the number of cubic centimeters required per active unit is of the order of 10^2 for the computer and 10^{-7} for the brain. Moreover, the energy used by the entire brain is of the order of 10 watts, an amount comparable to that expended in the same time by *a single tube* of three electrodes.

But the greatest difference does not lie there; it resides in the *time* factor. While the reaction time of a neuron between two stimulations is about 10^{-2} seconds, in a tube of three electrodes or a transistor it is about 10^{-7} seconds. That is to say, briefly, that the brain is proportionally constituted of more units which work more slowly; the computer of fewer units which work much more swiftly. Von Neumann concluded from this difference that the brain will have a tendency to consider as much information as it can in *parallel*, that is to say *simultaneously*, and it is this which gives it the appearance of logic; while the electronic machine will do these things in *series*, that is to say *successively*.

This temporal difference is loaded with consequences, for whatever the rapidity of successions in a series, it can never be equivalent

---

[1] John von Neumann, *The Computer and the Brain* (New Haven and London, Yale University Press, 1958).

to the simultaneity of intellectual consideration. This means that the "logic" of the machine will always be different from the "logic" of human automatons, at least in its premises and its processes, even if there is sometimes a coincidence in its conclusions. With great lucidity, von Neumann expatiates on this *temporal* difference which touches on the very mechanism of the memory, the chronometric element par excellence. To use the terminology of the engineer, on account of the all-or-none principle of nervous impulse, the intensity of the stimulus is transformed into a pulsating frequency by the very fact of the number of bits of information transmitted per unit of time, which is relatively equivalent to fostering frequency modulation.

The minimum time of this unit of time is on the order of that described earlier (in 1910) by Lapicque[1] as the time of neuromuscular chronaxia—the excitation time sufficient to give a response to a stimulus twice as great as the stimulus of the rheobase (that is to say, to the threshold stimulus below which there is no muscular response, even to a prolonged excitation). An interval of around 50 milliseconds is needed to distinguish, and thus to record, two perceptions. If the brain worked constantly on this rhythm, in the waking state the number of perceptions recorded would be on the average 10^6 per day, and, for an entire average lifetime, on the order of 10^{10}, a figure roughly comparable to the total number of neurons in the brain.

These considerations and these figures do not account for the rest of the intimate mechanism of the functioning of the memory, for the retention of the order of succession, the differentiation of recent and distant memories, or for the integral, and no longer symbolic, reactualization of the past, such as Penfield (1954) achieved by the direct electrical stimulation of a posttemporal lobe.

But now let us see whether we can come to grips with the problem of an especially conceived and adapted electronic "model," such as the one Albert M. Uttley[2] (1956–59) conceived and built at the National Physical Laboratory at Teddington (Middlesex, England).

---

[1] Louis E. Lapicque, *L'excitabilité en fonction du temps: La chronaxie, sa mesure* (Paris, Presses Universitaires de France, 1926).

[2] Albert M. Uttley, "Imitation of Pattern Recognition and Trial-and-Error Learning in a Conditional Probability Computer," *Biophysical Science—A Study Program*, J. L. Oncley, Editor (New York, John Wiley & Sons, 1959).

Nature, he explains, is the engineer that builds the hazardous bridge which will eventually link structure and behavior of living systems. While the psychologist is only occupied with behavior and only vaguely interested in the structures capable of eliciting it, the anatomist and the physiologist are occupied with the structures themselves and wonder what functions they are supposed to perform. It could well be, Uttley concludes in all innocence, that only the professional engineer may be able to fill in the gap between the structure and the function of biological systems.

With this in mind, he set out to build a computer model capable of discriminating the bits of information and of learning from conditional experience, necessarily based on the following:

1. The model will be capable of discriminating one series of signals from another series: it will be selective (a computer of the binary type), again because of the "all-or-none" principle characteristic of the nervous system.

2. The model will be capable of counting signals and coincidences of signals.

3. The model will be capable of appraising time, thanks to the introduction of delaying circuits.

4. The model will have to have a "plastic" behavior such as to enable the system following conditional probability to connect past events with future responses. That is to say that the computer will be capable of *inductive inference* (the essential quality of the intellect); it will have to have a memory bank of facts and to be capable of counting them with *discrimination*, that is, of comparing numbers of occurrences or nonoccurrences in a nonlinear manner. This will be then, out of necessity, an analog computer and, at the same time, a binary computer, as stated above (in selective condition number one). But this is not technically impossible.

5. In order to avoid supersaturating the system with numbers or series, a sort of *systematic leak* must be established. This will have the two added advantages of allowing the system on the one hand to give more weight to recent memories than to old acquisitions (therefore to differentiate them), and on the other hand to adapt more rapidly to new, recorded bits.

6. Finally, the model must be capable of appreciating relations and therefore of dividing numbers. As is well known, divisions are very easily performed by the use of logarithms. But it happens that a computer provided with the "leak" system described above pro-

29

duces automatically and very accurately, a logarithmic calculation. The relation will thus be established simply by measuring the difference between the conditions of two units. The "condition" consists precisely of the voltage placed in reserve in the computer. It is quite evident that the effect of one active unit of the computer on another to which it is connected depends on the state of their reciprocal charges. The latter relation is fundamental in that it allows the machine *to learn by profiting from acquired experience*, to make attempts and eventually to correct its own errors.

All these unreasonable demands are realizable, for the model is in existence and is functioning. It imitates the sense organs, of course, since it is fed by information coming from outside; what is more, it discriminates among them and is capable of choosing them, of storing them in its electronic memory, of appreciating their context and their real relation in an intelligent manner, in view of an outside action which simulates the will.

For example, in one of the models actually built, a little electric cart attached to a computer was taught to recognize the white and black on a complicated layout and to follow the white track to the limit of the black contour. Furthermore, given the conditional probability established in the electronic selector, this electric vehicle, which theoretically should discriminate only between white and black, proved to be autodidactic and learned to direct itself.

This means that an electronic system established in view of a certain function is capable not only of storing a memory but of profiting by experience and of learning in the proper meaning of the term—that is, of perfecting both its function and its functioning.

One imagines, given the huge number of brain cells and neurons of the brain, that a *very small number* of basic principles and mechanisms would be sufficient to allow a considerable number of functions to be successively acquired and perfected. Of these multiple functions of the brain, the one isolated as described above, through the computation of conditional probabilities, has been singled out among a great many; since this one function, through what it includes and induces, appears to be crucial in the over-all mechanism of the brain and in the very "timing" of its action.

Chapter 4

Intervention of External Time and of
Space in the Creation and Conditioning
of Internal Time and Memories

I have emphasized the description of the Uttley machine for two reasons: on the one hand its electronic potentialities have been designed with finality in view to achieve a determined purpose; on the other hand its very mechanism and the very way in which it deals with the time element throws a light upon the similarity of mechanism of the human memory that it copies, and thus seems both to account for it and even explain it. Whereas up to now memory and the notion of time inescapably have been looked at in these pages only from a theoretical point of view, philosophical and static, from now on I shall try to consider them from a biological viewpoint, *i.e.*, dynamic and statistical.

It is trite to say that, without memory, there is no notion of time, but reversing that idea, we can say that without *apperception of the succession of phenomena there is no possible construction of memory*. The apperception of external reality in its sequence, described below, is going to play a role analogous to that of the programming and conditioning of Uttley's computer, described previously.

Before engaging in this aspect of the discussion, however, I ought first to pay homage to Jean Delay, the great French psychiatrist, who, in a remarkable book, *Les dissolutions de la mémoire*,[1] undertook

---

[1] Jean Delay, *Les dissolutions de la mémoire* (Paris, Presses Universitaires de France, 1942).

31

the classification of "memories" on a physiopathological basis following the work of Hughlings Jackson [1] (1884). Jackson considered diseases of the nervous system as regressions of evolution, as dissolutions capable of experimentally dissociating the hierarchy—that is, the different stages of mental construction. This sort of *reverse programming*, which studies the arrest and reversal of development because of illness, thus follows the inverse route of that previously traversed in the evolution of the child. It furnishes us with a sort of pathological counterproof, so to speak, liberating and exposing mechanisms often less dissociated, hence less apparent, from the time of their evolutionary physiological formation. It is this physiological evolutionary process with which we are concerned here: the simultaneous formation of the notion of time (external or internal) and of the memory; and we refer again to Jean Delay [2] for the phenomena of destruction or of psychological liberation encountered in the course of amnesia, hypermnesia and madness.

It is interesting that in the child, as in the young animal, sensorimotor time is the first to be perceived. This is instinctive and internal time, a visceral time linked to the reflex mechanisms of hunger and thirst. Long before either the intellect or the memory exists, the first sensation of time certainly lies in the periodical recurrence of hunger and thirst, which are indistinguishable that early.

If this hunger and thirst are not immediately satisfied at the moment of their return, the *suffering* created probably constitutes the second sensation of time, followed by a third sensation, *pleasure*, in the satisfaction by the meal. The repetition of suffering alternating with pleasure would thus condition the newborn child to a physiological time cycle, as surely as when Pavlov made systematic use of *time as a conditional stimulant* for the establishment of a salivation reflex in dogs, who were given or shown a piece of meat at a fixed time.

Let me remark in passing that if the rhythm of breathing is not perceived it is because the succession of inhaling and exhaling remains unconscious in both the child and the adult unless something happens in the way of an obstacle—heart disease or an infection—to thwart this vital respiratory automatism, creating a thirst for

---

[1] John Hughlings Jackson (1834–1909), *Selected Writings*, Vol. 2, J. Taylor, Editor (New York, Basic Books, 1958).

[2] Jean Delay, *op. cit.* See also Chapters 12 and 13 of this book.

air. An instinct not thwarted or retarded in its cycle of evolution does not reach consciousness. In the same way, the rhythm of urination and the passage of fecal matter cannot intervene in the formation of the notion of time in the child, insofar as these passages, irregular and, at the original stage unopposed, still remain unconscious.

But these sensorimotor rhythms which unconsciously instruct the child and the young animal in the "sensation of time," whether they are the sensations of light or noise, hunger, thirst, of gas distending the child's abdomen, of waiting and crying, or satisfaction and sleep, are quite far from memory and still farther from a notion of time. They are *rhythmic* for the outside observer, for the mother or nurse who seeks either to satisfy or to regularize the original, instinctive needs of the child. The mother attempting to control the needs of the child by means of a schedule constitutes, in a way, the *first "programming" of the sensation of time* relating to periodic return in the young animal.

If this instinctive need is styled the "initial time," it follows from the observations above that it is quite special. It can be characterized as animal, compulsive, and visceral rather than mental; sensorimotor to be sure, but much more introceptive and proprioceptive than exteroceptive. It is moreover a time of the sympathetic nervous system, an autonomous time of hypothalamic origin, a pulsional and automatic time, as is shown anatomically by the absence, at this stage, of real cerebrospinal connections and physiologically by the possibility of its persistence in animals experimentally decerebrated.

The automatism in question is brought about by a physiochemical mechanism or equilibrium encouraged by a congenital constitution and programmed by the mother. It could easily be imitated by an engineer, who would compose a selective binary computer with retarding circuits capable of recognizing the recurrent cycle of a circumstance already encountered.

This last word *encountered* (instead of *experienced*) marks, at this stage, the specific difference between a vital phenomenon and its eventual electronic reproduction. The sensation of repetition felt by the child, the recognition of repetition by an electronic machine already more intelligent and obligatorily selective because of its construction and the adult who constructed it—these are different sides of the same essential and initial element which is the *seed of*

33

internal time. There is as yet no memory in the child, and electronic registration is certainly an assessment but, as we shall see below, assessment is not memory and does not deserve the name.

But let me pass—with no other transition than a few days in the young animal that can walk or a few months or a year in the young child—to another stage, where time is perceived from the outside now and associated, whether we wish it or not (and well before the relativists came along to characterize it), with the discovery of space. This is a fundamental period in which not only spatial time comes to be progressively formed but also social time, objective time, the conscious rational time which constructs the memory and the intellect, insofar as it conditions the brain cells.

Before coming to grips with this study, we must, with Bergson, make an important digression. It seems that it is this very delay of about one year, necessary before the young human child can walk, which gives impetus to the development of his intellect. His dependence on his mother and his immobility force the child to perfect data from his sense organs, and from sight in particular, thanks to a minimum of muscular verification. Thus, for example, distance will be that which he cannot reach with his hand, while for the puppy distance will be the space he must travel to get something. The relative immobility and absolute dependence of the child of less than one year lead him in a way to *construct his knowledge around the perception of the world seen from his cradle* by means of images which are *already mental*, that is to say already *intelligent*. And it could very well be that the child's impatience to grasp what he cannot reach, by steps as yet impossible, infuses in him the first notion of objective time, indissolubly linked to a space that he cannot yet cross.

Experience also shows that this unaccomplished act, or act somewhat thwarted in its accomplishment, pushes the child from the desired image to the *idea*, which is at first only a persistent image, and to language, in order to obtain *indirect* accomplishment, by means of those around him, of the act which he cannot yet execute.

Later, when the child at last is able to walk, thanks to the more complete establishment of the cerebrospinal nerve fibers, the benefit will not only be in the praxia, that is in the development of possible movements, but also in the parallel development of the brain's capacity, which will become above all an instrument to *select* the movements to execute, in order to obtain, to grasp, to reach. But to

34

reach is also still *to wait*, and precisely in the "time" of waiting, to traverse a certain space.

This is to say that in the reflex tendency to act in order to fulfill the desire to grasp, there does exist a certain amount of suspense and indetermination. This constitutes a crucial moment, since the feeling of this very *delay* inaugurates both the judgment and the appreciation of the nature of interior time. In short, after a stage which one might style Pavlovian, during which the newborn child conditions his reflexes with his sensorial analyzers, he becomes secondarily capable of using his praxical effectors to grasp objects.

This delay is fundamental to the development of his brain, his intellect, his judgment, because of the *connection which it establishes between the time of expectation and the distance from satisfaction*. It is a remarkable fact that when Uttley set about to realize an electronic computer capable of learning from experience and of reacting differently when faced with an outside element already received (we deliberately do not say perceived) or a new element that is capable of differentiating between the new and what has already been submitted, between the equivalent of the present and the past, by establishing a relationship, he was obliged to introduce *retarding circuits* into his reception system. In the same way that the instinct of a child becomes sharpened because of delay and the suspense of waiting, the electronic machine becomes capable of selecting and of exercising choice, that is of simulating intelligence, thanks to the introduction of temporization by a retarding circuit.

Whatever this new time may be, once formed it is no longer an individual time; it is a *social time*, it is the impersonal time of physicists and astronomists and the *time of men, rational and conscious time*, cerebrospinal time of voluntary action, official time which can be measured on a watch or a chronometer, arithmetic time which is always a measure—or can be reduced to a measure— of space traversed or energy spent. It is an internal time no doubt, but is capable of cutting up duration or outside space objectively, even if artificially.

To this new time, rational, impersonal and yet very human, if not exclusively human, will correspond the formation and the development of a memory, which is also rational and in some way social.

Nothing is more characteristic in this regard than our date of birth, which society symbolically and repeatedly requires of us for

35

every official act in order to fix us in time. Thus, as men, we are situated in society by *rapport* with the time of the stars, and, under pain of being considered "alienated" from society, we must have consciousness and measure of what is past, present, and future, and must be capable of identifying them with dates. Here there is a sort of superficial translation, almost administrative, of internal time and memory, and also of identification by the time of society. This kind of translation is not as important as a search for the mechanism by which the memory is formed, that is to say, the process by which the present is recognized, the fashion in which a remembrance is formed, in which it is evoked and recognized as past.

Bergson [1] has masterfully described the initial phenomenon; we shall cite it in its entirety, for nothing can equal the finesse of his analysis nor the relevance of his description and the elegance of his style. "The present," as he said, "is at all instants in its surge divided into two symmetrical spurts, of which one falls back towards the past, whereas the other springs towards the future. The latter we call perception; it is the only one in which we take interest. Why should we indeed be concerned with the memory of things as long as we are holding them. Since practical consciousness discards this remembrance as useless, theoretical reflexions consider it as nonexistent. Thus arises the illusion that memory follows perception!" But this is only an illusion! Each moment of our life offers thus two aspects, actual and virtual, perception on the one hand and remembrance on the other. But beyond appearance, these two aspects are synchronized and therefore *contemporaneous* at least in their origin. Nevertheless, as Janet says: [2] "The construction of the present prevents a precise determination of its duration."

This synchronization of perception and remembrance, which passes unnoticed by most adults, is naturally ignored by all children from one to five years old. That is why until this age, although they can conserve some images, they do not have authentic memories: they have fixed some impressions but they do not know how to make them actual, to classify or symbolize them, to put them in opposition to

---

[1] H. Bergson, *Matière et Mémoire* (Paris, Félix Alcan, 1896); *Matter and Memory* (New York, Humanities Press, 1962).

[2] Pierre Janet, *L'évolution de la mémoire et la notion de temps* (Paris, A. Chanine, 1928).

the past or to integrate them. To live in the present is not to identify the present, still less to construct it so that it can dwell in the memory at a level where one can visit it at leisure and make use of it, that is to say, evoke it and recount it. This fact accounts for two things:

1. Contrary to what Freud affirmed, if the infantile memory below the age of four seems devoid of remembrances, this is due not to a protective repression but, much more simply, to the fact that remembrance, as true memory, cannot possibly be formed in a child of that age, who is incapable of real mental synthesis. He does not yet have a social memory, although he plays, eats, drinks, sleeps, and defecates in family and social time. Here again, we find a new verification of the *precession of social time* over the rational memory, which is equally social and which will be extricated from it later.

The child under four years of age is an image-chaser capable of reminiscences, that is, of reawakenings without recognitions—without the precise localization in space and time characteristic of true remembering.

Let us note in passing that certain children, called "retarded," remain at this stage permanently, without ever having a present, because they do not construct an account of it, and without ever acquiring a memory, since the events which they have lived have passed without realization, without consciousness, and can never become symbols, remembrances or past.

2. During sleep, the most normal adult loses the notion of time to the extent that he loses his consciousness and the "unconscious" alone reigns as "master." The dream puts the dreamer back automatically to an inferior and more primitive stage of mental life, and there is no need to imply, as Freud does, the necessity of a repression, or of a frustration, or of a desire in order to explain the dream.

The conscious is simply *disconnected* (in the electrical sense of the term), the circuit is broken. There is no longer any time: past, present, and future are all one, since there is no longer a possibility of presentification. Since there is no longer a reality, there is no longer a memory: since there is no longer any reason, there are no longer remembrances. There is no longer anything but the images unrolling without logical sequence, kaleidoscopically associated or dissociated by the play of similitudes, symbols or chance. There, where there cannot be time, there cannot be reality; there, where

37

there exists neither reality nor time, there cannot be a connection between phenomena, nor a true relation that characterizes consciousness, as it characterizes rational memory.

Is this to say that this dream time, oniric time, or autistic time as it is called, does not deserve description and does not have "its own" memory? The time in question is no doubt different from the others, completely shut inside the sleeper's brain. *A living interior time even if it is not lived* in the usual sense of the term, a time important by its very duration, which is around twenty-five years for a man who lives seventy-five years—*a third of his life!* An unconscious time, individual and emotional, affective, impulsive, a time discontinuous to the point of being anarchic, without measure or proportion, hierarchy or relation. The time of the soul in Greek mythology. The time of nightmare and of drama. The time of madness, if the man is awake and under its permanent yoke. The time of intoxication and of drunkenness from alcohol, opium, mescaline or lysergic acids. Time dilated in subjective duration—seconds seem hours, hours seem months, days seem years—and contracted in space, repressed inside the body.

Does this time merit, without risk of confusion, the name of time? To tell the truth, we do not think so, and for two reasons:

1. If this subjective and purely arbitrary time can indeed last several hours in a man who is intoxicated or hypnotized, a third of the life of a normal man while he is asleep, the whole life of a madman who is awake, objective appraisals of the duration and of the arbitrary nature of this time cannot be evaluated by the subject; they are made from *outside,* and *the arbitrary, like this so-called time, exists only for the arbiter, for the outside judge.*

2. Here, there is nothing which resembles the sensorimotor times and the rational times previously described, which were capable of conditioning remembrance, memory, and reason or, at least, their habits and reflexes. If there is an evocation of remembrances or of images in the dream, they are born of, hence now preceded by, the autistic memory. The authenticity of this latter oniric memory can be argued, since it is made of bits and pieces detached from the sensorimotor memory and the rational memory, but stripped of their order, their hierarchy, their context—in a word, of their reality. They are perhaps meaningful from the emotional point of view, but certainly not meaningful from the point of view of reason. This is true for the reason of the sleeper awakened, as

well as for the reason of the interpreter of dreams, soothsayer or psychoanalyst, who seeks to instill in these images a logic, a sequence, and a pseudocausality which they certainly do not have. The only thing that can bring about this whirlwind of dreams detached from time and space, hence from all memory worthy of the name, from all consciousness of any reality, is the *immense number of affective images* localized in relation to the relatively small number of authentic remembrances retained.

This would lead us to think that one of the most important faculties of the rational memory would be the faculty of forgetting. To understand this, we must anticipate here and make a short trip into the domain of pathology, where the different functions of the normal memory will be found dissociated by illness, presented as if through a magnifying glass by pathological dissociation and by neurotic or experimental exaggeration.

Ernest Dupré,[1] the great psychiatrist of the Préfecture de Police in Paris, described around 1905 the mental childishness of "ecmnesic" old men. Falling back on childhood or adolescence, they relive entire slices of their past. They find themselves on the scene of the past as if they were still actors in it, instead of recounting it as spectators of times gone by and as commentators on the present. Formed memory is confounded with forming memory; the time of the past action replaces the time of the present narration by mistake and is substituted for it.

The dreaming hallucination of the sleep of pyrexia and of anaesthetics, like these emotive mental confusions, frequently reveals the states which Penfield,[2] the Canadian neurosurgeon, was able to reproduce directly by electric excitation of a parieto-occipital post-Rolandic region. According to the patient, the scene was not experienced but *relived*, with the illusion of an actual present and a wealth of details which he believed had been completely forgotten.

This oniric hypermnesia helps to explain the role of the notion of time in the social memory and the reason: the past is no longer recognized as past; it is brought to the present in a hallucinatory

---

[1] Ernest Dupré, *Pathologie de l'imagination et de l'émotivité* (Paris, Payot, 1925). See also Chapter 13 of this book.

[2] Wilder Graves Penfield, "The Cerebral Cortex and the Mind of Man," in *Physical Basis of Mind* (Oxford, 1950). *The Excitable Cortex in Conscious Man,* Sherrington Lectures, No. 5 (Liverpool Press, 1958).

39

manner. The memory confuses memorization and remembering and has lost its essential characteristic of discrimination, of selectivity, of differential integration—not only between the present and the past, but between the useful and the useless. This chaos of undifferentiated retention, with neither order nor classification, has nothing in common with rational and social memory; the latter has been eclipsed and therefore, through a process of involution and Jacksonian dissolution, a more primitive autistic mechanism which, as we have said, scarcely deserves the name memory, has been liberated.

It is perhaps in this sense that we could say that *forgetting* was the protector and guardian of the memory, an assertion which is paradoxical only in appearance. At the perceptual stage, indeed, there is already an experimental hierarchy of sensation, that is to say, sorting out and, consequently, elimination. At the conceptual stage, whether it is a question of placement in reserve by means of symbolism or of integration, or of secondary evocations of the remembrance, the memory selects and eliminates quantitatively "redundance" and, qualitatively, the useless. In other words, it forgets, it erases (like the head of a tape recorder which both erases and records). (*Cf.* Table II, Chapter 10.)

If this last assertion is exact, to the effect that the memory eliminates qualitatively what is useless (and clinical observation seems to bear this out in normal men), this would be one of the most important functions of the memory: to choose, to rank in order, perceive connections, establish relations. This is the *precise point where the memory becomes intelligent* and returns to the outside world what it originally received from it: impressions of the reality of the world, of the contour of things, of the aspect of beings situated in space . . . and in time. And it does this in the same proportion as this new intelligent exteriorization, the secondary expression of a past impression, retrieves or re-creates these things, these beings, this space and this time *by following a route the inverse of the first: from the inside towards the outside.*

Since this task is executed by the memory and the intellect with a view to *action* in the outside world or on the outside world, it is in this sense that it can be said that memory is the faculty of adaptation between the virtual and the possible, between the potential and the real. One step further: if this memory, evoked and projected back from the inside, has *become intelligent,* in order to act on the outside world it ought to distinguish the real from the imaginary and, of course, to distinguish the present from the past, or at least before from after. One step still further, and the world, where it is projected with its own personality, becomes its reality, "a world as will and representation," to borrow Schopenhauer's expression.[1] Moreover, Bergson, in his book *Matière et Mémoire*, implies this unity of memory, intellect, and will, and their temporal connections and oppositions. "There is certainly something else between past and present than difference in degree. My present is what interests me, what lives for me, what provokes me to action, whereas my past is entirely impotent." And this is just what happens in psychological reality. On the other hand, in pathological cases, whether of hypermnesia or of amnesia, intellect as well as will are seen to disappear in the wake of memory. In cases of amnesia particularly, whether it is a question of mental confusion or of madness, the subjects lose, with their memory, their autocriticism: they lose their will. (For further details, see Chapters 13 and 20.)

This does not mean that all remembrances are abolished—far from it. They occupy and nourish the insanity. The subjects make up stories about their past, thinking to evoke it or even to relive it. They lie without knowing that they are lying. This last point is important to emphasize, for starting from memories blemished by the imagination, the normal man, enjoying his fantasy, can, when he daydreams, describe for himself a world in reverse. But he knows he is inventing and that he is distorting the real, only in fun. He knows that he is lying and most often keeps his lie to himself. He is not the same as the mythomaniac who has a passion for the lie and spreads it about. Nevertheless the dreamer and the mythomaniac know the truth, even if they take pleasure in fooling themselves or in fooling others. The amnesic, on the other hand, confused or mad, lies to himself unconsciously, ignorant of the truth; he is his own victim, his own fool. The fabrication of amnesics is not a story, it is a delirium. Experimentally, with the memory and after it, the intelligence of the real has disappeared and also the possibility of action which depends on memory, that is to say, the will. As we shall see further on (in Chapter 13), these differences can

---

[1] Arthur Schopenhauer (1788–1860), *Die Weldt alles Wille und Vorstellung; The World as Will and Idea* (New York, Humanities Press, 1964).

be explained simply by the fact that the amnesic is cut off from time; he receives neither information nor communication from it and is equally alienated from—that is to say he is a stranger to—space, which leads to his total disorientation.

Having reached this stage, physiological facts and their pathological modifications already allow us, on the one hand, to presume that space and time are capable, through the medium of man's nervous system, of conditioning his brain and, on the other hand, to realize that memory, imagination, intellect, and will are encompassed in a *unique, interior, temporal* function which assures their exercise. The dissociation brought about by studying them separately is not really psychological or functional. However, the different stages observed in the progressive formation of this function in children, as well as the no less different stages observed during the progressive disintegration of the same function in older people, entitle us logically to study this separation of a unique entity. In short, either physiologic evolution in the child or pathologic involution in the old dissociate in a similar way the elements of this temporal function, and justify this artificial study of individual elements. It should be noted also that the very terms, "progressive," "evolution," "involution," include and necessarily imply the *common interior time factor*, artificially altered and dissociated in disease.

With this idea of time in mind, I am going to try in the following chapters to specify the nervous mechanisms that preside over this function or its disorders. Without a doubt we shall again have to compare and study a succession of phenomena, but without ever omitting the possibility of parallel and simultaneous action. In order to do this, we shall, in succession:

1. Envisage cerebral structure and function in the form of a cybernetic model and, by testing this imitation, find mechanisms which explain certain functions of the human brain. (*Cf.* Chapter 15.)

2. Return then to the functional anatomy (if it can be called that) of the brain, but this time, enlightened by cybernetics, we shall have to strive to see to what extent the "electronic model" has copied the original brain and in what respects the latter is nevertheless different.

3. Finally, in a last stage, we shall have to seek, beyond the differences, for the common denominator that binds the model to the

42

original. This will obviously be their common electromagnetic nature, which presides over the functioning of the computer as it does over that of the central nervous system and of the electric currents (nervous influx) running through its afferent and efferent nerves—which presides over all its connections and all its variations.

Such will be the object of the following chapters; but we must clearly note in advance that if the study of the parallel functioning of electronic machines and the brain is capable of shedding light on the latter mechanism and its intimate functioning and, more specifically, on the functions of the human nervous system, on the other hand it cannot solve the problem of the profound nature of the *mind,* a phenomenon peculiar to man, a characteristic incomparably superior to any machine, however perfected it may be.

Chapter 5

The Brain Considered as an Electronic Information and Communication Center

To give a general idea of these phenomena, we shall anticipate a bit by following, point by point, in Table I (p. 46), the possible parallelisms between an electronic computer and the human nervous system, from the point of view of the electronic mechanism for receiving information, of the programming of this information, of its transmission, of the registering of this communication, and of its possible secondary action.

As will already be apparent in this chapter, and as all the facts analyzed later will tend to prove, here comparison will become reason, given the identity of the electronic mechanism of action in computers and the flow of electric nervous impulses in man. In order to analyze the common function, I shall dwell equally on the parallelisms established by modern physics, on the common mechanisms recognized among phenomena so disparate in appearance as thermodynamics and electronics on the one hand and entropy and information on the other.

The result of this preliminary study will show that the common denominator of these phenomena lies in the law of large numbers, such as one encounters, even in a restricted space, in dealing with the molecules of a gas or the electrons of a current of information, when one considers them on the fundamental microscopic scale of matter or of energy.

44

In looking at this table, one cannot help being impressed by the parallelism between electronic computers and the nervous system in general, the human brain in particular. As F. H. George, of the University of Bristol, said in a remarkable book published in 1962,[1] four years after von Neumann's studies at Yale, the human brain behaves like a computer, *is* in fact an electronic computer.

At the outset, however, an essential remark must be made: this comparison is only valid and acquires all of its epistemological validity only if it is not forgotten that the electronic computer was built and programmed by a human brain. Even admitting the objection that one computer can program a second one and that the human brain in the course of evolution was itself programmed from the outside only serves to put off the problem without resolving the essential difficulty; the difference of essence, though not of mechanism, remains untouched.

One also notices, thanks to this table, that all that is known of the human brain and of the functioning of the nervous system can today be imitated and programmed on an electronic model; sometimes not without difficulty. But the very process adopted to overcome this difficulty calls attention to the probable mechanism of the psychological process which one is seeking to copy. Once the model has been realized, the conditions of functioning can be varied *ad infinitum* and the responses can be measured. These two advantages would suffice to justify the study of cybernetics. (For details, see Chapter 15.)

Just as in thermodynamics the study of the entropy of a system allows one to calculate the coefficient of disturbance produced in the system in transformation, in the same way the measure of the bits of information furnished to an electronic system accounts for the variation inside this system, and actually for its entropy, that is, its coefficient of disturbance. Louis de Broglie (1955), following Léon Brillouin, states this similarity, and compares Shannon's[2] formula concerning the probability of information signals, with Boltzmann's[3] constant, which expresses entropy, in a thermo-

---

[1] F. H. George, *The Brain as a Computer* (Oxford, Pergamon Press, 1962).
[2] Shannon: $al. \Sigma_i p_i \log p^2$, P_i giving the probability of a succession of signals.
[3] Ludwig Boltzmann: $S = K \log P$ (S: entropy of a thermodynamic system; P: probability of the system in a determined state [the molecules being considered as statistical aggregates]; K: Boltzmann's constant).

45

TABLE I: Structural and Functional Comparison Between

ELECTRONIC COMPUTER

A. *Reception of Information and Code*
1. Arising from the external environment
2. Receptors of a programmed code
B. *Transmission Mechanism*
3. Input conductors
4. Communication networks
5. Valves, amplifying or selector relays, tri-electrode tubes or semiconductors, transistors, diodes, capacitors, and eventually luminescence
C. *Registration of the Communication*
6. Conservation of magnetic impulses
Hysteresis
Polarization at level of semiconductors; ferromagnetic coils, electromagnetic tape
D. *Association Networks*
7. Interconnected circuits

Eventually, feedback
8. Means to avoid overload of circuits
Depolarizing (erasing) heads
Leakage or stochastic process
Electronic safety valve
E. *Internal Handling of Information*
9. Alternation between polarization and depolarization
Circuit resonance

10. Study of conditional probability by procrastinating circuits and delay stages; mercury, piezoelectric quartz. Computer can profit from previous experience, to select and "learn"
  (a) 1 or 0 (binary digital computer)
    "on" or "off"
  (b) employed to compare functions, and to integrate and develop them (analog computer)
F. *Action of Communication*
11. Electromagnetic reactivation of registration by a special current capable of restoring hysteresis
Emission through depolarization
12. Emissive circuit (output)
G. *Retransmission of the Communication*
13. (a) external: automatic models
    (b) internal: correctors, substitute and restorative calculations

14. Character of action appears voluntary but is in fact predetermined

Electronic Computer and Human Nervous System

HUMAN NERVOUS SYSTEM

A. *Reception of Information*
   1. Arising from the external or internal environment
   2. Sense organs already code-programming
B. *Transmission Mechanism*
   3. Afferent nerves
   4. Anastomotic networks of neurons
   5. Synapses or junction plates, basal gray nuclei, cerebral cells, membrane potentials, single and selective electrochemistry (refractory states) and eventually catalyzers and hormones
C. *Memory*
   6. Conservation of impressions (traces) *Cf.* Chap. 15

   Polarization at level of cerebral cells of basal gray nuclei (sympathetic)
D. *Association Networks*
   7. Anastomotic interconnection of nerves (interhemispheric, thalamo-cortical, hypothalamic, hypophyseal, etc., fibers)
      Feedback
   8. Forgetting
      Relative depolarization through action of time elapsing
      Selectivity between old memory (long fibers) and recent memory (short fibers)
E. *Internal Handling of Information*
   9. Probable alternation between polarization and depolarization
      Electrochemical equilibration
      Adjustment of chronaxies
   10. Procrastination, permitting perception of relations, simultaneous utilization, in parallel or in series, of comparisons, contrasts, relationships, memories
      Summation of impulses often necessary to avoid the "nothing" and admit everything; yes or no
      Awareness, reasoning

F. *Communication of the Action*
   11. Recollection and *evocation,* re-creation by symbolic reactivation of image or idea of code word

   12. Efferent nerves (output)
G. *Transmission of the Command*
   13. (a) external: striated muscles, inclusive of language words
       (b) internal: basal gray nuclei, thalamus, cerebellum, sympathetic nervous system, viscera
   14. Character of action appears to be from free-will choice but is perhaps unconsciously determined

H. *Connecting Systems*
  15. Replacement and substitute circuits, servomotor automatisms, *autonomous,* interior to the system, with feedback and feed ahead

  Linkage of binary computing systems, digital and analog

I. *Acceleration in Retransmission*
  16. Apparent automatic "habits"
      Reaction of action on the very activity of the internal system, leading to a sort of conditioning of circuits

J. *External Expression*
  17. Can trigger and direct any other mechanism or even program another computer, either arithmetic (digital) or logarithmic (analog)
      Source of new information and communication
K. *Disconnection of Internal Motor*
  18. Current remains connected but tapes do not revolve
L. *Current Cut Off*
  19. Temporary arrest

dynamic system, in statistical terms. In simple, nonmathematical language, there will apparently always be an inverse relation between the information transmitted by the signals and the probability that these signals are *received in a meaningful way in a sequence of time.* It is in this sense that Brillouin has qualified as *negative* entropy the quantity of information transmitted, which can only diminish, if simply because of the distortion produced in the system of transmission, that is to say, the system of communication or of information itself. At any rate, in a closed system, whether thermodynamic or electronic, the total of the information and of negative entropy can never be increased.

These few generalities provide a presentiment of the great importance the reception of information will have for the development of the cognitive network as well as for the exercise of its functions as a system of communication. This is less apparent in reality than in a superficial assertion, if only because, in measuring, imitating, evaluating, and producing the functions of an infinitely complex

TABLE I: Human Nervous System (*cont.*)

H. *Connecting Systems*
15. Extraordinary multiplicity, even redundancy of replacement circuits, linkage to *autonomic* nervous system (sympathetic), electrochemical "instinctive" automatisms
    Tournade's law, servomotor equivalent:
    the mechanism to be corrected constitutes the specific stimulant which triggers the correcting mechanism
I. *Acceleration in Retransmission*
16. Actual unconscious habits
    Reaction of activity on the functioning of the nervous system, facilitating secondary action
    Conditioned reflexes (Pavlov)
J. *External Expression*
17. Can trigger and direct (through intermediary muscles) another mechanism, especially the voice—through an initial programming code, the word-concept now becomes pragmatic
    Source of new information and communication, especially social
K. *Sleep*
18. Static "activity"; dream
L. *Current of All Neural Impulse Cut Off*
19. Death

nervous system, there will necessarily be *opposition* between the information of the cognitive network, an entity necessarily and functionally growing, and the "organic" negentropy of the brain which will have a tendency to become debased, following universal law and, in particular, the thermodynamic principle of Carnot.

And let me first specify, with L. Brillouin, the cybernetic relationships between information and entropy.[1] According to him, entropy corresponds to a state of disorder in a physical system, disorder connected with a lack of information. Lack of real information, corresponding to real disorder, bearing on the microstructures of a system: one can conceive that by the eventual measure of the one, we might better approximate the idea or the action of the other, and *vice versa*.

---

[1] L. Brillouin, *La science et la théorie de l'information* (Paris, Masson and Co., 1959); *Science and Information Theory* (New York, Academic Press, 1956).

This is precisely what can be done cybernetically: since this measure will augment the information of a system, it will permit the entropy, that is to say the disorder of the system, to diminish, or, as we have already said with Brillouin, its negentropy to increase. Since negentropy means *absence of disorder*, perhaps it would be preferable for the sake of clarity and to avoid a double negative to say: *presence of order*, that is to say, organization.

In short, the more information one has on a system, the better one will be able to understand its organization and to measure its function. In the precybernetic period of physics, the first endeavor of this kind was ingeniously made by Maxwell, through his "demon," which was gifted with magical power and which, without inertia and with a power of discrimination touching on sorcery, was able to recognize and to direct the exchange of molecules in the current established thermodynamically between two recipients in mutual "communication," containing gases at different temperatures. Thanks to the information acquired by his "demon," Maxwell arrived at a classification of the different molecules according to their speed and temperature, thereby establishing greater order in the classification of molecules.

To illustrate more clearly that, inversely, disorder accompanies lack of information, R. Schafroth [1] gives this simple example: a man may arrange his books and papers in an apparently *pêle-mêle* fashion; nevertheless he knows exactly where everything is. This means that for him the disorder is only apparent, order is real. But a second person may see only confusion; for him the *apparent disorder merely results from a lack of information*.

As Costa de Beauregard [2] remarks on this subject in a remarkable book: "This is the manner by which, at first sight unexpected, the subjective conception of physical probability makes a spectacular entry on the scene." And he adds, "It must finally be probability (negentropy and information) which operates as the *hinge between the objective and the subjective, between matter and mind*, where one is knotted to the other and reacts on the other." Be that as it may, since the cybernetic era one can, as Brillouin says, "exercise"

---

[1] R. Schafroth, *Selected Lectures in Modern Physics* (London, Macmillan, 1960).

[2] O. Costa de Beauregard, *Le second principe de la science du temps* (Paris, Editions du Seuil, 1960).

Maxwell's demon, and not only imitate it but fill its place electronically, and so verify that all the acquired information leads to the possibility of greater order in a system, permits its negentropy to be augmented and, if necessary, to be reconverted, coded this time by the electronic machine as a new bit of information.

Costa de Beauregard remarks that there is an essential and reversible bond between negentropy $\rightleftarrows$ and information. In the first case, negentropy $\rightarrow$ information (corresponding to the process of observation), the word "information" is taken in its current modern sense: acquisition of knowledge. In the second case, information $\rightarrow$ negentropy (corresponding to the process of organization or secondary action), the word "information" is taken in its obsolete sense, the way Aristotle understood it: that is to say, the power of organization.

These facts are full of consequences, for they illustrate in a scientific manner, insofar as they can be verified electronically and reproduced cybernetically, Bergson's assertion cited above (cf. p. 36), to the effect that "the present is at all instants in its surge divided into two symmetrical spurts, of which one falls back towards the past, whereas the other springs towards the future." In fact, these two streams correspond to information and to negentropy. There is no essential difference between the nature of the image of perception and the projected representation and the physical or psychological action which accompanies it, follows it, or even precedes it. Nor is there a difference between information and perception, between organization and action, nor even, going a little further, between imagination and will, to the extent that, for the electronic machine as well as for man, what is visualized by imagination entails what will be actualized in the future. What is seen presses on what is willed and hence on what happens.

Is this Maxwell's demon become man, or man become demonic, through the power (cerebral or cybernetic—electronic) to produce or to reproduce a situation, or even an action, born of an image, which is itself born of a bit of information, and all this beyond time? Not that time does not exist in this operation, but it remains a contingent element which affects directly neither the phenomenon nor the action which eventually flows from it. What counts in this operation is neither its origin outside or inside the system of information, nor the precession or succession of the negentropic modification of order or of action; what counts is the

51

price in energy of these transformations and of these reciprocal convertibilities, and this price is always a certain electronic debasement, analogous to the thermodynamic debasements according to the principle of Carnot.

As Gabor remarked,[1] "You can't get anything for nothing, even a bit of information": this information will not cost very much in negentropy. On the other hand, Brillouin[2] shows that to produce negentropy, one must pay "very dearly" in information. As we shall see later on, whether cheap or costly, these "expenditures" have a value beyond estimation, given their yield in the physical, human, social, or even commercial domain (for example, the information network of the American telephone system).

The assertion of Janet, cited above, will now be better understood: "The construction of the present prohibits a precise determination of its duration." In effect, what counts in the yield of a system is the energetic price of the expense in the reciprocal information-negentropy exchange—but not the speed, that is, the time during which this expense is made. Of course, this does not mean that the temporal circumstances are not very important, but only that we have *dissociated* them for the clarity of the explanation. Indeed, they are fundamental, since they illustrate *the utilization of time in the functional behavior of a system in activity.*

Before I go further, a simple comparison will elucidate this explanation. In the "economics" of a system, time acts like a bank account, a credit ready to be used. When the interaction described above (information-negentropy or *vice versa*) *is paid for*, there will always be a certain delay in payment (principle of delayed action), if only because the check is never given in advance. And that is true for a very simple reason, at once physical and logical: one never knows the cost of the operation before the interaction has taken place!

This simple fact is rich in consequences, for if one translates the experiment in terms of statistical mechanics, as Reichenbach[3] and Grünbaum have done, it is apparent that "These isolated states of order are always consecutive and are never anterior to an

---

[1] D. Gabor, *Massachusetts Institute of Technology Lectures* (Boston, 1951).
[2] L. Brillouin, *op. cit.*
[3] Hans Reichenbach, *The Direction of Time* (Berkeley, University of California Press, 1956).

interaction." This statement perhaps explains why the past can be recorded, but not the future. The fact is less obvious than this last sentence seems to indicate although it is implicitly contained in the very etymology of the term "recorded."

Boltzmann,[1] with his feel for change, foresaw before the theory of relativity that these ideas were not useless, since they necessarily implied the intervention of the human observer and of his personal system of reference in the interpretation of the observed phenomenon. This is why, he remarked, given the thermal equilibrium which prevails in the universe (with very few variations, always small and of short duration), it is impossible for this universe as a whole to set apart or to discern two directions in time. Whereas, for a living being in a determined phase of time, a designation and a direction will probably be earmarked for duration in the direction of increasing entropy, rather than decreasing entropy.

Since Einstein, it is generally accepted that the matter of this universe is *no less deployed in time than it is extended in space.* Also, as Whitehead remarks,[2] relativity consists much more of a temporalization of space than of a spatialization of time. From this point of view, there is no material objective boundary between the already accomplished and what is going to be accomplished. In a word, everything *is* actual for the material universe, space or time; the latter is no more than the famous "fourth dimension" of space: *i.e.,* another coordinate. And it is in this sense that, in our comparison, we described *time's account as always a creditor,* since it is always deployed, whether or not it is employed by a system . . . or by a man.

For a man, as Costa de Beauregard remarks,[3] the information of the cognitive structure is an essentially and vitally growing entity (in contrast to the negentropy of the brain, which is debased, according to the fatal law of Carnot). This is to say, this author adds, "that the internal flow of cognitive life is linked *in an essential manner to a flow of entering information.*" This is another way of expressing what Boltzmann had already foreseen: "Given

---

[1] Ludwig Boltzmann, *Statistical Mechanics and Lessons on the Theory of Gases.*

[2] A. N. Whitehead, *The Concept of Nature* (Cambridge, Cambridge University Press, 1920).

[3] O. Costa de Beauregard, *op. cit.*

the constant growth of this information, living beings, and in particular conscious beings, are obliged to explore the fourth dimension of space-time in the direction in which entropies are increasing, and not in the opposite direction." This is also what Heinrich Heine had perceived intuitively and described in his definition of experience: *"Erfahrung ist eine synthetische Verbindung der Anschauungen."* ("Experience is a synthetic bond of observations," and also of bits of information.)

I might say (and I shall return to this point in detail in a later chapter) that if an organism comes to be deprived of these bits of information by a disorder of functioning, whether of the receptive organs, or of the network of transmission, or of the integrating system, and is thus cut off from external, or internal, communication, it will seem disorganized in space and in time, alienated from these, as it is observed to be in neuroses and psychoses. There will be no need to look for or to allege a disorder due to lesions; the *functional* disorder alone, consisting of a malfunction of the system of communication at any step, will suffice to account for both the disorientation in space as well as for disconnection even from internal times. But before studying these malfunctions, we must better specify the physiological functioning of the nervous system and its relations with the very essence of biological time.

If I have dwelt too long on these considerations, it is because most scholars, including Bergson who implies it, have remarked that in biology the general tendency is to delay any augmentation of entropy. Now this fact is paradoxical, given the Second Law of Thermodynamics (Carnot, Kelvin, Clausius) and the inexorable evolution of the world towards an augmentation of entropy. And this leads us to examine how, in biology, this astonishing augmentation of entropy is effected, or, to put it better, how negentropy diminishes, a mechanism necessary for adaptation to the world, for the struggle for life, and even for preservation against death.

It might be said that, as in the atomic or subatomic level of the mineral world, survival and evolutive entropy are brought about, in biology, by *quantum mechanisms, that is, by abrupt bounds or mutations.*

It is indeed known, and Erwin Schrödinger dwelt heavily on this point, that inert matter would be unstable if there were not quantum discontinuity to maintain the stability of molecular and atomic structures, and thus the stability of this inorganic matter itself. Also the organic stability of biological cells throughout the individual, and above all throughout the species, is maintained throughout the ages, thanks only to a paradoxical instability, linked to quantum discontinuities. Without them the natural physical tendency would be progressive disintegration, in accordance with the Biblical expression: "For dust thou art, and unto dust thou shalt return." Like atoms, cells and genes remain stable only because they are unstable, subject to sudden and determined transitions, the only things capable of correcting and arresting the damages and disintegrations which the continuous variations of classical physics imply, and which would mean destruction, that is, in this context, death. These abrupt discontinuities are *mutations*, and De Vries has rightly insisted on their sudden and revolutionary character, in the light of a progressive and continuous evolution. These mutations constitute for the cells, that is, for organic matter, what the sudden bounds on the quantum level constitute for inorganic matter, the sole saving means of persistence, of discontinuous resistance to a continuous tendency towards physical disintegration; in a phrase, a quantum transition, dynamically adaptative and preservative. It is paradoxically in this discontinuity that *true natural selection* lies; it maintains and reinforces evolution to the extent that it prevents involution, by sudden revolution in the quantum-like mutations.

Do there exist, in the intimate cellular mechanism, other procedures to maintain biological stability by the instability of the exchanges which constitute life itself, in the sense in which Claude Bernard used to say that life is stable only because it is unstable? A living organism, in order to survive, must seek if not to arrest, at least to slow down, all the so-called irreversible phenomena that tend to augment its entropy, and therefore, by way of defense, it must seek to augment its negentropy. Certain products realize this possibility: these are the catalysts. By their temporary chemical-physical combination, they can introduce a temporary metastability, in other respects sometimes dangerous for the entropy of the system as well as for the continuity of metabolic exchanges. But fortunately most of them are more capable of changing the speed of the reaction than the actual equilibrium (or disequilibrium), to which they also often contribute by changing the sign

55

so that positives become negatives, and so favorably reversing a chemical-physical mechanism which they momentarily threatened to block or to exhaust. These biological catalysts are the enzymes or diastases, and their functioning is the basis of organic anabolism and catabolism as well as nervous propagation across the synapses.[1] Substances closely related to the glandular hormones, they are shown to be protectors of entropy and of the vital equilibrium and functionally linked to the hormones themselves, or released by them.

It is clear now why I have dwelt so much on the notions of entropy and negentropy, which are apparently more useful for the understanding of a thermodynamic system than for information about an electronic complex or about the functioning and the equilibrium of the central nervous system; it is because, contrary to appearances, these ideas are fundamental. They permit us to understand, *beyond the structure, the persistence of the function and its equilibrium in a determined time*, whatever the speed or slowness of the reaction itself. In statistical mechanics and in the reversible metabolism of the organism, *time remains an invariant element of the system*. Knowing this will permit us later on to understand more clearly how the human memory functions, for it behaves more in an electric capacity than in a volumetric capacity, capable (in an apparent paradox) of absorbing more the more it is given, if the individual concerned is healthy, that is, if the entropy of his system of information and communication is in active equilibrium.

Finally let us note that, from the biological point of view, it is important to define reversibility and irreversibility, as Max Planck has already attempted to do from the physical-chemical point of view, in his doctoral thesis. For him, an irreversible process is a process that cannot be done backwards, in popular usage cannot make the "trip back." From the biological point of view, this does not exclude the possibility that a final situation analogous to the initial reaction might be encountered again, restored, for example, by the catalytic power of the enzymes. In biology, systems are more complex and less "closed," that is, less isolated than in thermodynamics. Reversible processes are more common, either because they are authentically reversible, or because electrochemical phenomena lead back to an analogous condition, appropriate to good physiological functioning. Irreversible phenomena are more often

---

[1] The details of these mechanisms will be specified in Chapter 18.

the case with pathological states, because the rigidity of a function altered or destroyed by disease prevents the return to the initial state, that is, the *restitutio ad integrum* of health.

But, in biology as in thermodynamics, the *inexorable law of large numbers* must be considered. The brain cells are of the order of 10^{10}, and their actions and reactions, automatically, by their very number, cease to belong to the domain of precise causality and direct finality, and enter the domain of *conditional probability*, as in the case of the molecules in a vortex of a gas. At this point let us consider again the analogy between entropy and the information and communication in an electronic system, and recall Boltzmann's formula, cited in footnote 3 on page 45: $S = K \log P$. A simple inspection of this formula permits us to think that since S is additive, the entropy which it represents could easily be calculated or imitated by a binary digital computer; while P, being multiplicative, will easily be calculated and studied, in the variations of its logarithmic function, by an analog computer.

But, from the function, let us return for an instant to the structure.

The human brain represents, without a doubt, a most extraordinary combination of a series of digital and analog computers, capable of functioning sometimes in series, sometimes in parallel, and all in an extremely small volume. If there are miracles, this is the true miracle of evolution; and even if it has taken nature more than a hundred thousand centuries from hominization to psychogenesis, the present result, although very far from final, is already quite remarkable.

The brain cells, with their afferent and efferent circuits, their synaptic interrupters, their anastomotic connections to the cerebellar, bulbar, thalamic, hypothalamic, sympathetic or glandular relays, constitute a central nervous system nearly a billion times smaller than an analogous system built with triode tubes, a million times smaller than a system in which the circuits were established with transistors, and a thousand times smaller than a system constructed with the most perfected integrated microcircuits on film or silicon which we know of today (1964). Equally as amazing as the small volume of the brain, are, as von Neumann [1] emphasizes, the

---

[1] John von Neumann, *The Computer and the Brain* (New Haven and London, Yale University Press, 1958). *Cf.* Ch. 3, p. 27 of this book.

57

infinitesimal quantities of energy sufficient for its functioning: of the order of 10 to 50 watts per twenty-four hours.

Contrary to some popular opinion, it is not pathological-anatomical surgery, such as the marvelous work of Ramon Y Cajal,[1,2] which one must study in order to comprehend the constant activity of the brain, but rather its living, electric activity. We know indeed that the electric activity of the brain is *constant*, even during sleep, so that the electroencephalogram, while a relatively clumsy device, suffices to detect it. However, even when impolarizable silvered electrodes are used in the encephalogram, that is to say, electrodes not modified by the passage of the currents issuing from the brain, the currents are too weak, of the order of 10 microvolts, to be really significant. In fact, clinical experience proves that the variations in frequency of the oscillations are more important than their amplitude. The essential rhythm, termed alpha rhythm, is around 10 per second, and Wiener thinks that it is this basic rhythm which prevents the eye from perceiving images which last less than one-tenth of a second. We know, besides, that these rhythms are diminished during visual excitations and the active functioning of the brain; increased during certain phases of sleep or of epilepsy; diminished or deformed in certain brain tumors which these rhythms help to locate, according to the position of the bipolar electrodes. But these are, it must be admitted, relatively crude manifestations; one cannot interpret with certainty the details of the variations of these curves, nor recognize to what extent abnormality is due to parasitic currents, of external or internal origin. One must conclude that the information given by the electroencephalogram on the intimate functioning of the brain cells is still relatively accessory and superficial.

In order to appraise with more precision, not the artificial topographic anatomy but the internal functional anatomy of the substance of the brain, in brief, to appraise it in a manner more temporal than spatial, more rigorous methods are necessary.

Five techniques have shed a new light on the detail of the mech-

---

[1] Santiago Ramon Y Cajal, *Histology*. Translated by Nuñez from the tenth Spanish edition (Baltimore, W. Wood and Co., 1933).

[2] *Neuronismo o reticularismo. Las pruebas objectivas de la unidad anatomica de las celulas nerviosas. Consejo superior de investigaciones cientificas,* Instituto Ramon Y Cajal (Madrid, 1952).

anisms: (1) electromicroscopy, (2) the study of optical polarization and of the diffractions of X-rays, (3) the technique of ionophoresis and of the variations of the electrical potential of the membranes, (4) the imitation of the phenomena observed and measured by the first three procedures on binary and analog electronic computers, used separately or in conjunction, and (5) the replacement of the electromechanical electroencephalograms by totally electronic recorders. These recorders are capable of registering effectively, and isolating experimentally, certain cerebral excitations and of following their peripheral nervous propagation, or, on the other hand, of following an excitation from the muscular or sensory periphery along the afferent nerves to the brain; above all they are capable of counting these excitations and measuring them electromagnetically.

There is no doubt that until the last few years, the attempts at cerebral localizations were rather deceptive—the post- and pre-Rolandic sensorimotor localizations and certain language centers (the center of the aphasia of Wernicke, of Broca) apart—insofar as a surprising functional tolerance existed even in the presence of considerable losses of substance. Experimentation on animals, as well as posttraumatic surgery have confirmed the conservation of the memory, of the notion of time, and of most of the discrimination functions of intelligence after extended frontal lobectomies. More localized topectomies, originally performed by Penfield in Canada and Lawrence Pool in New York, conserve all these essential functions, but with a lower level of intensity, which permits their clinical use to reduce anxieties or the otherwise irreducible intensity of certain types of peripheral suffering. In these extended or localized losses of substance, it seems that, along with a certain number of brain cells and a certain volume of afferent and efferent fibers (except, of course, the bundles of pyramidal motor nerve fibers), a certain reactional and functional intensity, quantitative rather than qualitative, is being suppressed, leading to a diminution of the functions without changing their nature.

This proves that beyond the enormous number of the cells, of the circuits, and of their anastomoses, there exists a vast possibility of *substitute* nervous circuits, and that a functional replacement can be made by other zones of the brain often very distant, sometimes even situated in the opposite hemisphere. Let us, however, repeat that what seems true of the functions of memory, of association in-

59

telligence and notions of time and space, is not true of the bundles of motor nerve fibers, which have been determined more authentically, both anatomically and functionally: every lesion of the pyramidal bundle entails a paralysis in the domain of the corresponding efferent fibers and, consequently, of the muscular groups which they control. The same goes for other highly specialized centers, like the centers of language, vision, and hearing.

But, with these exceptions, it is established both physiologically and pathologically that *function far overflows structure and precise localization.* There is, however, in general, a functional predominance of one hemisphere over the other: the left hemisphere is dominant in right-handed people, the right hemisphere in left-handed people. This explains why identical anatomic lesions have a much more destructive influence, from the point of view of function, when the dominant hemisphere is affected than when the accessory hemisphere is involved. We can recall, in this regard, the classic example of Louis Pasteur, who, after a slight softening of the right cerebral hemisphere, had a left hemiplegia. The left cerebral hemisphere was obviously the dominant one in this brilliant right-handed man, judging by the importance of the discoveries which he made even after the hemiplegia.

In the same sense, Christian von Monakow, in his book, *Die Lokalisation im Grosshirn* (1914), destroyed the idea of topographical localization, in order to replace it with what he calls the "chronogenetic engram," his conclusion being that the story of what has happened to the brain cells is more important than their geographical (or topographical) situation: *function specializes more than location justifies.*

Likewise, the American physiologist K. S. Lashley, from Chicago, in 1929 published some experiments which prove, in the rat, that destruction of up to nine-tenths of the brain cells still allows the preservation of the memory of certain training previously given to the animal. He concluded that the memory behaves like a resonance which makes an echo in the whole cortex, rather than in a specialized zone.

We have already discussed Penfield's experiment. By stimulating the patient's brain directly with electric currents, he reactualizes the past for him to the point of presentifying it in all its details and making it lose the character of remembrance associated with memory. The weak currents which Penfield uses are nevertheless quite

60

strong compared to the physiological microcurrents,[1] and it seems that this cerebral overexcitation provokes a delirium of the "memory," analogous to that of hypermnesics. It is possible that the simple pathogenesis is analogous in the two cases: the stimulus is so strong that the subject who undergoes it cannot interpret it as a blurred recognition of the past, as a "trace," but only as a sharp consciousness of the present. In short, this is living proof that memory is never truly recall, but, as Bergson would have it, *recognition* and re-creation of a previous stimulus already undergone. When the stimulus is too strong, it can no longer appear to be past; it is so present that it becomes hallucination. Time and the possibility of recognition are erased experimentally to make room for a *present consciousness of suffering.* Thus the paradoxical words of Oscar Wilde,[2] "Suffering is a long moment," are at once exact and false, exact because suffering dilates the subjective impression of time, false because the moment, by definition, is torn from the duration which the subject cannot perceive, duration which therefore disappears by its artificial and destructive isolation.

By contrast, the alternating currents of higher voltage (110 volts and more) used for therapeutic shock-treatments, have an effect opposite to that of Penfield's localized currents of weak intensity. These high-voltage currents, given in a fraction of a second in a diffuse manner across the cranium with two electrodes, completely disorganize the cortical electromagnetic system, destroying by their intensity certain cells, their functions, and their connections, brutally overflowing the synaptic interrupters. Following the shocks, there is a loss of the memory for recent facts, loss of the notion of time, diminution of intelligence and will; in short exactly what is observed in the hypoamnesias, both anterograde and retrograde, of the great toxic alcoholic psychoses described by Korsakoff. The memory of very old facts is relatively conserved, as if the intoxication or the electric shock affected primarily the more sensitive and more labile mechanisms of the cortex and recent memories, the better to spare the memories sunk deeply in space and internal time: subcortical memories, hypothalamic memories, conserved in the old, vital sensorimotor reflexes of the being's infancy. With time, two to three months usually, the original circuits

---

[1] For the details of these mechanisms, see Chapter 18.
[2] Oscar Wilde, *De Profundis.*

or contiguous ones are re-established, the electrochemical potentials of the membranes of the synapses are restored, and the functions of intelligence and memory are progressively re-established; nevertheless, their potential for activity and for precision remains largely diminished. This is to pay dearly and blindly, if not dangerously, for the relief of depression, obsession, mania, or anxiety. I shall return to this point in the specific study of the pathological cases where these methods have their value, when they are well adapted and sufficiently repeated to relieve, sometimes to cure, a blocked bit of information, or a missing communication link. For the moment, let us be content solely to note, on the level of theory, that to electrical disorders of conduction, we shall oppose in practice a shock, *directly or indirectly electric,* if we wish to counteract them and "liberate" them.

Chapter 6

Some Meta-Physical and Meta-Physiological Remarks

The discussion in the preceding chapter confirms once more that Bergson was right to say, "Time is creation or it is nothing at all." But can we go a bit further in making use of the correlation among the physical, biological, and psychological or psychiatric facts described above?

To be sure, existence implies time, but it does not explain it. And the notion of an absolute time, restricted in the definition of an equally absolute space, such as Newton describes, can of course serve as a practical measure in everyday life, or for approximate astronomical estimation, but it tells nothing about the real essence of time or about its function.

To go as far as to say, with the relativists, that time is a fourth dimension of space, can facilitate the calculation of certain functions or the description of certain phenomena, but at the price of some confusion among nonmathematicians. For if the three directions of space can be represented by a cube, time is not a supplementary direction, but a *distinct* numerical dimension, a supplementary quantitative appraisal. And to state this, moreover, throws no light on the fundamental quality of time.

In point of fact, nothing we have studied about macroscopic times, their interpretation or their human measure, has served to advance the problem. It is on the microscopic, or more exactly ul-

63

tramicroscopic, the atomic, and above all the electronic scale that we have encountered elucidations. It is from these that we must set out if we wish to attempt a philosophical synthesis wherein time serves as a common denominator of physical and biological phenomena, to take on a general meta-physical meaning.

All observations about time and related concerns—its transport, its communication, its revelation, its function, or its real measure (that is to say, whatever the system of reference or of information) —indicate that time is an electromagnetic phenomenon, whose least unit may be approximated with a maximum probability and defined with precision in relation to the mass and the charge of the electron (the chronon).[1] In other words, I am saying, not without serious philosophical consequences, that time is finite, that it can be defined by the nature of the electron.

Let us take up again, from this point of view, the evidence which I have cited in the preceding pages.

And at the outset, as a first example, let us return to the propagation of light, surely an electromagnetic phenomenon. Its velocity of propagation in space implies, by the very definition of velocity, the notion of time.

Without repeating the details described above, let us here recall, to cite only Einstein and Louis de Broglie, that this phenomenon of the propagation of light can be considered sometimes as the propagation of particles of matter, sometimes as the propagation of waves and energy. It can pass from the one to the other, from matter to energy, either in an imperceptible manner, or abruptly in a more discontinuous manner, as when, for example, the light beam strikes against a material object. But in both cases, whether material or electromagnetic, the temporal element is qualitative; it will only become quantitative secondarily, if we wish it to: the perception of time is qualitative, its appreciation already conceptual, that is, internalized.

Considered as attached to matter, time is irreversible; considered as attached to energy, it is transformable, and in certain extreme cases reversible (cf. Boltzmann and H. Reichenbach).[2]

---

[1] See Chapter 17.
[2] H. Reichenbach, *The Direction of Time*, 1956. Following Stueckelberg (1941) and R. P. Feynman (1949), who demonstrated that on the subatomic scale the exchange of quanta between source and receiver cannot be detected,

This is important, for it makes it necessary to conclude that the symmetry attached in general to causality and to finality will have to disappear when large numbers are involved (here of electrons), to make room for purely statistical considerations and for conditional probability. Indeed, time can no longer, in these conditions, find its origin in the elementary phenomena which, theoretically, were supposed to produce it, but on the contrary it is reborn, practically at each instant, of the atomic chaos, a whirlwind which can only be estimated statistically. These findings, revolutionary in physics, touch on the very principle of the sequence of causalities and finalities, as we understand them on the macroscopic scale. If, paradoxically, the ordered and directed times of the macroscopic scale nevertheless persist, this must be attributed to the ephemeral existence of the positrons and other chaotic antiparticles, in the face of the statistical preponderance of the electrons which, themselves, conform to the rule and the general direction of time. There would then be a statistical asymmetry [1] of the duration of negative and positive charges on the subatomic scale which would form the basis of the unidirectional asymmetry of the macroscopic times.

That these considerations do not have a merely speculative value are startlingly confirmed by biology.

Just as on the atomic scale the space traversed by the electrons and the antiparticles has relatively little importance, so, on the cellular scale, the paraphernalia of nervous information and communication seem to lend little aid in the distinction between what is time and what is space. What counts is the electrical energy used to "alert" the equilibrium mechanisms and the electrical energy used to "maintain" this homeostasis.

Let us recall here that the term homeostasis, created by Cannon,[2] refers to the mechanisms assigned to the maintenance of

and that the *positron* (an antiparticle of opposite sign to the electron, but of similar mass) behaves like an ordinary electron "traveling backwards in time," a phenomenon recorded photographically in Wilson's cloud chamber.

[1] Young and Lee (1957) also demonstrated that there is not complete "parity" in the phenomena of nuclear disintegration, electrons, protons, neutrons, and neutrinos. The interreactions are rendered still more asymmetric by the fact that there are no left-spinning neutrinos, and that only right-spinning neutrinos exist in polarized light, a fact that has since been abundantly confirmed.

[2] Walter B. Cannon, *The Wisdom of the Body* (New York, W. W. Norton and Co., 1932).

ceaselessly variable equilibria in the chemical, physical, electrical, and glandular systems, and that this maintenance is effected above all, physiologically speaking, by the law of automatisms described by Tournade d'Alger: "In the organism, the mechanism to be corrected becomes the specific stimulus of the corrective mechanism." As is known, this rule applies as well to the maintenance of the level of the blood sugar, or of the blood pressure, or of the hormonal rate. But it is the function of the nervous system to communicate the necessary information and to effect the adequate correction: About 15 per cent of the total electrical energy of the body is reserved for this very information, whose role is to keep the organism in a state of alert towards threats from the outside world or in the stability of the internal world. Fifteen per cent amounts to about 15 watts, since the total electrical energy used daily by the average man is around 100 watts.

In our study of the intimate mechanism of these biological "communications," three orders of phenomena seem important:

First. For a signal coming either from the outside (visual, for example) or from the inside (as, for instance, an anomaly of tension perceived by the carotid ganglion), it is the constant and present mean variation of the impression that counts, rather than its variation in time; that is, the electrical phenomena which can be recorded in most cases will have a tendency to transform an almost linear static pressure into a pulsed frequency, which is the equivalent of modulated frequency for a radio wave.

Second. Information is not gross, but for various reasons is already selective: because of the number of the sensitive recorders affected, or because an intensity (of light, for example) will be perceived less and less strongly according to the time it lasts, even if it remains equal to itself in intensity, or finally because there exists a minimum threshold of excitation necessary for a sensation to be recordable. If this intensity is below the specific threshold, the phenomenon is not recorded, unless there is a repetition and accumulation of stimuli.

Third. This leads us to the understanding that the organism, superior to the most perfect electronic machines, codes for itself the messages which it receives from the outside or from the inside, and that consequently *message and code* are integrated in their informative values and already discriminative. The alarm signal is al-

66

ready like the "anticipatory response" of a defense mechanism ready to exert itself.

As Otto H. Schmitt, the University of Minnesota zoologist, said (1959): "Biological organisms are mechanisms of probability, and their communications reflect their willingness to grasp a statistical chance of survival in a world full of risks, above all if the chances are good." The same author remarks that the nervous system that "communicates" these bits of information by its refined anastomoses is functionally superior to the transfer systems of the physicists. The latter sometimes correct their signals by means of "feedback," a current of retroaction which acts on the afferent current (on the "input"), as well as in servomotor mechanisms; but these mechanisms rarely show the refinement which biology often adds, namely a regulatory system of preaction, "feed ahead," which anticipates and moderates or exaggerates, according to the requirements of the "cause," the intensity of the afferent current itself. Naturally, the two systems—feedback and feed ahead—are often found in combination, acting in symbiosis, if not in synchronization, and creating a relatively autonomous autoregulatory system (amplificatory or not according to the ideal needs of the afferent or efferent nervous system).

This refinement makes possible in the organism, not only operations of simple transfer, which can be imitated on an arithmetic, binary digital computer, but also functional, logical, nonlinear operations, which approach the complexity of the logarithmic functions of an analog computer. This phenomenon will seem even more remarkable if we add that it all takes place on the periphery of the nervous system (sense organs), or in the ganglions of the autonomic sympathetic system, without yet calling in the temporal function and without utilizing, or even reaching, the cells of the cerebral cortex.

In summary, the modulated frequency of the bits of information and of organic communications is constantly on alert—it would be more exact to say constantly in oscillation—to maintain homeostasis. This electrical nervous network, with its exteroceptive, interoceptive, or proprioceptive sensory antennae, receives the bits of information from the outside or from the inside, beyond space and time, absorbing them into its own frequency, that is, into the organic rhythm. If the excitation coming from outside or the stimulus

67

coming from inside is too strong, the automatic mechanisms of "feedback" or "feed ahead" intervene like a safety valve in order to stabilize, as much in advance as in retrospect, too strong a modification, which, without these stabilizers, could produce too intense a reaction, more disequilibrating than the original excitation. The cure would be worse than the possible disease! Selye sometimes encountered this reaction in situations of prolonged stress; when the reaction of alarm seemed to have overflowed, and the nervous and glandular protective corrections exceeded their goal. A stage of exhaustion then succeeded the stage of resistance, following the initial shock. In this general syndrome of adaptation, Selye recognized the fundamental role of the nervous system in the "alarm" and in the hypophyseo-suprarenal defense mechanism. He also realized that, in the interpretation of the stress syndrome, what proceeds from the threat and what proceeds from the defense must be included. If in spite of the perfection of the nervous system and of the regulatory mechanisms, there is a momentary lag in the transmission time, it is no doubt because of the disturbance, probably electrical, produced in the mechanisms of regulation and transmission during the period of initial shock.

Shock, as we know, is at once vascular, capillary, glandular, and nervous: it upsets the electrochemical mechanisms of defense and disturbs also the potentials of membranes. This is why the re-establishment of a hydrostatic equilibrium of pressure and of a mineral equilibrium is fundamental in allowing the action of the nervous system to be restored.

But let us leave these brutal shocks and inhibitions thereof to return to more moderate, more physiological, and more common conditions, namely, the mechanics of the process by which the organism receives information through the sense organs. This will be the subject of the following chapter, with particular emphasis on the mechanisms of vision and hearing which, more than all the others, communicate to man his feeling of space and his notion of time.

Chapter 7

The Role of the Mechanisms of Vision and Hearing in the Construction of the Notion of Time and Imagination

I will begin by citing three names: Theodore Holmes Bullock[1] and H. K. Hartline,[2] who recapitulated the modern theories of the mechanism of vision and of its neuronic propagation; and Harry Blum[3] who, not knowing of the work of the preceding men, foresaw theoretically and almost precisely, through electronic research, what an artificial model of the visual apparatus would have to contain in order to reproduce the natural function.

From the work of these three men we shall be able to examine to what extent there is selection, differentiation, and temporal integration at the peripheral stage of vision, before the impression reaches the memory or the cortical centers.

The sense organs in general, and vision in particular, serve as detectors and as transformers in order to record the physical events of the outside world and convert them into physiological events in

---

[1] Theodore Holmes Bullock, "Initiation of Nerve Impulses in Receptor and Central Neurons," *Biophysical Science—A Study Program*, J. L. Oncley, Editor (New York, John Wiley & Sons, 1959).

[2] H. K. Hartline, "Receptor Mechanism and the Integration of Sensory Information in the Eye," *Biophysical Science—A Study Program*, J. L. Oncley, Editor (New York, John Wiley & Sons, 1959).

[3] Harry Blum, "An Associative Machine for Dealing with the Visual Field and Some of Its Biological Implications." *Biological Prototypes and Synthetic Systems*, Vol. 1 (New York, Plenum Press, 1962).

the organic world. How are this information and this communication processed on the level of the retina?

The eye is a photoreceptive organ, extraordinarily refined, though limited, since it takes luminous information only from the domain of ultraviolet up to but excluding the domain of infrared. The bits of electromagnetic information are concentrated on the retina by a wide-angle lens. This crystalline lens does not constitute a static replica, a photograph, of space, but rather a dynamic interpretation, already geometrical and temporal, of space and its content.

We know that all electromagnetic radiation, in order to make an effect on a material system, must give up a part of its energy to it. This certainly occurs in vision: There is absorption of a part of the spectrum of light by the photosensitive receptors of the retina.

These receptors consist essentially, as we know, of rods and cones. "Rhodopsin" is a photosensitive protein concentrated at the end of the rods, joined to an aldehyde, retinin (a carotinoid substance), whose corresponding alcohol is vitamin A. This explains the better night vision of subjects whose food is rich in vitamin A or in carotin, and inversely the deficiency of photosensitive pigments in A avitaminosis. Iodopsin is the photosensitive substance of the cones. These two pigmentary substances, *in vivo* as well as *in vitro*, are subject to photolysis, and then to regeneration, which accounts for the absence of permanent images and therefore for the possibility of successive images on the retina.

Let us note, before going further, two important anatomical facts: first, Sjöstrand,[1] of the Karolinska Institute of Stockholm (1963), has found, through electromicroscopic study, that the ends of the rods have a *lamellar* (foliated) structure, favorable to the exercise of the membrane potentials and the phenomena of semipermeation and semiconduction; second, it is a well-known fact that the deep layer of the retina is, in anatomical, embryological, and phylogenetical terms, a layer of *brain* cells, located for once on the periphery. This means that the communication between the superficial sensory layer and the deep cortical layer of the retina will be very *short*, and therefore very quick. This also means that there will be little occasion for loss of energy in the transport of information.

In point of fact, the human eye can discern energy as weak as 100 quanta of light energy, a phenomenon all the more remarkable in

---

[1] F. S. Sjöstrand, *J. Cellular Comp. Physiology 42–15* (1953).

that 90 per cent of the quanta are absorbed by the internal media of the eye, and only the remaining 10 per cent strike the retina. That energies so weak can be discerned is due to two functional circumstances: one, these numerous rods and cones can be affected by just one light stimulus to reach the threshold of visibility; two, the absorption does not take place in a uniform manner, neither quantitatively nor qualitatively. Quantitatively, the frequency engendered is relatively proportional to the intensity received. Qualitatively, on the one hand, the retina is more sensitive to variations and to their suddenness than to a continuous excitation; on the other hand, the distribution of the absorption is discontinuous: each sensory cell absorbing electromagnetic energy inhibits its immediate neighbors, which has the effect of heightening the contrast.[1] We see already that the "representation" of the retina is more useful than faithful. This usefulness, moreover, is primarily for self-protection: the proportion noted above between the intensity and the frequency is of the logarithmic order (Fechner's law: small changes in frequency relative to large changes in luminous intensity); also, a persistent luminous excitation makes relatively little impression on the retina during its state of summation, however long it lasts. The maximum is always perceived at the moment of change, that is, at the time of the appearance or disappearance. All these phenomena leave the rods and cones with greater dynamic plasticity and receptivity for new impressions and at the same time induce, in the discharge of impulses, a sort of modulation, which, I repeat, constitutes a frequency modulation.

Given these specifications, one can understand how these electromagnetic excitations, selectively absorbed by the cones and rods of the surface layer, record colors, forms, displacements, hence velocities, and even times. But how are these excitations transmitted?

This is a complicated mechanism, for to these external times are added internal delays and supplementary selections, resulting from the mechanism of the nervous discharge and of its centripetal propagation in the cylindraxes of the neurons and across the synapses. I should say at the outset that the mechanism is both electrical and chemical and also that the all-or-none principle, which I have re-

---

[1] The greater portion of these phenomena could not be verified for the vertebrates, but were found in the retina of the common crab (Limulus), where the retinal cells are more dissociated.

peatedly described in order to simplify my discussion, does not come completely into play in a receptive instrument as highly specialized, sensitive, and refined as the eye.

In a general way, every excitation produces a depolarization of the membrane of the nerve cells which increases the probability of a discharge. Inversely, polarization or hyperpolarization tends to inhibit the discharge. These diverse processes are not, as one might suppose, solely linked to stimulation coming from the outside, but are in large part owing to the *delay* which these nerve cells themselves produce in their execution. In short, this means that the transmission of the discharge, "of the communication," will also be a function of the previous state of the nerve cells themselves, of the axons, of the synapses, of what might be called the rest potential.

It has been observed through electromicroscopy that the synapses are plates of junction—here, between one nerve and another—and that they are not anatomically continuous, only extremely contiguous. Communication across these relays, which act like unidirectional valves, permitting the passage of current only from the presynaptic fibers to the postsynaptic fibers, is accomplished by a chemical mediator, acetylcholine.[1] This substance, even in an infinitesimal dose, has a facilitating action on the permeability of the electric relay which the synapse constitutes.

The phenomenon is further complicated by the fact that the neurons themselves are traversed by basic microcurrents, which are called spontaneous, insofar as they exist independent of any outside stimulus, and which occur in continual peaks. In a certain sense these basic currents protect the neurons against the explosive depolarizations of an abrupt external stimulation, for example at the reversal of an excessive repolarization. Electronically, they may have the drawback of constituting a "noise," that is, a continuous parasite that will always have to be distinguished from the principal signal. But they are what prevent the crudeness and rigor of the "all or none."

The details of these phenomena suggest that nervous transmission might well not be linear.

Thus, independent processes of the variations of the membrane potentials, linked to the structure of the neurons as well as to the function of the synapse, come to modify anew the times of nervous

---

[1] See Chapter 18 for further details.

propagation, according to whether their previous state induces a facilitating action or not, that is, retards or accelerates propagation in the nerves. It is true that these phenomena especially come into play for weak excitations, below the threshold of normal intensity. But these mixtures of excitation and inhibition in the propagation of information are important to retain if we seek to copy their intimate mechanism in an artificial electronic model. Let us keep but one rule to this end: a neuron, with its synaptic valves, will have a response differing over time according to its own condition and its activity immediately previous, that is, according to its "hysteresis."[1]

It is as if the neuron and the synapse already "remembered" functionally, although there cannot yet be any question of real memory. The cells of the cortex have not yet been reached; the afferent fibers which will constitute the optic nerves are not yet constituted, and they are far from having reached the centers of vision of the occipital region in the area of the Calcarin fissure. But, as we have described, visual electromagnetic excitation has nevertheless already been absorbed, selected, differentiated, programmed at the periphery, and integrated in the proper sense of the term.

Let us add to all this the various muscular movements involved in vision—the synchronized movements of the head, the movements of the extrinsic muscles of the eyes, the contractions of the intrinsic muscles of the eye in order to adapt the convergence of the lens to distances or to contract the iris or diaphragm of the eye (the first electronically controlled automatic diaphragm!), according to the intensity of light—and we may marvel at the complexity of the synergic, if not always synchronic, mechanism which permits binocular vision and consequently, outside of flat space, the vision of objects in relief.

To facilitate their judgment of light or of space over a period of time, men have the "habit," in this case purely symbolic, of coding what they see in language. This coding gives them increased speed in judging what has previously been seen. For example, to see an upright chair is to be aware immediately that it has four legs, without concentrating one's attention on them, for one knows through many previously coded and decoded experiences that the chair would not be able to stand upright otherwise.

This language code permits more rapid recognition of all colors,

---

[1] See Chapter 15 for details concerning the phenomenon of hysteresis.

all forms, all objects seen before. The proper names of casual acquaintances are also part of the code, for by the code name one can verify the identity of a person almost without taking the trouble to look at him. The time of recording bits of visual information in the memory will therefore be reduced. For example, one is able, in a flash, to establish that there are two tables, four armchairs, two chairs, a piano, two bookcases, and four lamps, in a room. Closing one's eyes one can easily see them again, re-evoking them through the internal word which helps to decode the memory and to restore the images around the symbols of the names, clothing the objects in light intensity and dressing them with colors. For the imagination, in its restorative expression, remains or becomes impressionistic.

As the imagination restores the programming of symbols, the "*déjà vu*," by means of the language code, it can, in a certain sense, hinder future visual perception, by withholding the necessary attention. One comes, by laziness in concentration, to accept only what is analogous to what one has seen before, rejecting the details of the new perception.

For example, a traveler in a train sees the countryside slip past and records almost automatically houses, fields, animals—codes, words, stereotypes—but not *these* houses, *these* fields, *these* animals. As he does not fix his attention, he does not record accurately and he commits other sensory errors: he has the impression that the telegraph poles are moving with the train and that the countryside in the background is moving in the opposite direction. He accepts this error. If asked at what point this illusory and paradoxical optical inversion takes place, he does not know. In fact, the point where the pivot of this illusory axis turns is precisely the point at which he fixes his glance.

When the message of a sensory receptor is not accepted, the whole system of information and communication is falsified. The notion of time is lost along with the notion of velocity, an internal analogic vision is confused with the real external vision, which is allowed to slip past.

But in contrast to these frequent cases where imagination and memory hinder perception, there are others where, on the contrary, they sharpen, correct, and complete vision. Thus a lover of painting familiar with the style of Van Gogh or Manet, when viewing an unfamiliar painting by the same master, can see infinitely more, and more quickly, than an individual who lacks this particular kind of comparative and anticipatory imagination.

74

Better still, speculative imagination can correct a real error of optics; it is a classic fact that a stick half immersed in water seems bent, as a result of the difference between the index of refraction in air and in water. This optical illusion is "real," if indeed these two terms, "illusion" and "real," can be paired at all. (By the way, we know that a photograph will reproduce the illusion, and thus the error.) But the corrective imaginative judgment knows full well that water cannot bend a straight stick. La Fontaine, in the fable of the heron, makes an allusion to this correction by the imagination: *"Quand l'eau courbe un bâton, ma raison le redresse."* (When the water bends a stick, my reason straightens it.) In fact, the straight-line connotation of the word stick (when it is not accompanied by a corrective epithet) helps to correct the communication of the erroneously transmitted bit of information. The geometrical vision of forms facilitates the vision of spatiotemporal space and its pertinent interpretation.

It is remarkable that the modalities of this mechanism of human vision can at last be verified, by their imitation on an artificial electronic apparatus. Such an apparatus was conceived and described, but not realized, by Harry Blum [1] (1962), director of electronic research at Bradford (Massachusetts). Without entering into details for which the interested reader can refer to the original publication, I shall say merely that the author gives proof of the possibility of such a realization. In this connection, Harry Blum insists on the value of a simplified physical and experimental method which, on the one hand, does not have the logical limitations or the complexities of a mathematical theory, but which, on the other hand, possesses all the practical plasticity of experimental physics, "imitating" the organism according to the requirements of the "cause," or more exactly *according to the necessities of the effects one is attempting to reproduce,* that is, to understand and evaluate. This is a flexible experimental application of what cybernetics predicates and investigates.

Thus, to cite only a few essential points, Harry Blum starts from the principle that all man's sense organs, except hearing and smell, give essentially spatial information, for the most part in two dimensions. That is true for touch, and still more so for vision, which is, from this point of view, the most refined apparatus. Studying electromagnetic wave propagation, he distinguishes between two kinds

---

[1] Harry Blum, *op. cit.,* p. 224.

of space: a space of transformation and a space of association. He demonstrates that the first is a *function of time,* because in the absence of excitation, intensity is 0, and when excitation is set up it becomes 1 "for a certain time interval." In addition, the receptors of the periphery, such as the cells of the retina described above, are excitable in a *"determined time,"* *i.e.,* at the moment the front of the wave reaches the receptor and transmits an afferent excitation, which is proportional to the angle of attack and to the number of receptors touched *"at each instant of time."*

Without going further in the description of this first space, which Blum calls "neurospace," let us pass to the second variety, space of association, that is, of communication and, if we will, of amplification. This can become a vehicle for the exchange in parallel of the functions of time. A spatial memory, thus quantized in time, becomes in a way a continuous linear space, practically without limit, whatever the number of additions. Simultaneity is "represented" in this space by geometric figures rather than by arithmetic ciphers. The selectivity of interferences, the procrastination of nonrecognitions, underlines the importance of the *delays* whose maximum is a complete inhibition. Just as in Uttley's machine, delay (in the cells of the retina, there is also the inhibition of the neighbors of the excited elements) constitutes a selective, that is, a conditional, principal stimulus: it conditions by its peripheral reactions to the "input," that is, by afferent waves, the element which anticipates and provokes rapid central recognition. This element is important for the survival of the animal, because it enables him to recognize previous dangers or favorable situations. In the electronic model it is an element of rapid and selective functioning.

According to Harry Blum, all these conditions are realizable in a relatively simple (though complex) manner, in a system which combines photoreceptive diodes and magnetic elements for the space of transformation, and combines magnetic cores and amplifying or retarding filters with "feedback" and interconnections for the space of association.

But in the model, as in nature which it imitates, time always remains a *function derived from space* at the moment when it can be traversed in the geometrical perception of electromagnetic memory or of the cortical imagination. In this sense one might say that every image is a symbol of space and time, since it is perceived in space and conceived in time. This gestation by space and time (even if it

76

is infinitely weak) also takes place, like every gestation, *during* time; the trace develops, that is, becomes located and schematized in the memory, always ready to come to light again in image or action, which itself implies a new time for the order and its execution.

This long preliminary analysis has been necessary to make clear an important concept: the mechanism of vision is electromagnetic and perfectly comparable to that of television. The retina corresponds to the recording and scanning photographic apparatus which analyzes and converts for transmission *a model of space into a sequence of time.* The receiver apparatus synthesizes and reconverts this electrical sequence by an inverse mechanism and sends it across a second "scanner" to re-create the image of space on the screen.

It is more than likely, given the electromagnetic mechanism of vision, that this is the same process which creates the image of space in the brain and that herein lies the origin of the imaginative mechanism. The conservation of the image or of the inherent time would take place by polarization in the cells of the cortex, just as images are recorded in the "memory" of polyvinyl tape. And imagination in action would consist of the creation, the development, or the re-creation of an image or of a series of images coming, this time, from *inside* the memory, independent of any supplementary excitation coming from *outside* (such as the original image or the original record).

During the period of conservation—in a man's memory just as on tape—electrical intensity is zero. The memory is as a dead registration, since it is "crystallized" by *electromagnetic polarization or hyperpolarization,* without an actual effector current, without possibility of discharge. The image is in reserve, stripped of dimensions, hence of space, and excluded from duration, hence from time. But when a current 1, analogous to the current of the original registration, is re-established—which in a tape is done by re-establishing the current, and in a man by fixing the attention [1]—the image reappears, for it finds itself reinvested with a temporal quantity and with a spatial quality by a *depolarizing* mechanism which is the opposite of the one that held it in reserve and which provokes the discharge.

---

[1] At the fixation of the attention, the waves recorded by the electroencephalogram always show, even when the eyes are closed, a modification of the amplitude and the frequency of the rhythms. *Cf.* Walter Grey, *The Living Brain* (New York, W. W. Norton and Co., 1963).

In this sense the human memory, like tape recording for electronic machines, constitutes a sort of interior space, held in reserve with time 0 in the period of conservation, but always available when time is "retrieved" with an intensity 1, when the current is re-established. When we speak here of current, we mean a *simple electric current* and not the figurative current of a river, of a flow, which is wrongly appropriated to time.

The time which reappears at the re-establishment of an electric current, *is not the current* itself, but rather its consequence, that is to say, the electromagnetic revival of the primitively recorded datum which finds itself revealed anew. Thus considered, time would rarely be the *actualization* produced by this current capable of transforming the potential into the real, of revealing the virtual into the actual (in the differential and integral sense of these terms). It is no longer a space traversed, but space held in reserve for the security and success of the individual. In this context, success has its precise etymological meaning, *"that which comes after,"* rather than its common meaning, "accomplishment," which is only a consequence.

Let us note finally that physiologically, during sleep, the unconscious person reproduces purely spatial images, stripped of temporal character. It is as if the spontaneous currents of the dream period lacked the essential "scanning" connection, that is, the essential reconverting element which constitutes the consciousness and its attention, generator and director of current. To recall our comparison with magnetic tape: during the dream, it is as though the tape were unrolling without being connected to the fourth dimension, in the tape, sound, in the dream, time. The dream is a mute unrolling of images.

However this may be, organic experience, like experience with the electronic models, seems to indicate that the time of the original sensation is shorter than the time of the re-created feeling. In some instances, however, "habit" and hysteresis facilitate the traverse of the automatic circuits in a negative direction and tend to attenuate, without, however, entirely suppressing these differences. In electronic apparatus the filters, sometimes acting as detectors, sometimes as retransmission apparatus, are probably responsible for these differences; in man the analogous mechanism is the neuroglia of the brain, an element less noble and less specialized than the cells of the cortex, but which nonetheless constitutes an apparatus of transmission and of selective procrastination, a veritable filtering relay.

78

In the machine conceived by Harry Blum, as in the human brain, experience might be defined as the recognition of the coexistence of a certain spatiotemporal order, of an almost geometric image in this space-time combination, which resolves itself in an integral differentiation when, from being static, it again becomes dynamic, again a variable function of the space and the time in which will or desire reconstitutes it, and reprojects it, in some fashion, from the *inside* towards the outside.

In this sense the will originally would be merely the desire to re-create in the outside world the circumstances of coincidence and simultaneity of an image which has met the test: the test of security, of pleasure, of efficacy, or simply of meaning. In this sense also, the so-called free arbiter of voluntary choice would be only an appearance, since it is limited in reality by the determinism of a previous choice, resulting from an experience stored up in the memory. Still more briefly, will would be merely the choice of recognizing in the present an image, and hence a consciousness of the past, and of *reactualizing it in an activity which leads to action.* In other words, a conscious choice is unconsciously determined. *Volition becomes capability only if capability is already knowledge.* Experimentally, this formula is verified in the action of man as in the function of the machine.

The details that I have given on the communication of elctromagnetic spatiotemporal information by the eye will permit me to be more brief on the subject of its reception by the ear. But I must remark at the outset that this appraisal requires, in general, the synchronization of reception by sight and hearing. When one sees lightning in the sky and there is a hiatus before one hears the thunder, one receives an immediate gift of the notion of distance, a more precise gift if one knows that the visual reception of the lightning is almost instantaneous (an electromagnetic phenomenon propagated at 186,000 miles per second), while the wave of the material propagation of sound in the air is around 1,100 feet per second. In contrast, it will be observed that a blind man, even if his sense of hearing is overdeveloped, will have a less pertinent appreciation of time and of space and of the notion of velocity than a normal man, in the same way that a man who sees will be more easily "disoriented" in space and time, if he is hard of hearing.

The material waves of sound are characterized by a direction of vibration, either longitudinal or transverse, in relation to the axis of

79

propagation. These waves are defined by two essential properties: (a) their pressure, that is, their force per unit of surface (expressed in general in dynes/cm²); (b) their amplitude, that is, their temporal rhythm (usually figured as a sinusoid and expressed in cycles per second).

We might add that these material waves (especially at low, audible frequencies) are easily reflected and diffused by the air, so that they are not stopped by the passage of material objects. The frequency of sound waves extends from practically 0 to 1,000,000 cycles per second. But the human ear can only perceive waves from 20 to 21,000 cycles per second, and it is most sensitive to waves between 50 to 10,000 cycles per second. The most useful register for emitting or receiving communications is obviously that of the human voice (50 to 500 cycles per second). The sound register of a piano extends from 27.2 cycles to 4,138.4 cycles per second. The speed of sound propagation is, in the air at 32°F, 1,087 feet per second, a speed independent of the frequency. This last fact is very important, because it explains why the high and low notes of an organ or of an orchestra are received synchronously.

Let me add that the intensity of sound perceived diminishes in inverse relation to the square of the distance from the source of emission and proportionally to the square of the amplitude of the wave (in the audible zone of course). Finally, I should mention that the human ear, at the extreme lower limit, is sensitive to a variation in pressure of 0.0002 dynes/cm² (that is, corresponding to the extreme minimum of material agitation in our outside environment) and that at the upper limit of tolerance it is sensitive to 200 dynes/cm². It is thus a register of phenomenally high sensitivity, since it goes from 1 to a million. For practical purposes, the human ear finds its maximum of sound receptivity at an amplitude of 1,000 cycles per second.

This is not the place to describe the outer ear which, although fixed in man, has folds of cartilage that reflect the sounds and direct them towards the external auditory canal. If these folds are evened out with wax, hearing is very much diminished. Nor shall we dwell on the transmission apparatus which is made up of the three articulated little bones of the middle ear: the hammer, the incus, the stirrup. We shall rather concentrate solely on the cochlear apparatus of the vestibule of the inner ear. It is at this level that *the mechani-*

80

cal wave is transformed into an electrical wave, that is, into a nervous influx.

Without entering into the details of the vestibulary apparatus of the inner ear, let us simply say that when a sudden noise strikes the cochlear membrane, the cavity of the labyrinth seems to be divided into three compartments by the membranes: an upper compartment called vestibulary, communicating with the oval window, through which the sound waves penetrate; a lower part called the tympanic, which communicates with the middle ear through the round window; and between the two, the middle or cochlear part, the most important functionally, which contains the basilary membrane and the organ of Corti. The bipolar auditory cells which constitute the organ of Corti, with their internal and external vibratory filaments floating in the liquid of the inner ear, seem stretched between the basilary membrane below and the tectorial membrane above. It is their afferent axons which constitute the auditory nerve, the eighth cranial pair.

Until the last few years, it was thought, following Helmholtz, that these cells constituted only resonators vibrating selectively according to the frequencies of sound with which they harmonized. Today it is known with certainty, thanks to the work of G. von Békesy [1] who won the Nobel Prize in 1961 for his study of the physiology of hearing, that hearing is essentially a matter of a *piezoelectric* phenomenon. In the same way that the deformation of the surface of a quartz crystal engenders an electric current,[2] the movements of the basilary membrane in the ear, mainly under the influence of sound waves, deform the cells of the organ of Corti and engender a current by variation of the potential of the membrane of the cells. Von Békesy measured these currents, which are linked to the orientation of the atoms of these biological structures, and he concluded that they were not sufficient to account for all the energy of the phenomenon. He demonstrated that a continuous potential was added to the currents, resulting from the difference in potential between

---

[1] G. von Békesy, "The Ear," *Scientific American*, 1957; *Journal*, Acoustic Society of America (Vol. 24, 1952).

[2] It is known that, inversely, when an electric current is applied to both faces of a quartz crystal, a sound is produced which is proportional to the intensity of the current. This inverse piezoelectric effect permits the production of the whole gamut of "ultrasounds," audible or inaudible.

the *scala media,* which is positively charged at +50 millivolts, and the cells of the organ of Corti, which have a negative polarity of −50 millivolts. Thus, there exists a sort of continuous microphonic cochlear potential (the Wever-Bray effect) [1] that can be modulated: *frequency modulation* probably, set in motion by the piezoelectric currents, linked to the movements of the basilary membrane, from the reception of the sound wave.

Thus, as in the mechanism of vision, where a bit of electromagnetic spatial information is transformed into a temporal sequence, here the material information and the spatial mechanics are transformed, as in a microphone (or a telephone receiver), into an electric wave, a *temporal* modulation of frequency, ready to be propagated in a centripetal nervous influx towards the cortex by means of the auditory nerve, which merely transmits the communication.

I shall intentionally not speak here of olfactory information, for although it is also extraordinarily sensitive and selective, the spatial communications which it reveals are very limited and the temporal relations are almost nonexistent, without being totally absent (E. D. Adrian).[2] Nor shall I dwell on the organs of touch, distributed over the whole cutaneous surface, for the information received from them is mostly spatial and only becomes temporal insofar as, through feedback and association, the organs enter into proprioceptive communication with the muscles following their posture or the work they have done.

On the other hand, we cannot bring this chapter to a close without highlighting the extraordinary *functional synergies* between the apparatuses of seeing and hearing in the judging of time and space, in the harmony of behavior and of equilibrium, which the human being requires in order to live in space and act in time. To be sure, the functioning of the two eyes contributes more to vertical equilibrium and that of the two ears to lateral equilibrium. And just as there is always a cerebral hemisphere which is functionally, if not anatomically, dominant, in the same way there is always a directing eye (which guides, even if one is aiming a rifle with both eyes open) and a directing ear which predominates functionally and musically. That is why a lesion in one side of the mechanism of sight or hearing

---

[1] E. G. Wever, *Theory of Hearing* (New York, John Wiley & Sons, 1949).
[2] E. D. Adrian, *British Medical Journal* (No. 1, 1954).

will have greatly varying consequences, depending on whether or not the directing side is affected.

These phenomena can, moreover, be verified physiologically in the extraordinary functional associations between the ear and the vocal cords.

As Tomatis [1] points out, there exists a remarkable symbiosis between our apparatus of auditory information and that of spoken communication, between the ear and the voice, and for a simple functional reason, though one often forgotten: a man is his own primary audience. The human voice is essentially under the control of the ear, totally dependent on it. Not only are those persons mute who are born deaf, a fact of common knowledge; but one can alter the voice of a subject with normal hearing either by "dazing" his ear with intense or continuous noise, or more specifically by introducing selective electronic filters to suppress the auditory control of the voice in certain specific frequency bonds. One then observes, even in good speakers, important alterations of tonality, of rhythm, and of words: the voice becomes monotone, it stumbles; one can even create stammering experimentally. John Lee and John Black, of the Ohio State University at Columbus, were able to specify the retardation which must be introduced into the feedback of the auditory control to provoke stammering: it is of the order of 0.15 seconds.

These facts are obviously pregnant with therapeutic consequences which clinical experience verifies. Pathogenically and by analogy with the electronic machines studied above, we see clearly that the auditory mechanism conditions verbal communication, not so much by simple information as by a *conditional temporal factor*, not only by feedback which regulates vocal intensity, but also by feed ahead which anticipates and corrects tonality, that is, quality.

One may verify this in a still more experimental way if one studies the phonograms and oscilloscopic sonographs of singers. When their directing ear is spontaneously altered by illness or experimentally obstructed, one witnesses the formation of vocal "holes," proving beyond doubt that any loss of musical sense by expert singers depends directly on the disturbances of their auditory apparatus.

Just as the retina can undergo temporary inhibition when it is

---

[1] Alfred Tomatis, *L'oreille et le langage* (Paris, Editions du Seuil, 1963).

83

dazzled by an excess of light, so can the ear undergo temporary inhibition from an excess of noise. It is in this sense that we speak of "auditory scotoma," by analogy with visual scotoma. But it is interesting to note that auditory scotoma is always accompanied and followed by vocal scotoma. We shall come across these mechanisms again at their maximum in certain cases of total aphasia, following what has been called "verbal" blindness and deafness.

There is no doubt that these deficiencies are auditory and visual, before becoming verbal.

Chapter 8

Information and Nervous Communication,
Their Probable Process of Cerebral
Integration

All the fragmentary facts that have been described successively
in connection with the mechanism of seeing and hearing—the conditional models of Uttley, the functioning of the memory, the study
of electromagnetic times, the relations between information and
negentropy, the continuous subjective relativity of our knowledge
in regard to the discontinuous objective absolute of the spatiotemporal elements insofar as they proceed by quanta of energy—
all these form a meaningful whole. They permit me now to make
my point and to take a general synthetic view of the mechanism
and of the nature of these diverse processes, as well as of the
ties that link and even unify them.

But first a preliminary remark is imperative, a remark that John
von Neumann [1] made in a written presentation for Yale, but which
his premature death did not allow him to deliver.

In describing influx or nerve impulses as they are propagated
along the neurons of the nerve tissues, across the synapses, and in
the nerve cells, one can speak of the electric current itself, of the
variations of the potential of the membranes, or of the chemical reactions, depending on the orientation of one's experiments or on

---

[1] John von Neumann, *The Computer and the Brain* (New Haven and London, Yale University Press, 1958).

one's particular interests. The choice of terms is not important, for on the molecular scale where these phenomena are studied, *there is no real difference, nor is a true distinction possible between an electrical, chemical, or mechanical phenomenon.* On the molecular or electronic scale, these phenomena are all in such close correlation that they are mixed up. "Bearing in mind," says von Neumann, "the fact that the thickness of the cell membranes of the neurons and of the nerve cells is of the order of a few tenth-microns (*i.e.,* 10^{-5} centimeters), a figure which is of the order of that of the large protein molecules, there can be no mechanical change in the position or the chemical composition of the molecules concerned, without a corresponding change in the electrical properties and the levels of electric potential."

Consequently, it matters little whether the initial electric stimulus is described as coming from the outside, following an excitation of the sense organs, or provoked by a chemical modification in the level of a dendrite receptor; the result is the same. What counts is the behavior of this provoked electrical nervous impulse which, we have seen, is of an intensity of the order of 50 millivolts and of a duration of around one millisecond. The important thing is that this nerve stimulation, depending on whether or not it passes the necessary minimum threshold for the excitation of the nerve, succeeds or does not succeed, exists or does not exist, in its action and its propagation. We have already marked out this phenomenon under the name "all or nothing." By its nature it seems that it should be recorded in a part of the brain which would be analogous to a digital computer, recording either 1, or 0, depending on whether the excitation passes or does not pass the threshold.

But beyond this completely binary and completely arithmetic initial simplicity, we know that nervous system phenomena are more complex.

To describe only some of the essential possibilities of nerve conduction functioning, let us first recall that the "all or nothing" is not so strict as it seems. An excitation which does not succeed nevertheless leaves a "trace" on the neuron, a charge; with a small additional charge, by "summation," the threshold can be reached or surpassed. Besides, several simultaneous neural excitations can converge on a single synapse in order to pass it. The synapse thus acts at times like a valve, at times like a condenser, letting the current pass in a single direction, slowing it down *in certain temporal*

86

proportions, which gives the appearance of choice and *probably creates the reality of the logical, analog intelligent process.*

In effect, reduced to these simpler terms, intelligence is only the selection of an appropriate response.[1,2] Now this selection, like this response, is only made possible by procrastination, as we have already pointed out in the formation of the notion of time in the child and in the functioning of Uttley's electronic models with their retarding "leaks." When we cease to consider only a single neural impulse in a single neuron (as in the simple binary response described above), and consider several neurons acting in *parallel* on a synapse, it is necessary to arrive at a notion of an organic complexity fulfilling, in the brain, the necessary conditions for the function of an analog computer.

This is the beginning of logic.

It should be pointed out at the outset that the analog computer of the brain is not created by the individual, but that the nervous current of many neurons creates and progressively conditions in its totality this very computer. One step further, and I shall say that this current creates the individual himself, his personality and his so-called personal logic, born in fact of the exercise of a conditioning function, itself the result of circumstances!

With von Neumann, we note that the brain's analog computer has the constitutional advantage of often functioning in parallel, not in series. When the nervous impulses of two neurons act *simultaneously,* the first operation and logical consequence is an operation of *conjunction,* which can be formulated by *and.* If one of the two impulses is retarded or disturbed in its development, the second logical operation is one of *disjunction* which can be formulated by *or,* accordingly as one or the other stimulation reveals itself in activity. Finally, if these two nervous impulses are negated, either by a lack of intensity or by a refractory state of the neurites, or by an electrical or chemical blockage of the synapses, the logical operation is *negation,* and the response formulated is *no. And, or,* and *no* sum up, in the "analog" behavior of the nervous system, the origin of logic, indeed the basis to which all the operations of

---

[1] Michael J. Pedelty, *An Approach to Machine Intelligence* (Washington, D.C., Spartan Books, 1963).

[2] W. Ross Ashby, *An Introduction to Cybernetics* (New York, John Wiley & Sons, 1963).

the intellect, as complex as they may be, can in all cases be referred and reduced.

Anatomically, the individual constituents of man's nervous system behave individually and ideally in a binary and digital manner for strong and simple excitations. *Physiologically* and functionally, however, the intricate and imbricated nervous network, ceaselessly traversed by weak impulses, which, depending on the circumstances, are added or subtracted or multiplied or divided in their effects, behaves like a group of waves. Consequently, instead of a simple, unequivocal arithmetic response, there are *pulsed responses*, more or less retarded, more or less periodic, whose frequency will always be a "monotonic" function of the intensity of the stimulus. It is this sort of modulated frequency of the information system which I have already pointed out in the functioning of the retina, where the intensities are translated into frequencies and into colors. As von Neumann has said, in dealing with an analog computer, "it is then the mean density of a sequence of impulses (over time) which will constitute the number to represent." In the organism, it obviously cannot be a question of number, but of a *message of statistical character*, in a way symbolic, which marks a specific occurrence. This symbolization very likely happens in the relatively peripheral cells: in the third cell layer of the retina (already cerebral) electromagnetic waves are "transformed" into colors; in the peripheral cells of the organ of Corti in the inner ear mechanical sound waves are "transformed" through a piezoelectric mechanism into electric nervous current. Symbolization supposes *transformers* (in the electrical sense of the term) which are *already interpretative*.

What these messages lose in mathematical precision, they will regain in logical security for the whole of the phenomenon considered, here of color or of sound. Paradoxically, this nonnumerical and, in appearance only, imprecise response, will gain in *functional efficacy*, as much for its logical interpretation as for its retention in the memory. In fact this symbolization constitutes an autoprogramming, coded in key words, which, whether formulated or not, *will in the future trigger the possibility of a swift response*, i.e., *quick action therefrom*.

These are essential problems, and ones that will confront us in the next chapters.

Chapter 9

The Functional Memories

From all the preceding—in particular Chapter 4, where we studied the development of the notion of time in the child and the progressive formation of the various instinctive, rational, or social and autistic memories, as well as their pathological exaggerations and reductions—we can draw an analysis of what the memory is not, before coming to a synthesis of what it is.

The memory is not, as it has often been described, an automatic element, isolated, unique, localized, static, capable of definitive and permanent recording. On the contrary, the memory, or rather the *memories*, constitutes a multiple, functional whole, diffused throughout the nervous system of the body, dynamic and capable of bringing about a temporary modification, facilitating an eventual secondary revival.

The memory is neither perception nor the communication of perception, nor its amplification, nor its conservation, nor its disappearance, nor its re-evocation. Rather it is all these things in one: *It is the function which places man in time, sometimes outside, sometimes inside space.* What is more, born of space and time, the memory is as capable of actualizing the real as it is of dissociating space and time, and can actually re-create them if external or internal circumstances prompt it or allow it.

To describe the memory as a function successively of recording,

89

of conservation, and of evocation, or again of apprehension, of fixation, and of recall, is both inexact and too narrow.

Inexact, because the use of the word "successive" implies, without explaining, the inclusion of the temporal element. Too narrow, because this fragmentary nomenclature excludes the possibility of *simultaneity*, an essential part of the function. Inexact and too narrow above all because, thus limited, the function of remembering and recollection is deprived of life, stripped of its essential quality: its pulsional constancy, its electrical or electromagnetic permanence, characteristic of the nervous influx . . . of life itself.

Unlike the magnetic tape, which is "dead" when the electric current is not plugged in, the spools are not turning, and the playback head is not functioning, the human memory functions constantly. The current can never be cut off when the man is asleep. If the current is cut off, the man is dead.

Indeed, the "Gestalt" psychologists long ago noted the absence of experimental difference between perceptions and memories. In this way they caught up with Bergson's concepts (*cf.* Chapter 4). For the partisans of Gestalt psychology, as for myself, there is no reason for really distinguishing among the concepts usually described under the names of perception, memory, thought, judgment: these various titles only dissociate artificially the modalities of the same psychological and electrochemical process, a process of nervous information and communication essentially neuronic and above all cerebral.

These electrical biological phenomena, moreover, can be reproduced, measured and examined more slowly in various complex electronic computers, such as the model constructed by Uttley or the one described by Harry Blum. More simply, it is possible to use electric units for this purpose which have been reduced to their essential systems of perception, of amplification and of response, such as Frank Rosenblatt[1] has described under the name of "perceptrons."

Isolated or associated simple circuits that imitate by means of their anastomoses and their artificial synapses, the configuration of the central nervous system—these "perceptrons," by the very fact

---

[1] Frank Rosenblatt, *Principles of Neurodynamics: Perceptrons and the Theory of Brain Mechanisms* (Washington, D.C., Spartan Books, 1962).

that they transmit an electric impulse, create a field of interaction of *selective* power. This power would by itself suffice to explain the transition which exists between perception, simple information, and already intelligent instruction. The phenomenon can be confirmed with simultaneous currents, but is still more obvious if the temporal element is made to intervene: a current that has passed leaves "traces" which themselves will eventually react selectively on a later current. It is as though the electrical units were capable of "recognizing" an analogous current (that is to say one that has already been felt) or a different current (a new experience).

W. K. Taylor,[1] of the Department of Anatomy of University College, London, goes further still: He demonstrates that a single element, a *maximum amplitude filter*, introduced into an electric circuit, is enough to construct a memory, insofar as this selective filter can simulate learning behavior by recognizing and isolating the strong signals, which it dissociates from the weak currents, and by blocking the reception of the latter. Using these maximum amplitude filters, he states he was able, by means of repetition, to train computers to learn each "chosen model" and, inversely, to forget previous associations.

It is interesting to note in this regard that the perfecting of the electronic machines and of their selectivity allows us today to go further than the partisans of the German school of Gestalt psychology. They, in effect, contented themselves with stating that there are biological structures whose functional behavior creates a whole which does not depend on the parts themselves. The perfecting of the electronic models allows two more steps, pregnant with consequences:

First. The elements of the models can themselves be an integral part of the function, or *even create it by themselves* (if they are selective, as in the cases cited above of the perceptrons and of the maximum amplitude filters);

Second. *It is the functioning itself that creates the function.*

In that second statement, we have come a long way from the old anatomical assertion, "The function creates the organ," for to declare that the functioning creates the function comes down to say-

---

[1] W. K. Taylor, "Computer Confirms Theory that Memory Isolates Maximum Electric Signals," *Science* (April 15, 1964).

ing that it is the passage of the electronic current, of the nervous impulse itself, which is the conditional *element* constituting the cognitive structure in general, the memory in particular.

In short, it is the *constituting current that creates the constituted memory. The organ yields to the organization, the organic to the functional.* There is no longer a need for a localized organ if functioning organizes the function itself diffusely throughout the nervous system . . . and the whole body. What is lost in precision by this diffusion is made up in security of the conservation of function, and hence of preservation of life.

Let us return, to throw light on these phenomena, to the same simple analogy with the electronic recorder, of the tape variety. (See also Chapter 10, Table II.)

A sound wave strikes a microphone, connected to a magnetic recording head which makes an impression on the tape as it unrolls. In a way, it is the electric influx that by its functioning has created the electromagnetic recording. To play back, to remember, is to exercise the function by an *inverse influx* which, coming off the tape, will make the electromagnetic head act inversely, and become this time synthesizing. If an amplifier is connected to this now efferent current, the music will be played back to the outside world; if there is no amplifier, but the tape is unrolling and the current is flowing, the playback head analyzes and synthesizes to itself, without audible externalization: this is the internal speech or music, as opposed to externalized words or music. I shall return to this point.

In the same way when the electric influx of the information gathered by the sense organs is communicated by a nerve impulse across the neurons, the synapses, and the brain cells, this very flow creates almost simultaneously the perception, the understanding, and its associations. If the functional retarding factor is introduced, internal psychological time is created: the memory is born.

It is the memory that conditions the intelligence and the judgment, by the possibility of functional comparison of the reactional images in *parallel* (*this is the realization of simultaneity*), or, on the contrary, in confrontation, with retardation and delay, in successive *series* (*this is the realization of the internal before and after*). From judgment proceeds, through inverted mechanism and through desire and need for action—that is, for re-externalization—recollection (playback), the motor act (acting and reacting), the appearance of

92

intelligent choice (inverted selection), and the appearance of will (the retrospective appraisal of the active direction chosen, opposed to the relatively automatic, unconscious determinism in its preconditioning, that is to say, its circuit).

If this is indeed the case, and observation and experience indicate it, the role of the memory is fundamental, and its function is linked to the crucial reaction times.

The memory is the intersection of the sometimes afferent, sometimes efferent actions of the nervous system; functionally, it is like the electromagnetic head in the tape recorder, sometimes a pickup, receiving and analyzing current, sometimes a playback, emitting and synthesizing current, that is to say, successively a factor of information, then of communication. When the memory plays back, recalls, remembers, it in fact *re-creates*—it reconstructs entirely. F. C. Bartlett [1] insists on this point: "In fact, if we consider evidence rather than presupposition, remembering appears to be far more decisively an *affair of construction, rather than one of reproduction."* For this author as for Koffka,[2] a new afferent stimulus communicates and reawakens a precoded "trace," which sets off a *series of reactions in a fixed temporal order.* But this stimulus has a predilection for "that portion of the organized setting of past responses which is most relevant to the needs of the moment," *i.e.,* of the awakening or reawakening of a similitude adjusted to the requirements of the moment.

R. H. Wheeler [3] also points out that reproduction is the result of an organization of electrical potential in the nervous system, which imitates the model of the original stimulus, with the difference that there has been maturation since the original stimulus and that the repetition is only partial. Comparing recall to perception, he describes recall as an *incomplete perception* which implies an interpretative factor of discovery and invention. It is, he says, "the perception of a certain detail in regard and in relation to a total situation." It is a phenomenon of upsurge.

---

[1] F. C. Bartlett, *Remembering: A Study in Experimental and Social Psychology* (Cambridge, Cambridge University Press, 1932).

[2] K. Koffka, *Principles of Gestalt Psychology* (New York, Harcourt, Brace & World, Inc., 1935).

[3] R. H. Wheeler, *The Laws of Human Nature. A General View of Gestalt Psychology* (New York, Appleton-Century-Crofts, 1932).

Indeed, this upsurge of Wheeler's is a "resurgence" which is not opposed to the "traces" described by Bartlett and Koffka, and already verified in practice by Uttley's electronic model. These traces of what has been undergone or already experienced behave in a way analogous to the permanent residual electromagnetic modifications subsisting in a bit of ferrite, previously placed under the influence of an electric current. This structural and functional residue in the atoms of a piece of magnetic iron constitutes the *hysteresis* of the physicists. As Rachewsky [1] pointed out, memory is a very special case of hysteresis: "Time enters explicitly into our equations. I would say that what is necessary to introduce for long term phenomena (of memory) is some kind of hysteresis." In short, the magnetic hysteresis [2] of a piece of ferrite, inducing retardation or modification of the action produced by the application of a new current, is comparable to the hysteretic action of the "traces" in the brain cells and may account for the Wheeler effects of maturation, which differentiates the phenomena of revival of memory with respect to the original perception.

Indeed, the nerve impulse is constant in the organism, as magnetism is in the ferrite, permanent electric or electromagnetic oscillation; the memory represents its *continuous action in time*. The memory is never photographic; rather it is selectively (one might say emotionally) *impressionist* in its apprehension of nature, and it becomes *expressionist* (of its own personality) in its return to nature, in motor action, or secondary psychological reaction.

If emotion plays a role in the recording of a memory, its role is very much more important in the mechanism of forgetting,[3] that is, in the apparent suppression of a memory in the conscious, which is equivalent to repression in the unconscious. For we have already seen that time does not operate for the unconscious but that everything in it stays definitively engraved, ready to be reactualized by a spontaneous excitation (awake, or especially in dreaming) or by an artificial electric excitation.[4]

---

[1] N. Rachewsky, *Mathematical Biophysics,* Physico-Mathematical Foundation of Biology (New York, Dover Publications, 1960).

[2] For a detailed study of the phenomena of hysteresis, see Chapter 15.

[3] David Rapaport, *Emotions and Memory* (New York, John Wiley & Sons, Science Editions, Inc., 1961).

[4] See Chapter 4, p. 39 (Penfield).

It is to Freud's credit [1] that he dwelt on the psychological mechanism of this apparent forgetfulness, under the double influence of condensation and distortion. Distortion operates essentially on the affective traces of the memories, while condensation bears on their aftereffects. The latter lasts indefinitely, for no time limit exists for the unconscious. Curiously, when the subject experiences an analogous affective circumstance, the memory, which was thought to have been forgotten, is resurrected from the unconscious, giving subjectively the impression of *déjà vu*, that is of having already been experienced.

Even normal subjects may be prey to "false recognition": what they think they recognize is a new objective situation; what they actually recognize is an analogous subjective sensation that awakens an unconscious memory and makes it pass back into the conscious. This false recognition of the object is a true reminiscence of the state (of the subject), that is, a *rebirth of sentiment which falsifies the recognition*. E. Bleuler [2] saw clearly the importance of these affective factors in constituting the connection between perception and memory and *vice versa*, in the phenomena of evocation where the emotions show themselves more capable than the conscious attention itself of bringing memories back to life.

However this may be, various stages exist between these phenomena observed in normal subjects and the false recognition which is encountered in certain amnesic neurotics, or in the course of Korsakoff-type psychoses in which, as we shall see later on, the subject invents and makes up what he cannot remember, "what he has forgotten."

If we compare these statements with those in Chapter 4 concerning the influence of time in the formation of the different memories, we shall admit that the affective emotional memories are probably primarily subcortical, thalamic, hypothalamic, central sympathetic, covered and controlled by a primarily cortical system of inhibition (which can go as far as forgetfulness). But should this vigilance of the cortex come to be attenuated as in daydreaming, in alcoholic or

---

[1] S. Freud, *Introduction to the Study of Psychoanalysis* (*Interpretation of Dreams*), and more especially in *Collected Papers* (London, International Psychoanalytic Papers, 1924).

[2] E. Bleuler, *Die autistische Undisziplinierte Denken* (Berlin, Springer, 1922).

psychedelic intoxication, or in sleep, the affective dream, with its emotional fantasies, may be reborn with all its original violence restored, or rather liberated, snatched from apparent oblivion.

This attempt at localization, which is, in truth, more functional than anatomic, more temporal than spatial, is not a contradiction of what was advanced at the beginning of this chapter, namely that the "memory" is diffused throughout the nervous system and that it is not a lot of specialized and isolated brain cells.

The peripheral muscular memories of pianists, of tennis players or golfers, of dancers, and so forth, suffice to prove this, even though the reflex arc which goes from the peripheral muscles to the central nervous system and back passes through certain nerve cells of the medulla or of the brain. The training of a local memory, of a local neuromuscular system, is part of the conditioning necessary for swift performance, beyond an ideation which does not have time to operate when these skills have been perfected. There is still more to be said about the training for speech or for singing. Indeed, the relations of memory, language, and time are so important that I shall devote all of the following chapter to them.

Chapter 10

Language, Memory and Time

Language is the code of memory. It is an instrument that arranges thought to establish information, develop this information and communicate it; but as this happens thought follows its own construction.

Between the image born of perception and conserved as a symbolic sign (such as we have described in Chapter 4), and the word, there is no essential difference. Their common quality is their symbolic character which simultaneously facilitates the appraising registration and the eventual secondary interpretative communication.

Like memory, thought which flows and language which expresses thought are continuous electrical phenomena: they exist just as much in the course of sleep (the symbolic language of the dream) as in the waking state. In the latter state, the persistence of language is not diminished during periods of silence, nor is it less symbolic. This inner language [1] is what exerts our thought, and, when we speak, our words search to express this same thought, to make it communicable.

Thus, before coming back to spoken language and its place in the world of communication, I must first mention more precisely its specific symbolic character.

---

[1] Victor Egger, *La parole intérieure* (Paris, Félix Alcan, 1904).

What is a symbol? As Erich Fromm [1] has defined it, in its simplest form in the course of a dream, "it is something which represents something else." This can be a very deceiving definition if one limits oneself solely to the consideration of "external matters," such as those communicated by the sense organs, but it takes on more interest when applied to an "internal matter," that is to say, to our affective reaction to an external experience, secondarily internalized.

The fundamental question thus becomes: what is the specific connection between the symbol and the thing that is symbolized? Between perception, information, and memory on one hand, and between thought, language, and intelligence on the other hand? What are the links which connect them and the instructions of the common "codes" for programming them?

In fact, three varieties of symbols exist: conventional, fortuitous, and universal. For the first two categories, there is not necessarily an intrinsic relationship between the symbol and the thing symbolized; consequently, for these conventional and fortuitous symbols, the "codes" will be artificial and acquired. Being artificial, they make it possible for their possessors to learn other "codes," e.g., foreign languages. On the contrary, universal symbols sustain their universality from the fact that they are intrinsically based both on the nature of man and on his common reaction to the matter represented. There, no error of interpretation can exist.

Let us take these symbolic categories one by one.

1. The simplest and best known symbols are obviously *conventional*, such as everyday language. Learned in infancy by the repeated superposition of the word and the thing, words become more than the things they represent, to the extent that each word comprises possible object variations and at the same time symbolizes the use of the object. Thus, to take only two examples: *chair, clock*. The first term suggests a great variety of chairs, large or small, in different styles, for different rooms of the house or garden, but automatically linked to this word is the common meaning: an object which functions as something on which to sit. In similar fashion, the word *clock* refers at once to large or small clocks, made of different materials, powered by different mechanisms, but all with the same function, to measure our customary time.

---

[1] Erich Fromm, *The Forgotten Language* (New York, Holt, Rinehart and Winston, 1951).

Evidently, as we have stated at the outset, the word has no intrinsic relationship with the class of objects it represents; the proof is that the word, the code, varies according to different languages: *stool* and *chaise* have nothing in common, neither do *montre* and *clock*, even though their conventional value is identical. However, it is necessary to point to certain conventional language symbols which have an etymological, or to put it better, an onomatopoeic relationship with the thing being represented: for example, the word *cracher* suggests the sound of expectoration of saliva, just as do the words *spucken* or *speien* in German, or *spit* in English. These are imitative sounds, conventionally referring to variations of the sound of expectoration.

In emphasizing the conventional signs of spoken language, we should not forget the existence, for communication and conventional symbolic representation among men, of other kinds of images: flags, statues, religious crosses or medallions, figures or letters for the language of mathematics or physics. Because of the importance of the last-mentioned and their tendency to be secondarily universal and to go beyond that which they originally symbolized, I will return to them in the course of this work, when I will also speak of musical notes, which are a part of symbolic analog characters.

2. The *accidental* symbols have usually a relatively individual meaning; for example, a relationship established between a color and a gay event, a landscape and a sad circumstance, a certain dress and a happy meeting, or a piece of music and an unfortunate occurrence. Simple coincidences can lead the individual to re-examine, or to dread, events which, for him, have apparently proved favorable or unfavorable. These accidental symbols sometimes cause the individual to protect himself by ritual obsessions, a phenomenon which one finds among primitive people who attach to symbols a special meaning, according to the accidental context of their unforeseen arrival.

3. In contrast to conventional and accidental symbols, the fruit of education and of personal and fortuitous circumstances, the *universal* symbols pertain to the nature of man himself and are expressed in psychosomatic reactions almost identical throughout the entire world, and similar throughout time. While the conventional symbols are completely conscious, and the accidental symbols both conscious and unconscious, the universal symbols obtain their universality precisely from the fact that they are in the domain of the

99

common unconscious, shared by all men and part of their reflex reactions. These symbols are expressive of the language of dreams, myths, and emotions. These are the tears that mean sadness or joy, the laugh that communicates gaiety, the blush that shows one's bashfulness or anger, the pallor that signifies dread or even the trembling of fear, finally the physical attraction which, symbolically and universally, predisposes men and women to love-making. But besides these universal symbols of intrinsic origin, there are symbolic universal reactions to some exterior phenomena.

Such is the universal symbolism connected with elementary natural forces, or their manifestations: the sun, fire, water, waves of the ocean, floods, high winds, mountains, valleys. . . .

However, there again, some corrections are indispensable. It would be more exact to call this symbolism *almost* universal. Thus the symbolic interpretations of the sun are obviously different in Nordic countries where the sun is always a beneficial element, bringing life and warmth, and in the tropical countries where it is sometimes a desiccating, parching destroyer. But they will be common to men living in the same environment, under the same physical and "moral" climate.

All symbols, whether conventional, accidental or universal, have a dual character: a *manifest* element (*expressionistic*) which situates them in space and time and ties them up again with common exterior reality, and a *latent* element (*impressionistic*) which individualizes them and idealizes them in the very concept of the person who speaks and, through the medium of these symbols, communicates his message, his reaction, his thought.

What we have said in Chapter 4 about the influence of time and its role in the formation of three sorts of memory can be related to the three kinds of symbols: social and rational memory finds its complement in the conventional symbol of habitual language, which serves as a code of expression and communication in everyday life; sensorimotor memory corresponds to certain accidental symbols, carrier of emotions or of a certain type of expressive rhythms; autistic memory corresponds to the universal symbolism of the dream, the common language of man with its superstitions, rites, religions, and periodic celebrations, which follow the movements of the elements. At the beginning, time was primitively defined for human awareness through rites and ceremonies, which became the basis for

100

the creation of the calendar. As Delay [1] has remarked, with the beginning of the calendar, "time ceased to be a purely individual, subjective, precarious representation; it had ceased to be emotional in order to become universal, objective, immutable." Time common to all is distinctly the work of the community.

But let us come back to conventional language and to the code which it represents.

Comparable to the electronic computer's code in that it is learned or fabricated, language is truly an extraordinary code. Code and information are done simultaneously by the same apparatus of nervous reception and transmission. Thus, the language process is in effect *self-programmed.*

These remarks will become clearer if we examine the simultaneous development of language and thought in the mind of the child. In studying the development of the idea of time among children, we have seen that they originally build their memories through their efforts to re-create favorable circumstances leading to *repetition* of *situations* holding satisfaction of their instinctual drives. In the same manner, somewhat older children who are already more conscious of their desires and pleasures, will attempt to imitate their parents, to seek what has an influence on their pleasure or brings them satisfaction, all through the mediation of language. From the beginning, the need which generates drives little by little begins to sustain social relations (with parents or a nurse at first) and semantic relations by gestures and words, out of which comes true speech. As Delacroix expressed it so well, at first "the child cannot yet disengage himself from his affective experiences. In order to truly have a language, it is necessary for him to abstract his thinking from his affective responses, to treat his own states of mind as things and establish relationships between them, that is to say, thoughts."

That is why, during his first few years, the child, captive of perception, impatiently desires satisfaction. His words remain indefinite, like his desire: he *feels* that he desires, without knowing exactly what. And the desire which underlies his wishes can be satisfied by any means which bring results. A child who cries because he is hungry can feel satisfied when he is picked up and held or even

---

[1] Jean Delay, *Les dissolutions de la mémoire* (Paris, Presses Universitaires de France, 1942).

101

when he is propped up in his carriage. And this is true of primitive peoples as well as of infants: the indetermination in the use of the verb form is prolonged as long as it remains vested in affect and continues to oscillate between a vague desire and a necessary satisfaction, but paradoxically indetermined.

Later in the development of the child as in the human culture, desire becomes more precise, the means of satisfying it become attached to words meaningful in bringing about the particular satisfaction. Little by little, he learns to place perceptions in sequence, by recognition and repetition of words associated with particular circumstances and visual images. But in the early stages, the code of language being formed will be imperfect: a word has meaning for the child only because his parents understand his particular usage; that is, they have learned his personal conventional symbol from him. For example, "more" means to eat or to drink, "hat" means to go outside, and so on.

Little by little, however, by repetition, habit, conditioning of reflexes, constant superposition of the word on the visual image, the language on the object, a relationship is established between the desire and each object. Language becomes meaningful. "Teddy bear" becomes the bear who is most cuddly, and candy the desired barley sugar. Suddenly, the word becomes the open-sesame of desire, the precise equivalent. In time, the child acquires simultaneously memory through repetition, a selective intelligence through word use, a will that can express a wish through language. And, the child is increasingly able to gratify *by language* this desire, to possess, to have, to become.

Thus, from his attentiveness to perception, from his anxiety to obtain, little by little the child builds up memory. Oddly enough, μέρμερος, in Greek, means anxiety and is also the root of the word memory. Recognizing by repetition has become knowing, to know, and by language to seek to possess.

In this sense, one might say that thought is born from the visual image; and the thought joined to the wish for the image has created the need for language. However, one must add as well, that language goes on to develop thought. When the child becomes a man, he continues to think in images; however, he also thinks in words which represent much more than pictures, words which represent their use, their eventual usefulness, their relation with spatiotemporal reality.

Little by little the meaningful word is elevated to the superior

102

rank of word concept. First it signifies desire, then, as it is inserted into a sentence, through the use of a verb it becomes action and through this action it obtains completion. The language of perception and desire has become a language of voluntary action and of representation of an object or an action in order to use it and to obtain satisfaction. Through the simultaneous development of thought and language, the self-image is built up in space, in time, and in human society.

From this point of view, the self-image would be only a relationship which states precisely where the person is with regard to the three given dimensions: space, time, and human society. Still more exactly, one might say that the self-image is situated and placed in the acceptance of this relationship, that is, in understanding it. This self-image, once built up, defines the individual and permits him, by a path the reverse of primitive vision, to take a distorted look from *the interior towards the exterior*, a look that is by this time *a thought*. This is the time of the birth of that original thought which, more than anything else, characterizes the ego, the base of the construction of other thoughts, of the development of man's intelligence and of his *idea of internal time*.

In this mechanism, one sees that the *code word* plays an essential role. It serves successively to receive information, to program incoming sensations, to store the communication (that is, the *impressionistic symbol* of the visual image); the code word alone can evoke (even through silence) the ensuing release by a reverse process (that is to say, *expressionistic thought*), to produce the transmission of the communication, meaning the order of action.

Since the word acts as a code, simultaneously receiving information, programming it, storing it, and later on eventually retransmitting it, until an action ensues, one can certainly well understand by what mechanism there will always be a parallel development of language and thought. What is language, indeed, if not mere words put into action or reaction, *i.e.,* in relation? From this very relation, the current of thought is born and develops. Words have become relation, which means concept, which means spirit.

As we have already seen, physiologically and psychologically, and as we will document still further by the study of pathological cases, this current, whether in electronic machines or in the human brain, is an electric current. To elucidate further this comparison between the human brain and a simple electronic recorder such as a tape recorder, we have established the following table which makes clear this parallelism. (See pages 106 and 107.)

All these considerations have serious consequences, but they point up the fallacy of using anthropomorphic terminology for common electromagnetic phenomena, since the former can lead to confusion. It is an example of extreme anthropomorphism to call the recording of an electromagnetic tape recorder the *memory* of the tape. How much better it would be, on the contrary, to call human memory an electric recording which leaves traces. (For details and discussion of traces, see Chapter 15.)

Having established a parallel between these two series of mechanisms, one will see everything clearly delineated with great precision, if, in the reverse of what usually happens, one uses for man the more precise terminology of electronic mechanisms.

In this intentionally schematic and simplified Table II, I have avoided the word "memory," because the word is vague by being too comprehensive. It unites, without specification, constituent memory and memory process, information, programming, communication, storage, recall, word code, word symbol, word concept, in total all the complex mechanism of memorization and of rememorization without making possible a separation of the elements, thus *without distinguishing the temporal stage being considered.*

Let us be careful to say that however impressive is the parallelism between the functioning of the human brain and the tape recorder, this parallelism could not be more deceptive when it is used to refer to the human mind instead of to the electric functioning of the brain.

The working of the mind is not just a matter of a systematic stereotyped thought reliably recorded, but of a construction, a retouching, a constant reconstruction, that is to say a *creation.* In fact, we never have a single thought, but always multiple thoughts. As Nietzsche said so well, *"Denken ist nur ein Verhalten der Triebe zueinander."* ("Thought is only an interaction of our instincts among themselves.") That is to say that thought cannot be unique, or unidirectional, and also that the relationship between thought and language will be the result not only of choice, but of an extraordinary condensation. It is in this sense that our internal language can be considered the richest, and our verbalization frequently likened to a Pyrrhic victory, when our memories and our instincts are defeated by the necessity for contact with reality. If thought is com-

104

pared to a deep current, language represents through spoken words only the mild oscillations of the surface of the water.

This explains why language may many times not translate thought at all, but betray it; not express it, but mask it. Speech is of value only through the associations in a phrase; but even the phrase is only a token, a symbol, which, to be totally comprehensible, to a certain extent requires knowledge of who emitted it, as well as who listens to it. Peirce [1] clearly insists on these necessities.

However, practically speaking, language is characteristic of man and his essential means of communication.

As Colin Cherry [2] has remarked, from the point of view of physics the sounds of language are linked in a temporal continuum: the vocal current, like notes of music, is among the *signals in time*, as compared to writing and pictures, which are signals in space. It is true that, on one hand, retinal functioning and eye movements can convert a spatial signal into temporal information, and that, on the other hand, one can combine the information obtained from space media and from time media by reading in a loud voice. In all cases, in studying data one must never confound that which is measured physically by frequency with that which is measured by intensity of sound or color, that is, sensation. One depends upon the other, but we must not confuse the two, any more than we should confuse the amplitude of a sound wave (an objective physical phenomenon) with its characteristic noise (a subjective mental phenomenon). This is so even though certain subjects, highly skilled in music, are capable, thanks to the memory of previous experiences, of recognizing unmistakably any note, which always corresponds to a certain frequency or to its harmonics.

In the *temporal continuum,* whether of the human voice or symphonic music, the pauses play an important part in the rhythm which contributes to the expression; the silence is not empty; significant vibration is prolonged in the pause. As Cicero has said, "The pause is the most important part of a speech"; for it is then that the orator continues to emit his thought and gives his listener time to

[1] W. B. Gallie, *Peirce and Pragmatism* (Harmondsworth, England, Pelican Books, 1952).

[2] Colin Cherry, *On Human Communication* (New York, John Wiley & Sons, Science Editions, Inc., 1961).

TABLE II: Functional Analogy Between

HUMAN BRAIN

A. *Exterior phenomena:*
electromagnetic or material

B. *Information received by*
—sense organ: In this category the inner ear, retina, cutaneous receptors, and olfactory receptors
—preselective: *cf.* basilar membrane of the cochlea
            cf. rods and cones of the retina
—electric or piezoelectric

C. *Transmission*
—electric or electrochemical by central core of the afferent nerve fiber
—across synapses, relays which selectively change or amplify as needed

D. *Storage*
Pseudohysteresis by electrochemical "residual magnetism"
—by polarization in cerebral cells, both cortical and subcortical
  (Possibility of forgetting through depolarization with the passage of time or by electric shock treatment)

E. *Recall*
—by depolarization of nerve cells creating electric currents in the efferent nerves

—released by
  (a) an analogous or identical external sensation calling forth a stimulus current or return of activity,
  (b) internal emotion provoked by association (similar or opposed), thought, visual image
     code word producing intentional or pseudointentional program
  (c) internal language, word codes activated or as a reaction to the electric current of thought

F. *Communication of action*
—by the intermediation of efferent nerves
—accessory circuits with effective or selective "feedback," "affirming" the choice following synaptic relays and reflex releases, and recurrent association fibers
—exterior manifestations
—by neuroelectric muscular motor plaques, provoking movement and notably speech and language according to the quality of the incoming electric nerve impulses and the choice of means of execution

G. *Examples of difficulties in functioning*
—Confusion of efferent and afferent circuits:
  confabulation and delirium of hallucination: constituent memory and constituted memory confused; the past is taken for the present
—Information is received, thought is possible, action or language impossible, a variety of motor aphasia

* Translator's note: Hysteresis is used here to denote the residual magne-

106

the Brain and a Tape Recorder

TAPE RECORDER

A. *Exterior phenomena*
   electromagnetic or material
B. *Information received by*
   —microphone or photoelectric cell

   —preselective: analytic pickup through the electromagnetic head

C. *Transmission*
   —electric or electromagnetic by input electric circuits
   —by means of transistors or diodes which limit or amplify as the case
   may be
D. *Storage*
   Hysteresis *
   —by polarization on plastic tape or electromagnetic ferrite
   (Possibility of demagnetization with the passage of time or by depolarization by electric current)
E. *Recall*
   —by depolarization and unwinding of the tape, this time generating
   an electric current for the electromagnetic original analyzer, which
   becomes now a playback head; *i.e.*, a synthetizer
   —released by
   (a) re-establishment of an electric current, brought about by the
       unwinding of the tape
   (b) an electric current initiated by specific programming at a defi-
       nite point on the tape
   (c) the silent unwinding of the tape puts the electromagnetic head
       into a generating phase

F. *Communication of action*
   —by the electric conductors of output
   —accessory circuits with effective or selective feedback simulating the
   choice according to relays and conditional probability
   —external manifestations·
   —by the vibrating membranes of electromagnetic loud speakers
   —or by television, that is to say photoelectric reconstruction producing a picture or music or speech according to the quality of the incoming electrical impulses and the choice of the equipment for retransmission (scanning)
G. *Varieties of trouble in functioning*
   —accidental confusion of the input with the output. The reproduction
   is taken for an original production: the representation for a presentation
   —the tape unwinds, the current flows, but it is not transmitted to the
   loud-speaker

tism or the electromagnetic field or the record of the electric impulse.

receive it, time to take it in, time to comprehend it, in the original and profound sense of this term.

In physical terms, the musical pause continues vibrating during the sonorous silence. So the pause in language corresponds to thought which "plays the pedal on its intellectual piano," so that electromagnetic "chords" do not cease to vibrate with thoughts, visual images, and words. . . . These, even though they go temporarily unexpressed, are far from being absent! On the contrary, the momentary suspension of language plays an integral part in communication, to the extent that, while keeping the listener in suspense, the pause is *temporally in harmony with the rhythm* of the speaker and augments his own receptivity.

Let us open a parenthesis here—the equivalent of a pause for written language—and take up again the successively recorded values in the word. Three, which are fundamental, can be separated: the *code* word, the *concept* word, and the *pragmatic* word. While the first two categories are symbolic and conventional, the last is stripped of any symbol and becomes accomplishment, that is to say action (in Greek πρᾶγμα means action).

The code word has a purely semantic, informational value. The word become concept takes on a syntactical value when it is inserted in a phrase with a verb. It can attach the subject to a direct or indirect complementary object, and thus become action, that is to say, a pragmatic word (that which creates the object and utilizes it by purposeful action). It is not just by chance that this group of words is called a "phrase," in the same way that a group of musical notes, following a certain rhythm, is called a musical phrase. In either case, the *temporal element of the rhythm of spoken language,* as well as of musical language, constitutes the *constructive element* of communication, that element by which suggestion becomes consent becomes action. It is the pragmatic conclusion which differentiates thought (an essentially human function) from the cerebral electromagnetic mechanism (comparable, as we have seen countless times in the course of this text, to electronic machines).

Whatever be the mechanism of information, of transmission, and of communication of this electromagnetic brain,[1] it is remarkable to note that this human "computer" has itself created its code and

---

[1] Or electrochemical. *Cf.* Chapter 18.

its programming, in the same manner that, through its own functioning, it has created thought. There again, as in the formation of memory,[1] it is the *functioning itself which has created the intellectual function* and develops it to the extent that it continues to function in time and that, by activity, it is exercised in space. We shall see further on the crucial importance of this cerebral functional recovery between time and space, because it is from this juncture that thought is born.

These conclusions can justify the pragmatic doctrines of C. S. Peirce and William James, which affirm that the sense of concepts (and of the words which express them) must be sought . . . and found in their practical consequences: that the *function of thought is to be a guide to action*. Equally, in this sense the truth of a belief can only be proven and tested in its practical consequences, in its possible realizations.

Although born of time, and developed in time, thought remains an *incomparable* mechanism, specific to man. Although it is verifiable in its birth, its development, its expression by words and ideas, and its affirmation by action in reality where it finds its own act, man's thought nevertheless remains a *unique* phenomenon in nature and to a great extent inexplicable. Say that it is a creation and function of time, that it expresses its ideas through words, that it constructs its action in space, that it is at once both communication and action—all this is correct, but it is only an approximation, a registration of small portions of the total, because the peculiar quality of thought is to be "universal" and to exercise its limit where perhaps there is none.

If thought is an artifact born of the functioning of the brain, it is uniquely the privilege of man and his evolutionary (that is, temporal) crowning in nature. It is that which seeks to establish a *continuity of certainty*, where there probably is nothing but discontinuity of matter and chance encounters.

Given this essential characteristic of man, to seek to contribute by this continuity to the permanence of his security, it is not astonishing that most of his myths, beliefs, or religions try to extrapolate this continuity and this certainty beyond his life, in a spiritual survival after the death of the individual. Of course, the mechanism of

---

[1] *Cf.* Chapter 9.

the formation of this idea of survival is explained in its sentimental value—it is satisfying for the individual "soul," but has no scientific justification.

At most one could say that the spiritual consequences of the passage of a man on earth should be *communicated* to other men who will receive the message of his words and his writings or the benefit of his actions; thus, in a certain very relative measure, the individual would persist in *the species*, thanks to this transmission in time.

Chapter 11

An Attempt at Temporal and Functional Classification of the Electrical Neuro-Physiological Disturbances of the Human Brain

This title may surprise the reader, because it alludes to phenomena that one often meets but refuses to perceive. However, this electric-temporal classification of psychological and psychiatric phenomena touches on and constitutes a necessary consequence to all that has gone before. Only the wording of the title may suggest an arrogant or audacious theory by the unity it imposes on facts classically considered isolated, separated, or even opposed.

In fact, to apply temporal, functional, and electrical qualificatives to this theory is to refer to its essential physiological mechanism, which will deter future authors from identifying it only with my name. Not that I hesitate to take the full responsibility for the examples which preceded, or for their consequences which I will reveal in this chapter; but I intend, as I have said, to capitalize on the experimental results and theoretical considerations by others who preceded me in their personal and fragmentary research. Besides, I am always of the mind that a new approach, whether it be a pathogenic theory or synthetic classification, is of value only if it is in agreement with the facts, and if it *takes them into deeper account,* not only because the facts are susceptible to proof, but because, introduced into a new framework, they go further in explaining the true nature of the phenomenon under consideration, as well as of its pathological deviations.

111

Finally, I have no doubt that this *temporoelectric functional theory*, although it corresponds to the reality of clinical facts and is based on all the data formerly separated out of the physiology of neuroses and psychoses, constitutes only a method of approach and a *new tool for study*. Certainly, a number of modifications will be required to capitalize on this temporoelectric functional theory and to account as much as possible for psychic mechanisms and their disturbances. Because in science, above all in medical science, a new theory does not constitute the solution of a problem; rather it leads up to the emergence of another problem.

Following Paul Valéry's axiom, "To pose a problem correctly is often to solve it," I have abstracted in the synthetic table below (Table III) the natural applications of the facts revealed in this research. Let me repeat: this table does not represent a static conclusion; it is a theoretical table for the dynamic study of psychic manifestations and their functions in health and in sickness. Its goal is to be a workable instrument for practice and research; its only merit rests on the validity of its facts and the authenticity of electronic comparisons which make it possible to compare the mechanism of the functioning of man's central nervous system to a set of computers, digital and analog at the same time, concentrated in a highly organized and confined space, and economical in their expenditure of energy. All the second half of the book will gather strength from the demonstrations of the experimental validity and the practical as well as clinical utility of this view.[1]

Before studying the application of the preceding table to the analysis of the various clinical mental syndromes presented by man, whether normal, neurotic, or alienated, two remarks should be made.

First. An historic remark: The history of medicine demonstrates that for each organ of the body practitioners have tried to state precisely the origin of each "illness," first by research on pathological anatomical lesions, then by a study of causes, and finally by a pathological-physiological study of the functional syndromes. The study of kidney diseases constitutes a striking example. At first, researchers tried to explain them by macroscopic and microscopic

---

[1] Many of the facts which seem assumed here will actually be verified and demonstrated in the following parts of the book, notably in Chapters 15, 18, and 20. If I seem to present this table prematurely, it is only with the goal of sharing with the reader the connecting thread of my thought, and to associate it henceforth in this progressive search for the truth.

anatomical studies of the noble tissue of the kidney, then by an etiological classification of the various known causes of acute and chronic nephritis. At these two stages, it must be asserted, they understood nothing of what was happening in each individual case of nephritis, and were neither able to establish, for a diagnosed patient, the individual functional "balance sheet" necessary for a prognosis and for appropriate treatment, nor to follow the developments in the patient in order to evaluate the treatment.

To say that a patient had parenchymatous or interstitial nephritis hardly threw light on the case, particularly when this diagnosis was frequently made retrospectively, by examination of the kidneys in an autopsy! But when the great French clinician, Fernand Widal, in the course of work undertaken between 1905 and 1914, systematized the renal examination into four major *functional* syndromes, everything became clear:

(a) Urinary syndrome;

(b) Syndrome of chloride retention with or without edema;

(c) Syndrome of nitrogen retention, urea in particular;

(d) Syndrome of arterial hypertension.

It became recognized in the clinic that these syndromes could exist in the course of nephritis, either singly or variably associated. It became possible to figure out a schedule of kidney function, permitting in different cases, or even for a single patient in the course of his progress, determination of the prognosis with an indication of therapy.

What we have just said about kidney disease could be repeated, *"mutatis mutandis,"* for illnesses of the digestive tract, diseases of the liver, disturbances of the glandular organs, diseases of the blood-forming organs, etc. In all these cases, it has been recognized that there is no necessary parallel between the extent of the lesions and the intensity of functional difficulties. One can even come across considerable functional inhibitions without any lesions which can be detected at the microscopic or even the most minute submicroscopic level.

Under these conditions, is it not surprising that we continue today to reason about the central nervous system and its diseases as we did in the nineteenth century about nephritis? We become infatuated with looking for anatomical lesions which we generally do not find (and which for the most part do not have to exist to account for the functional trouble), or to look for an etiology which, in the

113

TABLE III: Theoretical Classification to be Used in the Temporo-Electrical Functional Study of the Processes of Information, of Communication, of Action, and of Reaction of the Human Brain

A. *Disturbance of reception* (or of input of current):
Deficit or alteration of information

Syndromes or distortions in the receptive area: because of "redundance," that is to say, multiplicity of systems of information, these symptoms often must be very advanced before being perceived.

(a) of exogenous origin
Difficulties in perception and in sense organs—exteroceptive.

(b) of endogenous origin:
Difficulties with interoceptive or proprioceptive information, leading to irregularities of functioning of the central sympathetic system and of the hypothalamus

B. *Disturbances in afferent communication*
(a) Syndromes or distortions of transmission: common characteristic or rather common consequence is disorientation in time and space, leading to "alienation" in them (Time, space)
(b) Syndromes or disturbances in the programming of information: Diseases of recording
—insufficiency of codes for the constitution of language (syntactical aphasia)
—difficulties in conceptualization
—difficulties in symbolization,
—difficulties in *constituent* "memory"

C. *Disturbances in conservation* (or *of feedback*) (*faulty hysteresis*) (or of residual magnetism),
(a) *Insufficiency* or *absence of polarization:* distortions in learning
(b) Difficulties in the circuits of association: distortions in recognition (impossibility of establishing relationships leading to an alteration of intelligence)
(c) Difficulties with the obstruction of circuits: anxiety, obsession, mania
(d) Distortions in the recording (of the feedback or of the feed ahead): Difficulty of recall, distortions in *constituted* "memory" (forgetfulness, repression, suppression)

D. *Disturbances in efferent communication* (or *of output of current*)
(a) Insufficiency or absence of depolarization: distortions of will or motivation
(b) Absence of efferent electric nerve impulses: illnesses in the sphere of activity
External consequences: paralysis, catatonia

114

TABLE III (*cont.*)

Internal consequences: loss of critical observation, hebephrenia, loss of ego, and *of the idea of internal time*
Mixed consequences: the "aphasias"
(c) Abnormal deviations of the current: visceral conversions, gastric and sexual conversions, etc.

All of these difficulties can exist separately or in various combinations and associations, creating clinical diversity.
(*Cf.* Table IV, Chapter 12 and Table VII, Chapter 20.)

majority of the cases, remains indeterminate, or even when individualized, is not of great help in evaluating the prognosis or the treatment. Moreover, we are still more astonished to discover that given the highly specialized and very complex nervous system, lesions (apart from the exceptional cases of localized lesions), when they exist, are diffuse, or diffused by compressions from a distance, and that difficulties involving them are also apparently functional.

To use a simple, nonmedical comparison, let us say that when an automobile misfires, the good mechanic looks for a functional trouble in the engine (not enough gas getting through, trouble in the ignition, etc.), rather than for a lesion in the carburetor or the cylinders. In the nervous system, as in the automobile motor, the functioning is everything, the lesion is rare, and even when it exists, what counts is the additional functional trouble which accompanies it. It is this which indicates the seriousness of the trouble, and suggests the eventual repair, that is, treatment.

Second. The second preliminary remark is at once experimental, simple (everyone can understand it), and philosophical. Sir Arthur Eddington [1] was the first to state it clearly in his seminars at the University of Edinburgh, in 1927.

If an individual cuts off visual information simply by closing his eyes, and if he turns his thoughts inward, he persists in feeling that he exists, that he "endures," but he ceases to feel any relationship whatsoever with space (he does not feel himself "extensive"). This is to say that we have an internal sensation of *time* and of internal duration which is live and *direct*, although our external awareness

---

[1] Arthur Eddington, *The Nature of the Physical World* (Cambridge University Press, 1928, and Univ. of Michigan Press, Ann Arbor Paperback, 1958).

of space and space-time, that is, external time linked to objects traversing space, is *indirect*, like the rest of our knowledge of the external world.

From these observations alone, one can foresee that a simple disorientation in space will be less serious, from a prognosis viewpoint, than a disorientation in time. A simple disorientation in space can mean trouble only in the perception of information issuing from this space, or in its secondary transmission, while a disorientation in time will always imply a profound trouble in the mechanism of internal association, that is to say a disintegration of the personality which immediately becomes, by this fact alone, estranged, alienated in the proper sense of the term.

One can also understand that isolated spatial disorientations can exist, but that a temporal dissociation can never be isolated and is always accompanied by spatial disorientation, as well as by many associated serious functional troubles. And it is helpful to observe that when the sense of time is lost, there is a "disconnection" with reality, *i.e.*, dementia. The famous French psychiatrist Esquirol has said: "The man who is suffering from dementia has lost the faculty for suitably perceiving objects, for grasping relationships, for comparing them, for preserving a complete recall of them, from which results the impossibility of ordinary reasoning." Esquirol's remarks remain perfectly pertinent, but they are perhaps not described in a satisfying chronological order: the dementia he describes is a trouble of afferent communication which provokes memory difficulty, which in turn precedes difficulties of association and of apperception of relationships, the qualities that make intelligence possible.

It seems to follow that, in dementia, information may not only be cut off from the outside, but also internally. This is what we have called in our table deficiency of endogenous information. Without this information, there are no more normal proprioceptive and interoceptive communications and the subthalamic nuclei of the central sympathetic nervous system lose temporal sensation and their ability to communicate normal rhythms, to regulate homeostasis. Thus dementia is almost always accompanied by secondary functional somatic difficulties.

From the moment that we accept the idea of examining the central nervous system of man uniquely from its functional aspect, the same criteria can serve for normal, neurotic, or psychotic man. There are only differences of degree or temporal differences between

116

the various states, and all manner of connections exist between them.

It must not be forgotten that a normal man is normally delirious each time he dreams or suffers from an infection with fever or from a temporary alcoholic intoxication, any of which can make him a subject presenting difficulties of reception, transmission, association, recall, etc. He becomes temporarily a neurotic subject with hallucinations, amnesia, excitability or depressions capable of turning him into a dangerous aggressor towards himself and towards others, a subject genuinely demented since he has lost all possibility of self-control.

To return to neuroses and psychoses, no satisfactory distinction can be made between them by analyzing their characteristics because, practically and functionally, there is no difference in the essential nature of the two, but only differences in degree, according to the proportion in which, for each given moment, there is an involvement of each of the mechanisms of reception, communication, association, of conservation, or of externalization of the data which are fed into the nervous system.

Bowman and Rose [1] are of the opinion that the difference between psychoses and neuroses is essentially superficial, "legal, social, and administrative," in fact external to the subject. It is only an artificial ruling by a doctor who needs to assess the responsibility of the patient in relation to society and the extent of his contact with reality. From this point of view, perhaps Freud [2] has given the best comparative and differential definition of neuroses and psychoses. "The neurotic does not deny the existence of reality, he only choses to ignore it; the psychotic denies this reality and tries to substitute something else of his own."

Translated into functional language according to our table of physiological studies, Freud's definition will be found simplified and explained. The neurotic continues to receive information from the outside, communication with reality persists, but obstruction of the circuits by anxious repetition makes it possible for him to avoid facing the original reality, right or wrong, by provoking this same

---

[1] K. M. Bowman and M. Rose, "A Criticism of the Terms Psychosis, Psycho-Neurosis and Neurosis," *Ann. of Psychiatry* (108, 1951).

[2] S. Freud, "The Loss of Reality in Neurosis and Psychosis," *Collected Papers*, Vol. II (New York, Psychoanalytical Press, 1924).

anxiety, *i.e.*, this overcharge of the circuits (called affective). But to say that the psychotic "denies" reality appears inexact to me; for perhaps he has not received it, or it is not registered on him; in which case he cannot know it, much less recognize it and evaluate it. Thus, the characteristic of a psychosis is not a negation of reality at all, but an absence of contact with it. When Freud adds that the psychotic looks for something else to substitute for this reality, this statement seems doubly false to me; since there is an absence of perception of reality, there can be no question of substitution, and since the psychotic is estranged from this reality, alienated from it, he looks for nothing; he perceives only what his internal currents, poorly programmed, falsely symbolized, and poorly recalled, reveal to him at the moment. These are almost dream-interpretation phenomena, without anything in common with normally constituted logical intelligence, which is constantly equilibrated by the double control and "feedback" of a rational memory and by constant contact with external spatiotemporal information, both of these nonexistent with the psychotic.

It already appears evident that the functional and electrotemporal study of the various troubles of the "humor," as Jean Delay [1] calls it, can be very useful for the establishment of a psychopathological chart for each individual, whether his troubles are secondary to an evident cause, or, on the contrary, primary, and then called essential, in the absence of any known cause (and this is the most frequent situation).

For example, the condition called euphoria, a loss of self-criticism, a megalomania, can be due either to syphilitic encephalitic meningitis in the course of a general paralysis or can come on without identifiable cause. Certainly, I do not ignore the importance of antisyphilitic treatment in the first case, even though, for most of the late syphilis cases, it does not bring any improvement, whether psychological or humoral. (One knows that the persistence of a positive reaction of the Bordet-Wassermann in cerebrospinal fluid, in spite of intense antisyphilitic treatment, constitutes one of the sad lots of the general paralytic.) But whether the clinical psychiatric syndrome comes with an accepted general paralytic or from an unknown cause, the same functional troubles of the cerebral circuits

---

[1] Jean Delay, *Les dérèglements de l'humeur* (Paris, Presses Universitaires de France, 1946).

are at stake, and it is these troubles which must be recognized and treated.

In the same way, certain hallucinatory troubles—deliriums, obsessions, wine intoxication—can be secondary, accompanying an infection, an exogenous intoxication, an autointoxication, or a tumor, or primary—as in most cases. It matters little at the moment when they are treated and when (if possible) the cause that primarily brought them on is put down. Alas, too often mental troubles persist beyond the suppression of the cause; even in so temporary a case as that of cerebral edema, one observes, after the disappearance of the compressive phenomena, a sequel of difficulties in mental functioning. These secondary troubles persist in the same way as troubles that are called essential and which they resemble. They constitute the psychiatric reality in 95 per cent of the cases, and must be functionally evaluated and treated according to their isolated symptoms, or whenever possible to the totality of a functional system. We will see further on that, under the influence of psychoanalysis, a purely psychogenic interpretation, i.e., an unconscious psychological mechanism, has been sought at great price for psychological troubles without apparent causes. This seems to postpone the problem without resolving it. We do not even know if these troubles, so-called causes, might not be, to a great extent, effects. Far be it from me to disparage the great work of Freud, or to dispute his genius as a pioneer in the interpretation of the unconscious. But it is in the interests of objectivity to note on the one hand the discordance between the analytic value of his method, which is impressive, and its therapeutic value, which is deceptive; to claim, on the other hand, that to seek to refine the functional value of cerebral electrical functioning does not contradict the analytic process, but, on the contrary, comes closer to the ideal mechanistic and chemical explanation which Freud himself wished for the future of psychiatry.

Let us remark in passing, and to illustrate the psychodynamic method, the investigative and therapeutic value of Table III, page 114, which refers to the domain of the so-called unconscious, primarily in paragraph C: difficulties in conservation, in "feedback," in association or in obstruction of the circuits. The role of the psychoanalyst consists precisely of an attempt to remedy these difficulties by bringing the so-called unconscious to the brink of the conscious, by augmenting the "polarization" through concentrating the attention of the patient, by stimulating the "feedback" and the repair of

119

memories apparently forgotten, by thus clarifying the multiple connections which brought about the obstruction of the circuits, by "isolating" the provoking causes of anxious repetitions or of obsessive continuities as well as associative confusions. From this point of view, the psychoanalyst can conduct himself like an electrical engineer, a repairer of circuit troubles or of short circuits. But moreover, he will know better how to localize the trouble and to combat it according to its functional and temporal predominance.

Chapter 12

Functional Interpretation of Diverse
Psychological and Psychiatric Syndromes
Considered as Electrical Mechanisms
Charged with Receiving and Communicating
Information

The purpose of this essay is essentially to test the functional study in Table III (p. 114) by confronting it with different psychiatric syndromes encountered in the human clinic. Let me say at the beginning that although this approach is not at all classical, it is nevertheless much more logical and less audacious than the habitual endeavor of seeking to localize anatomically the center of pathognomonic difficulties in the neuroses and psychoses.

My approach is more logical, because if, according to the conclusions of Chapter 4, the brain behaves in all respects of its functioning like a remarkably perfected electronic computer, it is of as little consequence for it as for the electronic machine to localize information, from the moment that it does exist. In the "memory" of the computer, as in the recordings of nerve cells, not one bit of information is strictly or uniquely localized; information coded in the recorded programming is always, by "redundance" and for the sake of security, recorded (by a standard of control in the machines) in a multiple manner and widely diffused. In both the brain and the computer, what finally matters is that the *function* of this information be "communicated" when it is required; in the brain this happens when the combination of neural impulses in specialized centers is requested or elicited. But it happens just as well in the machine as in man.

121

My approach is also less audacious for two reasons:

(a) In spite of the progress made in the study of cerebral localizations, this approach is still very gross, above all in regard to the great multiplicity and complexity of the functional syndromes encompassed;

(b) An anatomical lesion of a neuron, cell, or a synapse, or a break in a circuit, transistor or diode, is not serious in itself; the importance lies in what surrounds the lesions, because of their connections, in the precise and in the general sense of this term: in both instances, it is a question of a *"temporal" and functional connection rather than an anatomical or topographical one.*

We have seen above (p. 91) that in the central nervous system it is the functioning itself which creates the function, and in the electronic machine it is only the electric experimental functional test which can verify the resistance, impedance, and the capacitance of an element according to its theoretical structure. To sum up, only at the time of the passage of current or of the nervous impulse can one verify if the machine or brain functions well or not, and never when the current is cut off or the brain is dead.

Let me add that, of the billions of existing cerebral cells, localizations have been carried out on only a relatively small number. These localizations, moreover, are macroscopic and cortical, as for example, the sensorimotor areas pre- and post-Rolandic, or the speech centers. But in the large subcortical regions and their network of communications, which are of fundamental functional importance, localizations remain very imprecise, except in several very rare points: the thalamus, the hypothalamus and the eight groups of gray nuclei in the reticular formation of the brain stem, of which I must speak further on. Their individualization has been much more functional and physiological than lesional and anatomic. I will come back to this.

Another example of the limitations of localization can be found in the study of language: if one is solely interested in the center of spoken language (in general, at the base of the left hemisphere), one can account for certain purely motor aphasias, rare isolated stages, but one has to ignore completely all of the functions of interior language, so much more rich than spoken language, which precede and form the basis for it. Interior language is the link to all the functions of the brain, memory in particular, which allows us to understand the complex physiopathology of the true aphasias.[1] As

---

[1] For a detailed discussion of the problem of aphasias see Chapter 14.

122

we shall see, with these disorders, too, there cannot be a question of a univocal location: all of a system of communication, all of a complex network is certainly involved. Within this system and network, the localization matters relatively little, given its extension and diffusion through contiguities and associations. This explains, as we shall see in Chapter 14, why in the most common aphasias, difficulties in speech may be only an epiphenomenon, associated with generalized functional troubles in remembering, in thought, in will, the speech trouble being just an element of a generalized deficit.

In every case, it is the same. There is no clear limit between neurosis and psychosis. It seems that there is no longer a way, in the examination of patients, to separate those in the domain of neurology from those in the domain of psychiatry. All shades of transition exist between the two, and they are certainly most frequently associated.

However, the exercise of the temporal function, which we have seen is the basis for the involvement of the self in duration, appears to me to be the physiological common denominator lending itself most readily to estimation of the degree to which contact with reality is maintained by the patient. That is why I have developed the following systematic table (Table IV),[1] to indicate, in succession, what the six major syndromes are. These syndromes must be viewed successively if one attempts to diagnose temporally, that is to say, physiopathologically, a patient exhibiting neuropsychiatric symptoms. Afterwards, from this same point of view, I indicate the classical clinical, neuropsychiatric syndromes, according to the behavioral activity of the patients, *i.e., according to the degree of more or less conscious or unconscious activity or inactivity displayed in a period of integrated duration of this very behavior.*

If all of the preceding developments seem to warrant our endeavor—to establish a plan of diagnosis in order to classify these patients according to their engagement within time, or, on the contrary, according to their detachment from time—it is necessary of course to justify this plan with respect to the facts of clinical experience. Essentially, this is what will be done in Chapter 13 on temporal alienations and in Chapter 20, which deals with behavioral activities, the functional dynamism of various patients in relation to the external world, as well as to their internal world, on which

---

[1] The preceding Tables I, II, and III are interesting to compare with Table IV.

TABLE IV: Plan to be Used in the Physiopathologic, Functional, and Temporal Study of a Patient Suffering a Neuropsychiatric Disorder

(Confrontation of each individual patient with the following syndromes will enable the clinician to evaluate the interrelation between the patient's ego, duration, and reality.)

I. *Disorientation of External Space-Time*
   The subject's disorientation may be:
   —of exogenous origin: exteroceptive (disorders of information)
   —of endogenous origin: interoceptive or proprioceptive (disorders of communication and its registration)

II. *Disorientation of Interior Times = Temporal "Alienations"*
   A. Due to Deficiency
      1. Extrinsic to the personality
         —sensory agnosias: information not coded
         —motor apraxias: loss of initiative of gestures
      2. Intrinsic to the personality
         —global disorders of information, of coding, of programming (*i.e.*, of symbolization, of registration, of recall), therefore also of secondary execution, from which come:
         amnesias of memorization
         disorders of integration
         amnesias of recall
         disorders of establishment (of information)
         disorders of expression (language)
   B. Due to Excess
      1. Hallucinations of the *present* and *false recognition* (the registered idea is mistaken for one already registered)
      2. Hallucinations of the *past* and of *false new ideas* (the old registration is not recognized)
      3 Temporal falsification and *old errors* (absence of code or error in the program)
      4. Artistic equivalents: *false reminiscences*
      5. Experimental reproductions: infectious, toxic

III. *Alteration of the Code and Program*
   Language Disorders (the Aphasias)
   —primary and isolated: rare
   —secondary and associated—the rule: language disorder is only an incidental phenomenon

IV. *Association of the Circuits with the Ideas*
   —coherence = correlation: greater or lesser degree
   —incoherence = simultaneous loss of contact of ego with reality and duration
      therefore, loss of critical power and plan
   —consequences: in the command: lack of initiative: impaired will
      in the execution: no action ensues

124

TABLE IV (cont.)

V. *Activities of Behavior, i.e.*, Study of Action in Time and Reality
   A. Isolated Temporal Functional Disorders
   —hypersensitivity, indifference, anxiety, negativism
   —disorders of sleep, of dreams, of sexual life
   —disorders of imagination and emotivity, of attention
   —disorders of moral consciousness—appreciation of good and evil
   B. Associated Functional Disorders, Systematized and More Lasting
   1. *depressive* reactions: melancholia, cenesthopathies, depersonalization, asthenias and obsessions, psychosomatic phenomena, and stress
   2. reactions of *excitation:* mania, hypomania, aggressions, hates
   3. *cyclic* reactions: alternations of excitement and depression
   4. *obstructive* reactions
      (a) mental confusion, delusions, hallucinations
      (b) psychosensory disorders: delusions, aggressions, persecutions, plus feared loss of object
      (c) anxieties: phenomenon of withdrawal, conversion, dissociation, phobias (*cf.* when object is the ego = the subject himself)
   5. reactions of *escape:* hysteria, pithiatism, repressions, suppressions, compulsions (escape through activity), sublimations
   6. reactions of dissociation and disintegration (internal times are isolated and disconnected)
   —hebephrenia, schizophrenia, catatonia, catalepsy, paranoid psychoses = disintegration
VI. *Study of the Primary Functional Character—Pure or Secondary*
      (a) tumors: radiographic and electroencephalographic study
      (b) acute or chronic infections; infestations
      (c) acute or chronic intoxications
      (d) cortical and subcortical epilepsies
      (e) studies of associated conditions
          neurologic (meningitic, hemiplegic)
          vascular (hypertension)
          general (cardiac, glandular)
      (f) age and heredity
      (g) remote neoplasms (*i.e.*, not originally intracranial)
      (h) pharmacologic tests
      (i) question of the opportunity of shock treatment
      (j) problem of the opportunity of neurosurgery
      (k) prognostic functional evaluation and therapeutic conclusion

great light is shed by the outward manifestations of their behavior. The classification in Table IV comes close to the well-written books of Henri Baruk,[1] to whom we give recognition here, because

---

[1] Henri Baruk, *Précis de psychiatrie* (Paris, Masson and Co., 1959).

more than anyone else he has tried to reconcile his vast clinical experience with the experimental facts of psychopathology. It differs from his work, however, mostly because of the importance given to the temporal function, considered to be the physiological common denominator, through which can be evaluated, for each particular case, and even gauged, in a certain measure, the importance of the cerebral and intellectual disturbances of the patient under consideration.

This temporal conception derives directly from the conceptions of the great Ivan P. Pavlov,[1] who was not only the first to observe that time could constitute a stimulus capable of conditioning a reflex in the cortical system, but also the first to notice that if our observation of scientific facts takes place in space and time, *"the psychological facts are only concepts evaluated in terms of time."* This last fact, he added, suffices to suggest an incommensurable difference between the two modes of thought. It is to give practical value to this difference, which is manifested in an extraordinarily precise manner in clinical cases, that we have separated the study of the temporal function into two distinct syndromes, according to whether it is question of external time linked to space (I), or whether of *internal time linked to the actual functioning of the brain* (II). (See Table IV.)

Before going further, it will be useful for the reader to compare this table with the preceding tables, particularly with Table III.[2] Without entering into details of the impressive electrical and psychological functional parallelism which will be precisely explained in the ensuing chapters, one can see immediately that the syndrome I of Table IV (disorientation in external space-time) corresponds to paragraph A of Table III (disturbances in the reception of information). One will also realize that the temporal alienations (syndrome II of Table IV) will depend, in differing proportions according to clinical variations and pathological combinations, on different coefficients of difficulties B, C, D, of Table III (difficulties in

---

[1] Ivan P. Pavlov, *Lectures on Conditioned Reflexes* (New York, International Publishers, 1941). *Cf.* also K. Bykov, *The Cerebral Cortex and the Internal Organs* (Moscow, Foreign Languages Publishing House, 1959).

[2] To facilitate this comparison, the seven tables published in this text have been repeated at the end of this book, to make them easy to consult repeatedly and comparatively.

afferent communication, in transmission, in programming, in conservation, and in efferent communication). It is the same for the third syndrome of language which, in most cases, is a reflection of profound difficulties in internal communication (internal language) which become manifest in spoken language. The same is true for the fourth syndrome of association of ideas, of thought, of judgment, of motivation: these higher functions of relationship evidently depend on the same factors mentioned above. If they had been analyzed, one could foresee the coefficient of difficulty, which will be verified by a synthetic study of the fourth syndrome (Table IV).

As for the fifth syndrome of behavioral activities, it constitutes a rational physiopathological classification and a sort of frame into which the picture of the different psychiatric syndromes can be inserted, whatever their variations and combinations may be. (See Table VII, Chapter 20.)

In its baffling and temporary forms, a clinical difficulty can be referred basically to one of the electrical functions of Table III. But in extreme forms, in permanent illnesses of the major systematized psychoses—where there is a situation of great mental confusion, of paranoid states, and above all of hebephrenic catatonias or the schizophrenias—all the functions A, B, C, D of Table III are implicated: not only is the communication of the patients cut off from the external world, but their internal temporal functions are in anarchy. To say, as certain physicians do today, that these patients are disoriented in space and time, is an underestimation without either diagnostic or prognostic value! How can they not be, when their "ego" is totally disconnected from both the exterior and the interior of the brain. Through a process of dissolution (Jacksonian),[1] their own reality permits them at the most an autonomous vegetative life, depending upon basilar hypothalamic automatisms. Their self is disengaged from time and space, thence from reality. Henri Ey,[2] the great French psychiatrist, has insisted on these points in his dynamic conception of neuropsychiatry.[3]

---

[1] John Hughlings Jackson, *Selected Writings*. Vol. 2, J. Taylor, Editor (New York, Basic Books, 1958).

[2] Henri Ey, *Essai d'application des principes de Jackson à une conception do la neuropsychiatrie* (with J. Rouart) (Paris, Doin, 1938).

[3] Henri Ey, P. Bernard and Ch. Brisset, *Manuel de psychiatrie* (Paris, Masson and Co., 1963).

Chapter 13

Temporal Alienations

Here again, before attacking the heart of the matter, I will make two preliminary remarks which may help in making the subject more precise and in setting the limits which I have chosen to give it. First. In Table IV (p. 124) I have identified a first group of patients who, while maintaining their orientation in space, nevertheless suffered an alteration in their concept of external time linked to space, and another group who presented more serious symptoms of personality disturbance, having lost the concept of internal time through an alteration in the functions of the brain.[1] Here, *I shall give sole consideration to internal psychological times and their functional alterations.*

Second. Given the development of the notion of time in children, as described by Piaget, and the consecutive formation of different memories (*cf.* Chapter 3), one can conceive that in the course of complications induced by age or illness one would expect to see the reverse process, the dissolution of memories which time has created. And since this temporal functional dissolution essentially provokes different varieties of amnesia, all the functions which are linked with memory and dependent on it become dissolved to various de-

---

[1] "Autopsychic" and "allopsychic" disorientations, according to the terminology of Henri Ey.

grees. These are intelligence, will, power of action—all of the elements making up the personality—constituting the dynamism of the self as well as the very existence of an ego worthy of human quality. Successively, we will look at two classes of alteration of the temporal function: the first, more superficial, more peripheral, and if one can say it, depending on something extrinsic to the personality, which can be changed by the difficulty but not broken up; the other class is more profound, more central, an integral part of the personality, which it is in the process of more or less alienating from reality.

1. In the first class, two varieties of alteration can be distinguished according to whether they are predominantly sensory or motor. Both consist of localized deficiencies in the temporal function, leading either to forgetfulness in sensory coding or to forgetfulness in motor expression, but always to a forgetfulness which is limited and disrupting only to part of the function.

Jean Delay [1] and Bergson [2] have inspired this part of my study, and I shall follow their relevant observations, paying my respects to their ability to express themselves well. But I will refuse to divide, as they have done, the amnesias into neurological and psychiatric classifications. Considered from a functional point of view and above all from the temporal point of view which interests us here, amnesias always seem *mixed:* consequently, whether pure or associated with motor lesions (hemiplegic, for example), they will always affect *total* psychological functions, even if they seem anatomically localized to the point of being unilateral, as happens in certain exceptional cases. As we have seen from the preceding, perturbations of information cannot exist which are not followed consecutively, by difficulties in communication, whether in coding or in its eventual utilization. This functional electrical logic reveals itself, clinically and physiologically, to correspond to the reality of observed facts. In what manner?

In sensory troubles, whether visual or auditory, it can lead as far as blindness or verbal deafness, or it can produce tactile or even visceral troubles; in each instance, however, one can always ob-

---

[1] Jean Delay, *Les maladies de la mémoire* (Paris, Presses Universitaires de France, 1961).

[2] Henri Bergson, *Matière et Mémoire* (Paris, Félix Alcan, 1896); *Matter and Memory* (New York, Humanities Press, 1962).

serve that the trouble arises because the sensation is not transmitted, or is not homologated as such. To use the terminology of Sherrington, whether sensation be exteroceptive, interoceptive, or proprioceptive, the creation which accompanies perceptual information, as well as the re-creation of the symbolic image which depends on it, does not take place. In short, information is not coded. How then could it be programmed and, above all, used?

Even in the apraxias, that is to say, in motor forgetfulness, the temporal function cannot be exercised, because the information is missing, and because communication cannot be established to give consecutive order to muscular action. As Bergson said: "To recognize an object, is to know how to make use of it." That is, the knowledge must, temporally, precede the ability. The motor apraxics are not paralyzed: what has been lost is the initiative for gestures more than the gestures themselves, which can be elicited by indirect stimuli. This observation can be verified for all forms of voluntary muscular action, including the groups of muscles which control speech. Thus it is necessary to separate firmly from the aphasias (see Chapter 14) the anarthrias or dysarthrias of Pierre Marie, and according to the apt phrases of Alajouanine and Ombredane,[1] to entitle them "verbal apraxias."

In fact, in both sensory troubles and motor apraxias, the difficulties in temporal function of information, of coding, and of cerebral communication *do not constitute true amnesias*, and it is wrong so to identify them. Only the *appearances of forgetfulness* are there; what really exists is a misunderstanding and, as an immediate consequence of this, difficulty in secondary behavior.

2. This is not so for the second class of temporal alienations, which we have distinguished. Here, there is a complete disruption of the mechanism of information and conduction of the cerebral circuits: the totality of memory will be stricken profoundly and the personality disintegrated, to the extent that the self, becoming disengaged from duration, "will alienate itself" (in the true meaning of the term) from reality.

This syndrome of true amnesia is the basis of a great number of the functional symptoms encountered in the most diverse psychoses, whether they are accompanied by associated organic lesions or

---

[1] Th. Alajouanine and Marcel Ombredane, *Le syndrome de désintégration phonétique dans l'aphasie* (Paris, Masson and Co., 1939).

whether, as happens most frequently, they are purely functional. If the reader wishes to turn back to Table II (p. 106), a glance will be sufficient for him to realize that given the complex electrical functioning of the human brain, every disturbance at the stage in which electric coding of information takes place *necessarily* will bring later difficulties in the domain of communication, either in the conservation of this information, its evocation, its utilization, or finally, in the possible execution of secondary action. This is exactly what one observes in the clinical varieties of psychiatric amnesias. There are only names to change to take account of the different clinical syndromes which will vary according to the predominance of and association with such and such functional difficulties.

Thus one can describe the amnesias bearing most of all on the integration and memorization of remembrance. The patient, incapable of constructing his present, that is, of living it, seems to construct an amnesia which is above all anterograde. As Janet has said so well, "The recollection is not of the image, but of a judgment about that image in time." The patient who is incapable of making a judgment cannot temporally evaluate images. How can he not be amnesic since he is not able to acknowledge his present from the very beginning, and he is therefore even less able, retrospectively, to narrate for himself a history of his "former" present.

In most cases, amnesias will be mixed, anterograde and retrograde, just as they have been described classically by Korsakoff, particularly with respect to the disintegrative alcoholic psychoses.

In other clinical forms of amnesia remembrance is fixed, but there is no awareness of this fixation. This is the unconsciousness which accompanies the course or the waning of epileptic attacks (above all those which are localized). The memory is awakened only during attacks and never between them, exactly as certain affective remembrances coded during our waking life, but without our taking account of them, are awakened only through their repetition from dream to dream.

Freud, more than any other author, has emphatically stated about these amnesias of rememorization and about their emotional mechanism: that which he calls "voluntary" forgetfulness and repression equal actually an involuntary forgetfulness, since they are unconscious, and a consequent suppression by the patient. It is precisely the role of the psychoanalyst to awaken these uncon-

131

scious "traces," and to reveal them to the patient in order to try to suppress all of the associated functional inhibitions.

A state of forgetfulness is never pure; it always brings along with it others with which it is associated. One often speaks of the association of ideas and memories; *the association of states of forgetfulness is always considerably stronger* and much more inhibiting in its consequences.

But after this psychogenic parenthetical remark, which is also functional and temporal, we come back to forgetfulness and to the less elective amnesias, which are more global and which one encounters in the confused and in the paranoids. Whatever may be the coefficient and combination of amnesia, or, on the contrary, of excitation and hypermnesia, which one observes in these subjects, one can ask oneself whether these difficulties themselves provoke the mental confusion and paranoid attitude, or, whether, on the contrary, they constitute only secondary effects, as has customarily been thought. The question is far from being decided. I tend, from the functional point of view, to consider that these difficulties of the temporal function, linked to electric troubles in cerebral communication, are largely contributors to, if not instigators of, the phenomena of mental confusion or of paranoid attitude. *Why should they not be?* [1] I believe that the burden of proof rests on the proponents of the second theory, rather than on those of the first, which seems to me to be amply demonstrated. If one wishes supplementary proof, one should be able to find it in the fact that when patients improve, whether spontaneously or under the influence of electric shock, one observes that with the reintegration of the idea of time, the mental confusion tends to diminish. (We may call this mental confusion a confusion of circuits, because everything happens in a manner similar to what happens in an electronic computer when the circuits are blocked by an obstruction, and the remedy in both cases is electric shock.) That is, this mental confusion tends to diminish or disappear at the same time that amnesia or hypermnesia is effaced; at the moment when the patient reintegrates the present and reality, he differentiates it from his past, can recount it with-

---

[1] The complete response to this *crucial* question will not be given until the end of this book, in Chapter 20, when we will have acquired all of the elements necessary to evaluate internal time in the behavior of man and the role of these alterations in the behavioral psychoses (*cf.* Table VII).

out having to confound it and without having to relive it. This is a counterproof, but it is rarely observable, since amnesias which are at first localized more often tend to become generalized and progressive, both the progressive amnesias of the elderly arteriosclerotic and Wernicke's amnesia (wrongly called aphasia because, as we shall see in Chapter 14, aphasia is only a secondary epiphenomenon). It is interesting to ascertain the functional and temporal character of the regressions of thought and of language in the categories of amnesia, because they follow an inverse progression from that of their functional formation, as well as of their pragmatic establishment.

All the alterations and alienations of the temporal function, all the functional deficits of memory and its associated mechanisms of which we have just spoken, constitute losses, deficiencies. Those which we are going to study now correspond, on the contrary, to abnormal excitations of the temporal function, to excesses of memory also very dangerous in their consequences, and in general even more difficult to reverse.

In these disorders, the mechanism of coding (*cf.* Table II) memory, instead of conserving the hysteresis of a potential trace, ready to be reactualized one day, becomes the seat of a permanent reactualization, through a sort of polarization or even hyperpolarization, which blocks the eventual depolarization necessary to normal functioning. The common characteristic of all patients attacked by this sort of trouble is that their hypermnesic excitation *disconnects their ego from reality, and isolates it from duration:* hence the hallucinations of the self accompany the deliriums of memory.

One can group the clinical syndromes into three categories:

First. Those which fix impressions without true memorization: these are the paramnesias of false recognition. Constituent memory is taken as constituted memory, or, to use again the comparison with the tape recorder of Table II, recording is taken for that which is already recorded. The consequence is compelling mental confusion: the patient ignores his present, experiences it as past, or *vice versa,* as is so well described in the precise formula of Delay: "He flounders in a chaos of accepted unreality and misunderstood reality." Often his personality, as well as his thought, has a tendency to become divided before becoming more disintegrated, as if, because of his hallucination, he loses the "attention to life" which

133

Bergson says is essential to maintaining contact with reality as well as with duration.

Second. Other patients, on the contrary, seem to be hallucinated by their past: these are the ecmnesics who ceaselessly recall without rememorization. They are like the tape recorder of Table II: the music is played, but they do not know that the tape unwinds, nor that what is played is a former recording. In this disorder, constituted memory is taken for constituent memory. This is the case with the childish elderly of Dupré, who ceaselessly ruminate the remembrances of the past, without recognizing them as such; intoxicated by the constant repetition of their dream, they transform it into a nightmare.

Let me return to the comparison with the tape recorder: the synthesizing head no longer functions. (Oh, how true of the brain of the patient!) And the music no longer has rhythm or pauses and becomes cacophonic. Look again at the patient: memory, such as association of circuits, is blocked; images succeed one another kaleidoscopically without cease, that is to say without the protective forgetfulness of memory, which is indispensable to produce "the depolarization" that prevents the blockage.

Third. Besides those patients who constantly drag the "ball" of their past or of their unrecognized present, there are those who confabulate, who invent a past that does not exist. Suffering most frequently from a mixture of amnesia and hypermnesia, they invent to fill the gap of that which they cannot rediscover. The gap of their forgetfulness is unbearable, and they fabulate by substituting, without even knowing that they are lying, what they completely invent, because they are incapable of reciting a truth which has never been present. In this way, they are totally opposite to the mythomaniacs of Dupré (*cf.* Chapter 4, p. 39) who know that they are lying and who take great pleasure in it. But the mythomaniacs are not disconnected in time, they are *perverse* and *not demented at all,* as is the confabulator who, in his delirium, makes an offer of a false past. In his case, there is an error in programming, of code and of symbol, images unroll before him without his knowing that they are resemblances: *reality no longer makes sense, since time is absent from it* and the self "disconnected."

One often finds this syndrome of fabulation, associated with a

134

syndrome of megalomania, during the periods of excitation of general paretics or among schizophrenics when they come out of their hebephrenic periods, that is of petrification; one also encounters this tendency to fabulate at the depths of the "cunning madness" of paranoids.

Thus, it appears that when the temporal function of the brain is altered—either through an excess or through a deficit or with a combination of the two phenomena—in the three cases, temporal alienation disconnects the self from duration and makes the patient demented, alienated in the proper sense of the term.

It is interesting to note, however, that besides these extreme pathologic and psychiatric cases, there exist certain physiological circumstances, linked to age, to race, or to artistic temperament, where these temporal alterations exist in an isolated and attenuated state, without being accompanied by disintegration of the functions of intelligence, of critical judgment, of will, or of language.

As we have seen, children, according to Piaget (Chapter 2), in the course of their development, lack a certain distinction between the present and the past, between an account and a fable, but this lack is without real consequence for a self which does not yet exist in all its assertion and which, on the contrary, unconsciously seeks to experience reality in *play activities*.

No doubt, a similar mechanism operates among certain primitive peoples described by Lévy-Bruhl,[1] who by desire and custom raise the myth to the height of reality, or even above it. But here it is only a voluntary means to escape from the difficulty of the real, from the cruelty of the actual. The temporal function is vitiated voluntarily, or traditionally, by superstition or by rite.

In the same manner, certain artists of genius are sometimes accused of "madness" for having succeeded so well in disengaging themselves from the temporal function. But what differentiates them fundamentally from the demented of whom we have spoken is that this dissociation from the temporal notion is conscious, voluntary, that it is exercised in a purposeful sense, with the goal of

---

[1] Lucien Lévy-Bruhl, *Les fonctions mentales dans les sociétés inférieures* (Paris), English translation: *How Natives Think* (New York, Alfred A. Knopf, 1925).

freeing emotion from the chains of thought and necessity. Thus liberated and stripped, emotion will have all the fantasy of the dream: inspiration will be facilitated; expression, more colorful.

To this explanation, Marcel Proust devotes the first hundred pages of *Le Temps Retrouvé*, which constitutes a sort of preface to his early work, *À La Recherche du Temps Perdu*. In contrast to the *false recognitions* of diseased fabulators, Marcel Proust in this book exalts the artistic value of the reminiscence, but he seems not to take account of the fact that what he describes with so much talent are *false reminiscences*. We have seen that reminiscence is essentially, and contrary to remembrance, a "renaissance" without recognition. However, it is obvious that all of the work of Proust is developed only from remembrances of extraordinary precision, minutely localized in time as well as in space.

Similarly, Friedrich Nietzsche,[1] in *Thus Spake Zarathustra*, hid himself under the guise of a poet and magician to justify the illusion in the search for truth and the voluntary confusion of time in the thirst for eternity: "The poet and magician who at last turneth his spirit against himself, the transformed one who freezeth to death by his bad science and conscience," he who, at the same time "must deceive" and who avows that he does it "solely for amusement," but who concludes in a chant of despair:

> *The world is deep,*
> *And deeper than the day could read*
> *. . . Joy deeper still than grief can be*
> *. . . But joys all want eternity,*
> *Want deep profound eternity.*

At the very moment when the poet seems to detach himself from time and the reality of grief, he recognizes, through that and more profoundly, the joy which wishes to reintegrate him in eternal duration.

In an analogous search Henri Franck,[2] in *La danse devant l'arche*, at the border of the journey of his short life, tried to strip himself completely, to disconnect himself experimentally from duration; but carried away by his inspiration, he rapidly returned to this

---

[1] Friedrich Nietzsche, *Thus Spake Zarathustra* (New York, Random House).

[2] Henri Franck, *La danse devant l'arche* (Paris, Nouvelle Revue Française, 1921).

voluntarily abandoned reality: "The beautiful departure, how young I am and how serious my task. . . ." "To make a ring around me, the things clasped hands." And through the anxiety of this reality which he recognized, he made God descend to earth: *"Dieu n'est en chacun, que ce qui reconnaît tous les autres."* ("God's part in every man is that in him which recognizes all others.")

This supreme recognition, after a temporary and voluntary evasion, characterizes the artist and totally differentiates his experiences from the involuntary temporal alienations of dementia.

Chapter 14

Disturbances in Language Communication (Aphasia problems)

From what we have seen (Chapter 10) of the formation of language, of the value of the word as a code and programming of human thought, of its conceptual value for the development as well as the expression of this thought, and finally its pragmatic value as the motive power of human action, it seems essential to study it with regard to the fundamental disturbances in illness. But in doing so, it is not necessary to preserve, for purely historical reasons, a confusion which has become totally anachronistic.

The term aphasia, a classical term, is etymologically precise, but it unites under its aegis a potpourri of separate difficulties, which do not often have a common denominator if one takes a close look at them.

In human communication, isolated difficulties of external language are very rare; the most frequent difficulties, and also the most serious, touch on internal language and *on thought to which they are indissolubly linked*. It is necessary then to systematize and clearly and functionally distinguish between difficulties with external language and internal language. Here one will find a triple advantage: diagnostic, prognostic, and therapeutic.

1. *Isolated difficulties of output, that is to say, of efferent communication of language.*

External language is constrained by difficulties in articulation.

138

Internal language and thought are untouched. The word, even if it is inarticulate, or poorly articulated, conserves its conceptual value and significance.

These are the expressive difficulties of spoken language referred to by Jackson. Other similar difficulties are the motor forgetfulness of Jean Delay with asymbolia of expression and the anarthria of Pierre Marie (inability to articulate even though no paralysis is present). Also related, and it is necessary here to attack them functionally, are the corticomotor dysarthrias (which may or may not be associated with paralytic difficulties with language, verifiable by glossograms [1] of the cheek and mouth muscles,[2] often complicating a hemiplegia, particularly on the right side); there is also the orolaryngeal apraxia of Alajouanine and Ombredane.[3]

Sometimes, because of their slowness and the motor difficulty of articulation, these patients speak in a telegraphic style, which proves in itself that their intelligence is not suffering, because if one takes a close look at it, the condensation of a telegraphic style is a more difficult linguistic feat than the dilution of speech in daily language.

To sum it up, the patient conserves his intellectual ability, but has lost the motive power initiative, thus the power to make the muscles of the mouth, tongue, and larynx act, even though they are not paralyzed.

Rarely isolated in fact, these difficulties are frequently associated with internal language difficulties.

2. *Difficulties of language input.*

These difficulties are linked to the perceptive aspects of language, mentioned by Jackson, and to the agnosic sensory difficulties so well studied by Jean Delay: "Between the image such as we conceive it, that is to say, as a sign, a symbol and the word, there is no essential difference. Between tactile agnosia and tactile aphasia, where the only fault is the word evoked by tactile means, there is only a difference of degree, not of nature." In the same way, a verbal blindness, or alexia, can be the remains of visual agnosia (Pierre

---

[1] G. de Morsier, *Les troubles de la déglutition et des mouvements de la langue dans l'anarthrie.* Pratique oto-rhino-laryng (Bâle, 1949).

[2] E. Bay, *Die corticale Dysarthrie und ihre Beziehungen zur sogen, motorischen Aphasie* (Düsseldorf, Dtsch. Z. Nervenkrankheit, 1947).

[3] Th. Alajouanine and Marcel Ombredane, *Le syndrome de désintégration phonétique dans l'aphasie* (Paris, Masson and Co., 1939).

139

Marie and Charles Foix);[1] an auditory agnosia can leave a verbal deafness; an agnosia of the ear-vocal chord synchronizations, a dysprosody (Monrad-Krohn)[2] which leads to a certain monotony, through loss of the rhythm and melody of language. The agnosic no longer schematizes, no longer symbolizes, no longer synthesizes language; he can still sometimes pronounce and spell words in a monotonous voice; he acquires an accent in his mother tongue and is taken for a foreigner!

3. *Total difficulties:*
—of reception of information;
—of input;
—of conservation (polarization, hysteresis);
—of communication (of output).

These difficulties correspond to paragraphs A, B, C, D, of Table III on page 114. They lead to fundamental difficulties with internal language, and incidentally with external language. Articulation is conserved, but with a considerable intellectual deficit which constitutes a primary fundamental element.

There are two essential forms:
—forms with sensory predominance;
—forms with amnesic predominance.

(a) In the forms with sensory predominance, there is logorrhea and an abundance of paraphrases. The patients lose their critical sense, and are often euphoric, stumbling and totally unconscious of their errors in language. E. Bay[3] insists on the fact that these sensory forms can evolve into pure amnesic forms, *cf.,* (b), or *vice versa.* These disturbances arise from cerebral lesions or, in their absence, from the always preponderant functional difficulties. These patients suffer from a *loss of correlation* in their cerebral electric circuits; they are more or less incoherent through loss of the idea of time and reality, difficulty with the association of ideas, loss of self-criticism.

---

[1] Pierre Marie et Charles Foix, *Aphasies,* in *Neurologie* (Widal, Roger, Teissier), (Masson and Co., 1928).—Pierre Marie et Charles Foix, *Neurologie* (Paris, Maloine, 1921).—Charles Foix et Nicolescu, *Anatomie cérébrale* (Paris, Masson and Co., 1925).

[2] G. H. Monrad-Krohn, *Dysprosody or Altered "Melody of Language"* (New York, Brain, 1947).

[3] E. Bay, *Über die Beziehungen zwischen der sogennante amnetischen und sensorischen Aphasie* (Dtsch. K. Nervenkrankheit, 1957).

140

(b) Amnesic aphasia. This is the most frequent, the most serious, the only one which, if one desired to conserve the term aphasia, merits the name. This is the "old" aphasia of Wernicke, in which there exist profound troubles with internal language and with thought, even before external speech suffers. That is why the difficulties of aphasics surpass language difficulties. To give one striking example, deaf-mutes may become "aphasic" and lose the "language of gesture" which has nothing to do with speech (except through previous conditioning of an educational reflex of the Pavlovian type).

These aphasics are capable of proffering oaths or short automatic phrases. But all of the informative character of language has disappeared; it ceases to be a means of communication, and the word has lost all its conceptual value.

Bergson, in *Matière et Mémoire*, has clearly explained why, in language forgetfulness, the proper names are the first forgotten, then the common nouns, adjectives, and last the verbs: forgetfulness proceeds from words to gestures, he says, and because "verbs approach more closely action which can be mimicked," they are the last to go. As Delay says, "Thought and language are composed and decomposed together." This point is very important, because with the opportunity to study the amnesic aphasias, we are going to find a new example and a new illustration of the influence of the pathogenic action of the temporal function, in the formation as well as in the loss of concepts and of language.

Some time ago, Van Woerkom [1] showed that forgetfulness in the handling of temporal and spatial schemas preceded difficulties with the thought process in aphasics. More recently, E. Bay,[2] of Düsseldorf, described the modeling of simple objects made from memory by aphasics. He has published photographs of these models, which are impressive because, more than the study of language which is an insignificant epiphenomenon, the modeling permits one to follow with time a deterioration of analytic differentiation and a weakening of conceptual ability of the aphasics. According to R. Klein,[3] cited by Bay, "The disorder in the actualization of concepts con-

---

[1] Van Woerkom, "La signification de certains éléments de l'intelligence dans la genèse des troubles aphasiques," *Journal de Psychologie* (Paris, 1921).
[2] E. Bay, "Present Concepts of Aphasia," *Geriatrics* (New York, May, 1964).
[3] R. Klein, "Denkinhalt und Aphasie," Zbl. *Neurol. Psych.* (Berlin, 1929).

cerns *their temporal development,*" and the slowing down of concept formation is parallel to the slowing down of expression, whether of speech or in modeling. At its maximum, as Delay again expresses it in a brief formula, "This is not forgetfulness of a language; it is *forgetfulness of language.*"

One could extend this matter further, to speak, for example, of functional echolalias of elderly palilalics, a tendency described by Souques and characterized by repetition of words, or of parts of words, in senile arteriosclerotic deterioration and its associated functional difficulties. Or even the major schizophasias of Chaslin, where the patients are incoherent in their acts as well as in thoughts and words. But we do not wish to exceed the limits of this discussion. And the evidence given suffices to demonstrate that the term aphasia can no longer be justified functionally. It leads to confusion, since it brings together phenomena which are entirely disparate, where the language difficulty does not constitute the essential phenomenon. If, out of historic respect, one wishes to conserve the word, it would be best to reserve it solely for amnesic aphasia, pure or associated with hemiplegic difficulties.

Functional difficulties in efferent or afferent communication of language, whether they be apraxic and motor, or agnosic and sensory, should be qualified as such; the functional difficulties involving the meaning of language, as code or concept, must be related to the deficit of functional correlation in the brain and the weakening of memory and thought processes which proceeds in the amnesias. This precise evaluation is indispensable in making a fitting prognostic judgment and in choosing an appropriate treatment.

Chapter 15

Cybernetic Recall and Heuristic Theories
of the Functioning of the Memory of Man

Etymologically, the word cybernetic comes from the Greek Κυβερνήτης, the man in charge of the helm. In the sense of governing, and thus of controlling, Plato uses this term in *Gorgias* when he says that the cybernetic can deliver not only souls from the greatest dangers, but also bodies and goods! In modern times, Ampère and above all Maxwell have revived this term, and it has been applied to "feedback mechanisms" since 1868. But it is the American physicist Norbert Wiener,[1] who completely inaugurated the modern science of cybernetics and who based on solid foundations the tremendous future of its applications. This is not the place to tell the story of this science, and I refer the reader who is interested to the book by Wiener. Because my demonstration required it, I have put the "cart before the horse," and I have already described the cybernetic model evolved by Albert Uttley (*cf.* Chapter 3). I must now not only explain its principles and its intimate mechanism but take into account how it and other electronic "models," in their actions and reactions, imitate the behavior of the human brain, in particular its temporal interior function.

I cannot here describe the tortoises of Walter Grey[2] or the

---

[1] Norbert Wiener, *Cybernetics* (New York, John Wiley & Sons, Inc., 1948).
[2] Walter Grey, *The Living Brain* (New York, W. W. Norton and Co., 1963); "An Imitation of Life," *Scientific American* (May, 1950).

143

marvelous homeostat of W. Ross Ashby, which is conditioned to simulate the automatic finality and self-equilibration of the cerebral mechanisms. A masterpiece of ingenuity, its essential quality, in spite of its apparent complexity, is to present an application of the principle with extraordinary simplicity. The numerous works of W. Ross Ashby [1] are the results of a life entirely devoted to the study of these questions, first in London, then in Chicago at the University of Illinois. In the history of cybernetics in the twentieth century, he will be remembered as an outstanding pioneer who applied this science to the study of man and his central nervous system. Thus I will refer the reader, for the technical details of these questions, to the excellent works of this author, so satisfying to the imagination; I shall mention here only the conclusions used in our demonstrations.

For clarification of this work, two facts are to be recalled as a necessary preliminary, and must always be kept in mind if we are to appreciate the epistemological value of this discussion:

First. The possibility of a cybernetic governor rests on the principle of the servomechanism, perfected in its electrical functioning by the mechanism of "feedback" or retroaction. In brief, this is a procedure which permits the effect, by means of a recurring circuit issuing from it, to act upon the circuit of the cause which produced it. It is then, for a closed system, a mechanism of *internal self-control and equilibrium*. Obviously, the greater the influence of the effect on the cause, the greater will be this equilibrating tendency. This is what is called the *negative feedback* in which, as the amplitude of variation of the effect increases, stability is augmented and therefore equilibrium, in all its broad spectrum of efficiency.[2]

Second. Given the preceding remarks on the functioning of a

---

[1] *Cf.* the different works of W. Ross Ashby, *An Introduction to Cybernetics* (London, Chapman and Hall, 1956); *Design for a Brain,* 2nd Ed. (London, Chapman and Hall, 1960); "Computers and Decision Making," *New Scientist* (March, 1960); *The Mechanism of Habituation Symposium Mechanical Thought* (London, Her Majesty's Stationery Office, 1958); "Simulation of a Brain," *Computer Applications in the Behavioral Sciences,* Harold Borko, Editor (Englewood Cliffs, N.J., Prentice-Hall, Inc., 1962).

[2] In order not to burden the text uselessly, I say here that in the inverse case when the retroactional effect, instead of diminishing the "power" of the cause, adds to it, the feedback is called *positive,* the intervals of variation are reduced, the effect is in danger of disappearing because of restriction of its extent, equilibrium is unstable or "frozen," so it is no longer an equilibrium!

closed system wherein the effect becomes, at least in part, its own cause, one can foresee that the problem of causality will become a false problem, a poorly phrased problem which it would be better to pass over in silence than to try to solve. It is more logical and more conforming to the reality of facts to say that in a system conditioned with a certain goal in mind, that is to say, to a certain finality, causality does not intervene. Whether this system is a mechanical machine, an electronic computer, or a human brain, if it is internally controlled by a negatively regulated "feedback" mechanism, it will be independent of the apparent causality which affects the usual phenomena of the external world, from which by definition it remains isolated. But in its freedom from the stability contingent upon the habitual causal order, it finds *in itself* a more valuable stability, linked to its constant self-adaptive variations around a position of equilibrium. The theoretical order of the external world has been replaced here by an organization or by an internal "organization," far superior in its plasticity, its efficiency, and its capacity for survival. This idea was already implicit in Claude Bernard's studies of physiological mechanisms,[1] and this is why, a century ago, he said with great foresight, "Life is only stable because it is unstable."

Further along (Chapters 16 and 18) we will come to the profound epistemological consequences of these ideas and to the anatomical and physiological conditions of the central nervous system which experimentally verify these mechanisms by means of their anastomotic recurring circuits, truly feedback.

Having said this, we turn back a little to observe first how these questions were envisaged in the precybernetic period, and then how they are "simulated" in their evaluation by cybernetic models.

Before the cybernetic period, experimenters attempted to dissociate complex physiological phenomena in order to study them in isolation. All precise attempts to represent them mathematically, in the manner of physical phenomena, were naturally very artificial, and consequently tainted with error. The organic functions certainly are too complex to be expressed by a linear function, which on the contrary is sufficient for the majority of physical phenomena.

---

[1] Claude Bernard, *Introduction à l'étude de la médecine expérimentale* (Paris, Baillières, 1868). It is by design that we repeat this citation, because its significant contribution is crucial.

145

Recently however, F. George,[1] on one hand, and Pitts and Mc-Culloch,[2] on the other, demonstrated that by well-conditioned electric networks, one could simulate all of the behavioral phenomena of the nervous system. And I have already indicated that with the perceptrons of Rosenblatt [3] and with the maximum amplitude filters, one could arrive at the same results.

If these discoveries have not received all the attention they deserve, it is because interest has already been attracted by general electronic computers (a combination of digital and analog). Thanks to them, from now on, our physiological behavior, however complex it may be, may be simulated without necessitating dissociation from the function being studied, provided that one knows how to program the computer appropriately. A supplementary theoretical benefit, and of considerable practical importance: in the study of physiological behavior, one can consider that the electronic computer gives variable results, *independent of its structure,* if in the study of a function the initial states and the final states are analogous and coherent. This is another way of saying that for the study of complex physiological functions, in particular of the nervous system, the computers and electronic models represent, *for the organic functions, what differential and integral calculus represented for Newton in the study of the laws of physics.*

To cite only two examples: in the appraisal of the behavior of the phenomena of semipermeability, it matters little that the mineral elements of the electronic computers are "transistors" or semiconductor diodes, and that in the nervous system they are proteic elements of the semipermeable membranes of synapses or of neurons; it is also of little consequence that in the first instance the phenomena may be purely electric, while in the second they are electrochemical and ionic.[4] What counts, for a total estimate of the active behavior in these phenomena, is the common denomi-

---

[1] F. H. George, *The Brain as a Computer* (Oxford, Pergamon Press, 1962).

[2] W. Pitts and W. S. McCulloch, "A Logical Calculus of the Ideas Imminent in Nervous Activity," *Bulletin of Mathematical Biophysics,* Vol. 5, No. 4 (December, 1943).

[3] Frank Rosenblatt, *Principles of Neurodynamics: Perceptrons and the Theory of Brain Mechanisms* (Washington, D.C., Spartan Books, 1962); *cf.* Chapter 9.

[4] For details, see Chapter 17. We describe only the principle of the process of these phenomena here.

nator of electricity constituting the current of the electronic calculator or the nervous impulse in the brain. The system of relays acts in both cases as a threshold, whether as tunnel diodes, with a temporary refractory state, or, on the contrary, as the cause of the summation of excitations, that is to say, amplifying relays. If the model is set up properly, the effects will be comparable independently of the structure and of the nature of the constitutive substance.

This is the case in our second example: the study of "memory" —I would prefer to say, of the recording of facts already perceived.[1] And, given our ignorance in the matter, it is particularly fortunate that there is no necessity for knowing and comparing the structures. In fact, we do not know, even today, where human remembrances are localized; we suppose them to be extremely diffuse, given the data from surgical experiments. We know even less about the localization of the "traces" of perceptions received or of symbols previously utilized; certain authors go so far as to dispute their existence! [2] The word "traces" may be poorly chosen, since it implies a concept of matter, while these "traces" can only be potential and functional before being reactualized by the *passage or lack of passage* of a new current. As in the case of the maximum amplitude filters of W. K. Taylor,[3] this would be the permission for or resistance to passage of the current which would constitute the "trace." It would be better then to speak of *"laissez-passer"* while recognizing that before experience it is impossible to affirm the validity of the term.

We should rejoice that despite our lack of knowledge, it is possible to simulate the behavior of this "memory" and to compare

---

[1] We have already seen that although the term memory, established through usage, can and must be conserved in current language, the desire for clarity in objective research leads us to use less anthropocentric terms. Thus, rather than qualifying the recording of an electronic computer by the term "memory," it would be better, when one compares it to the brain, to use in both cases the term *recording*, electronic or cerebral. This is only a detail, but one which can avoid confusion.

[2] Erwin W. Strauss, "On Memory Traces," *Tijdschrift voor Filosofie*, Vol. 24, No. 1 (Amsterdam, March, 1962); Alan Pasch, *Experience and the Analytic: A Reconsideration of Empiricism* (Chicago, University of Chicago Press, 1958).

[3] W. K. Taylor, "Computer Confirms Theory that Memory Isolates Maximum Electric Signals," *Science* (April 15, 1964); see Chapter 9 of this book.

its function to that of the electronic registration in an electromagnetic core! However, in spite of our ignorance, we know that there is no electromagnetic core in the brain! And through a process of elimination, we can infer that organic phenomena are linked to diamagnetic or paramagnetic substances, that is to say, linked to the spin of intra-atomic or intramolecular electrons, the magnetic field being created by this rotation of the electron around the nucleus of the atom. Since *there is no* persistence or *residual magnetism* for these two varieties of substance, we can further infer—but as a hypothesis still difficult to verify [1]—that it is the resistance to inductive current which is likely to leave a "trace" *not magnetic, but electrochemical, in the synaptic membranes.* (See Chapter 18, with reference to opinions expressed by John Carew Eccles, Bernard Katz, Léo Szilard.)

If we now go on to ferromagnetic substances used for electronic computer recordings or for the construction of electronic models *simulating* the human recordings (human memory), we find ourselves faced with familiar phenomena, however complex they may be. Whether it is a question of a ferrite core or of a colloidal suspension of magnetic iron oxide [2] (Fe^2O^3) or of magnetite (Fe^3O^4) deposited on a support (polyvinyl, cellulose, or mylar tape), the mechanism of the electromagnetic phenomena is similar. André Didier [3] has recently presented a particularly clear and complete study of this matter, from which I shall draw the necessary elements to establish a functional comparison with the organic phenomena described above, despite their totally different structure.

---

[1] The magnetic moment is opposed to the initial induction for the diamagnetic substances, and in the same sense that this initial induction is for the paramagnetic substances. For two reasons the probability seems greater to me that in the nervous system the phenomenon will eventually be *diamagnetic;* (1) the magnetic moment which appears is independent of the temperature (this is not the case for the "paramagnetic"); (2) when the induction passes from zero to a determined value, its variation produces inductive currents which *are opposed* to the cause which produced them, which gives them every appearance of a phenomenon of *negative "feedback,"* a frequent finding in all cerebral mechanisms and within all physiological phenomena.

[2] This product Fe^2O^3, being more stable, has almost completely supplanted the magnetic oxide Fe^3O^4.

[3] André Didier, *Processus de l'enregistrement et de la reproduction des signaux par voie magnétique* (Paris, Acta Electronica, 1964).

It is known that magnetic recording, based on the existence of a residual magnetism of a ferromagnetic medium, causes intervention of a nonlinear character from the cycle of hysteresis, that is to say conservation of an effect after the passage of the current. Here hysteresis signifies a slowing and *eventual temporal distortion;* it is necessary to eliminate it for musical recordings on tape, to conserve it carefully for memorizing recordings.

André Didier demonstrated with simplicity that the polarization of a continuous current, or better (because it produces less noise from redundancy) the superposition of an alternating current on the signal current, permits one to obtain linear relationships, that is, a residual magnetic induction proportional to the signal. It would be beyond the limits of this book to go further into detail on the processes of ferromagnetic magnetism; for example, the spontaneously polarized domains (Pierre Weiss, 1907), their brusque discontinuous revolvements (Berkhausen effect, 1919), both phenomena which condition the bent of hysteresis and which it is necessary to surmount if one wishes to destroy the *residual magnetism which subsists in ferromagnetic substances, even when the magnetic field has become again of no force.*

About this last phenomenon, I must be emphatic, because if it presents a certain advantage in the electronic recording of a computer, it certainly constitutes a great inconvenience for tape recorders, and would probably constitute one for human memory as well, if it existed in the nervous system. (That is why we have made more comparisons to a tape recorder than to a computer; *cf.* Table II, Chapter 10.) To obtain a good recording, the magnetic band is first demagnetized by an erasing head, fed by (traversed by) an alternating current of heightened frequency. "The alternating field of erasure saturates the ferromagnetic medium and makes it run through a cycle of hysteresis—backwards, one might say—to finally reach its position called irreversible which passes through the source, and where the residual magnetism has no force."

Thus, a good recording requires that one instigate, for the tape, what we have encountered in the perhaps diamagnetic mechanism of human memory: a residual magnetism without force. In either case, a superadded secondary current is equally necessary for a recording without distortion.

149

I am indebted to the great French physicist Max Serruys,[1] professor at the Ecole des Arts et Métiers and at the Ecole Centrale de Paris, for having called to my attention the descriptions of hysteresis by André Didier, which illustrated and confirmed my clinical studies of memory, including my comparisons, stage by stage, with tape recorders. This book was already written when the last research of Léo Szilard appeared in July 1964. His hypothesis and mine differ on more than one point; however, as we will see in Chapter 18, they are complementary on many others. Both of them remain *working hypotheses* and only offer a large number of agreements with physiological phenomena and correlations between clinical and physical phenomena. Thus, they remain in the realm of plausibility and should be confirmed or rejected by subsequent experiments.

So, having made this favorable negative verification, which is the absence of residual magnetism in both the brain and the tape recorder, I am the first to recognize that I have here only one preliminary observation, which may well account for *forgetfulness*, but certainly not for memory! Besides, there is no tape which unwinds in the brain, nor any mechanism which resembles it, even remotely. Can one assume an identical mechanism in recordings which differ so much in their permanence? So many questions are raised, and, for them no one up to now has presented possible valuable comparisons—not to speak of explanations.

I have every justification for daring to undertake research on a likely comparison. This research will at least have this value: experiment, even with negative results, indicates what this cerebral recording cannot be.

Apropos of this, two remarks are pertinent. The first concerns the general history of the sciences. The second refers to what Ross Ashby demands of a model in order that it be valid.

1. The history of the sciences oscillates between many procedures. In one, *observation* of facts serves as the point of departure, the theory follows, the method finally develops through which the theory is verified by experiment or by experimental observation. Most of the discoveries of Darwin and Claude Bernard have followed this pattern. The latter said, however, that at the beginning it was often necessary "to make experiments in order to see," pilot proj-

---

[1] May he find here the expression of my gratitude.

ects conducted only to construct a theory. In other cases, the *discovery of a revolutionary instrument*, which increases man's power of observation and rolls back the horizon of his research, permits him to accumulate new observations and to draw from them a new theory. The telescope was for Galileo a revolutionary instrument, as was the microscope for Pasteur. The microscope had existed from the seventeenth century; it took more than two hundred years to capitalize on its possibilities. Finally, in still other cases, the point of departure is an extremely high intelligence capable of elaborating a *theory*, which leads to a method that the facts of observation verify. The discoveries of Bergson and Einstein represent illustrious examples of this category of procedure.

With the discovery of the electronic microscope and of the electronic computer, with which we are primarily occupied here, we have evidently entered into one of these revolutionary periods, where it is the *instrument* that is going to initiate the research; thanks to its tremendous breadth of performance, facts will be discovered, and the theory will come last to crown the task.

For our problem, the study of the internal temporal function in man and its cerebral mechanism, it is certainly very lucky that we are in one of these privileged experimental periods. Given the complexity of human phenomena and the law of great numbers (I cannot repeat often enough that there are ten billion cerebral cells), one can say that the study of their behavior and their functions before the advent of the electronic computer was comparable to the study of astronomy before the telescope. In both cases, the science was one of pure observation, in which one could not manipulate the variables of the phenomena experimentally. This fact is evident for astronomy: before the first feats in space (1957) and before photography by lunar projectile (American experiment in July 1964), the experimental objects were totally beyond the range of experimental intervention. The evidence is perhaps less clear for the phenomena of the central nervous system, in part because man, being the observer, has often believed that he can reach his object by introspection (that is to say by studying himself), and also in part because the almost experimental dissociating modifications furnished by infections, intoxications, and psychoses, permit a sidelong glance, but a glance nevertheless.

Great hope, which the facts will certainly justify, is about to be realized with the general electronic computer, the complexity of

151

which encompasses, imitates, and one day may even surpass (at least in certain of its functions) the cerebral computer complex.

2. In order to be able to build on this marvelous instrument created by man, and, in a certain measure, in the image of man, it is nevertheless necessary to know how to use it intelligently. This means not only to ask it intelligent questions, but to understand the new logic of this mechanism, which, if it is well interpreted, will continue to instruct this intelligence, criticize it, improve it, and in a certain sense reveal to it, this time from without, its own internal function.

Ross Ashby declares that in order for a model to be significant in this sense, "It is necessary that it be programmed in a simplified manner,[1] but conserving an equivalence of relationship or a quotient of the above, which is always compatible with the original plan, characteristic of the operation of the machine."

By "compatibility," Ashby means that the simplification of the problem must not lead to a nonsense solution; the simplified mode must always correspond to a machine, that is to say, to a plan.[2] This idea of a plan is fundamental; it determines if a model, electronic or otherwise, is suitable. Any model will be so if it adheres to a plan, and if this plan adheres to a constant relation. This is so for whatever kind of "model" it is, so that it may not matter whether the model is made of a particular kind of material (metallic, electric, etc.), or is even nonmaterial—a mathematical function or a conceptual expression of common language—*"provided that the latter is expressed with the strictest rigor and discipline."* [3] These

---

[1] According to Bourbaki, cited by Ashby: "In physics as well as in psychology, the state of a changing system depends upon its immediately previous state. A *machine* may be defined as a system the behavior of which corresponds to a *schematic diagram* which reunites these two states. If the machine functions by means of *input*, the successive states of the machine with respect to this input will be represented *'canonically'* by a double-entry table which could be programmed into a computer, capable of solving this differential equation." *Cf.* N. Bourbaki, *Eléments de mathématiques* (Paris, Hermann and Co., 1939); *Elements of Mathematics* (Reading, Mass., Addison-Wesley Publishing Co., 1966); *Théorie des ensembles (fascicule de résultats)* (Paris, Hermann and Co., 1959).

[2] We shall see in detail, in Chapter 20, how the *schematic diagram* and planning play an equally crucial role in the development of action behavior, which is proper to man.

[3] Every work of Bergson and of Einstein presented a picture of concepts and language capable of serving as a "model" long before there was a question of electronic computers and of simulating electronic models.

152

notions of rigorous adherence to a schematic diagram of relationships and this extension of the notion of model are of foremost importance for research and for the comprehension of the pages that follow.

Let me note in passing that one of the great benefits of the electronic revolution is that it provides increased *possibilities for logical symbolism* and capacities for expression of language, to expose more precisely *complex problems in their simplicity*.

In this spirit of simplicity, one can remark with Ross Ashby that all the qualities of the brain can be reduced to two, which are essential: *selectivity, activity*. Selectivity brings man the appearance or the reality of finality in the pursuit of his goals. Activity of the brain's behavior is in the service of an extreme sensitivity to the outside world (perception, information) or to the internal world (symbols, ideas, words, associations, reflections, judgment, plans, intentions, decisions). This double regulator initiates a constant oscillation, of the kind *pulsed between action and reaction*, permitting constant adaptation to outer and inner circumstances.

Undoubtedly, this mechanism is extraordinary and its perfection is the result of many millions of centuries of evolution and of progressive selection. Until about 1940, in the precybernetic era, this mechanism was, so to say, *unique*, so good that it appeared at the same time paradoxical and magic. Magic because one could not analyze it; paradoxical because one could not imitate it and because its systematic predetermined nature seemed in total contradiction to its ceaselessly adaptive characteristics. Today, since the era of electronic "feedback" by adaptive reactions (seemingly instantaneous for man), there are many operational behaviors which have "intelligent" appearances and which, by their mode of action, imitate the behavior of man. To cite only a few of them: the automatic pilot of an aircraft, photoelectric cells, the automatic focus in photographic equipment, the automatic reporting of distance by radar, the target-seeking aerial of submarine torpedoes, etc. Pierre de Latil,[1] in a beguiling book, demonstrates many aspects of the present and future for these systems, which he brings together under the title of *La pensée artificielle*.

It is also true that mechanical "servomechanisms" have existed

---

[1] Pierre de Latil, *La pensée artificielle* (Paris, Gallimard, Collection de L'Avenir de la science, 1953).

since 1788, when James Watt[1] ingeniously discovered the "flyball governor" of a steam engine; but the material inertia of these servomechanisms did not permit them to be instantaneous, intelligent, and anticipatory in appearance like the electronic "feedback."

In fact—and here I refer again to the epistemological point of view in Chapter 16—the common denominator of all of these apparatuses, as with the central nervous system of man, is that the *goal sought and the correcting effect to attain it, constitute, in themselves, the constantly corrective and adaptive mechanism.* In brief, it is the effect which perceives the necessary information for the carrying out of action in achieving its goal; in this manner, the corrective effect continues its initial predetermined strategy, but appears to modify it ceaselessly through tactical adaptive reactions.

Machines have become intelligent, and through the interchange of appropriate operational behavior, are going to give back to man, their creator, new information about the mechanism of his own intelligence. Many of the pseudophilosophical problems of the past will be answered thus and will disappear because they were wrongly expressed.

What is there to say about the general electronic computer? By means of its most complex organization, it can simulate the *schematic diagram* of all the little bits of mechanisms referred to above and execute them; it can even imitate the behavior of another computer (which is one means of verification); finally, it can imitate the complex behavior of the human cerebral computer if it is appropriately programmed; the electronic computer can thus serve as an imitative model of the complex human function without the previously necessary dissociation, which formerly made impossible the study of the *constitutive interactions of the function.*

After this long and necessary parenthetical remark, let us return to the study of the recording mechanism of electronic computers, in order to see if they can teach us something more about the mechanism of human memory.

The permanent, noncirculating, non-"volatile" recording is what I refer to now. In the majority of I.B.M.-type computers, these permanent "memory banks" are made up of little ferrite cores, in

---

[1] James Watt, "The Flyball Governor" (London, 1788), in Ernest Nagel, *Self-Regulation, Automatic Control* (New York, Simon and Schuster, 1955).

154

the form of rings approximately two millimeters in diameter, with vertical and horizontal electric conductors strung through them like balls on a net. When any current passes through, even if it is only a millionth of a watt for less than a millionth of a second, the core is permanently magnetized by magnetic polarity which depends on the direction of the circuit: 0 or 1.

In actual machines, each stage of the scale contains about four thousand cores, and, according to the design of the machine, the stages are more or less numerous. To isolate one of these cores in research, one transmits only half-current on the horizontal plane and half-current on the vertical plane, in all of the series of magnetic rings. Only those cores which are traversed at the same time by a vertical and a horizontal current will respond to this localized search, that is, only those that receive two halves of the necessary current. All of the other rings, receiving only a half-current, will not respond to the request. This process is the *equivalent of thresholds* in the physiology of the nervous system.

Once a ring has been chosen, there are two possibilities—first that this ring was at zero and the current reading will not change its polarity; second, that it was at one, which means that, on one hand, it is going to influence the current reading, and on the other hand, it is going to lose its own magnetization. Whether the magnetization be lost or only altered, it is necessary, in order to restore the magnetic information and to conserve the recording, that the current reading be followed by a new pulsed current (said "of inhibition"), which suppresses the effect of the reading and re-establishes the original magnetism.

Although this mechanism is very simple, it gives the impression of being complicated. I apologize to the reader for having described it, since there is no indication that an analogous mechanism exists in human memory. But by means of this description, I intend to emphasize the following facts:

1. Every recording which bears on a large number of elements is necessarily *complex,* even if the principle of it is simple.

2. We count the elements of computers by the hundred thousands, but in human memory, they are counted by the *billions.* Without doubt, as in the scales of the electronic computers, they are grouped in *systems.*

3. Although there are no ferrite cores in the brain of man and a residual magnetism does not necessarily exist there, an electro-

155

chemical residual magnetism at the level of the synapses,[1] can play exactly the *same* role and fill the same function; and the thresholds likewise act similarly to the maximum amplitude filters of Taylor.

4. Given the electrical passage of nervous impulses at the time of the "utilization" of a memory, one would expect that, as in the destroyed polarity of magnetism in the ring of the calculator after the passage of current, there would be forgetfulness after the usage of memory!

5. But one knows that the opposite happens, and that the more a memory is used, the less it is "erased"; let me even add: the more its subsequent evocation will be facilitated. There exists a mechanism of *restoration* in the organism as in the electronic machine, which imprints the synaptic relays more forcibly—in these circuits or their residual magnetism—in order to facilitate subsequent use. It is in this sense that as we have already said with regard to the human memory, the act of functioning creates and perfects the function.

6. This latter mechanism takes into account that for the brain, as well as for electronic computers, two sorts of memory exist: one *active, circulating, brought forth* by its actualization, creating habits, facilitating by repeated action the circuits of activity in the subcortical anastomotic recurrent regions;[2] the other, long-term memory, in reserve, in storage in the cerebral cortex and awaiting occasional excitation by the long fibers, without anastomosis or feedback.[3] The equivalent in electronic computers[4] of this long-term storage is the permanent storage recording.

7. Let us remember that according to von Neumann, even if man recorded the maximum number of possible remembrances, that is to say, one every fifty milliseconds (72,000 per hour), and each remembrance became fixed to a single cerebral cell, all the avail-

---

[1] The anatomic details and the intimate mechanism of the synaptic transmission will be described in Chapter 18.

[2] For the details of the anatomic structures of the brain and of the intimate electrochemical functioning within it, see Chapter 18.

[3] Walter M. Elsasser, "Reformation of Bergson's Theory of Memory," *Philosophy of Science,* Vol. 20, No. 1 (Baltimore, 1953). See also Chapter 20, p. 223, of this book.

[4] Harold Borko, *Computer Applications in the Behavioral Sciences* (Englewood Cliffs, N.J., Prentice Hall Inc., 1962); M. G. Hartley, *An Introduction to Electronic Analogue Computers* (London, Methuen and Co., 1962).

able cells would still not be used in a human life span! Given this abundance,[1] it is not to be doubted that remembrances become attached to many cellular groups, thus increasing their opportunity to be conserved as well as reactivated and to come into eventual action.

To conclude this chapter, I shall say:

First. That the study of the mechanism of the various recordings in computers shows us that we must *seek the equivalent* in the central nervous system of man.

Second. If the magnetic ferrite hysteresis does not exist as such in the brain, there are a number of organic functional equivalents which have the capabilities of "residual magnetism": thresholds, refractory states, synaptic "valvular" or electroionic function. They can act, either isolated, or more probably in combination. Given these multiple possibilities and the large numbers of cells involved, one can conceive that memory can be retentive. The absence of authentic hysteresis is of little importance, since the final result of recording is there: *analog.*

Third. Nevertheless, it is necessary to say that the piezoelectric quartz retarding circuits and mercury tube of the computers are very different from what one will find in the brain structure, where there are the subcortical anastomotic and recurrent circuits, with "feedback," which play such an important role. We shall study them in detail in Chapter 18. We must not be frightened by the complexity of their makeup, understanding the equally complex role they have to play. But their principle of action is simple and its interpretation is simplified by the study of electronic computers, which although of different structure, are also both complex and simple, if one tries to analyze them closely.

---

[1] Jan A. Rajchman, "Integrated and Superconductive Memories," *Proceedings of the National Academy of Sciences,* U.S.A., Vol. 52, No. 2 (August, 1964). (Electronic memories with "parallel access" simulating the life and logic of human memory.)

Chapter 16

Meta-Physical and Psychodynamic Considerations

All the observations I have reported, as well as all the demonstrations given in this book of the importance of the time factor in the operational electrical functioning of the human brain, are going to permit me to make a new meta-physical interpretation of certain classical proofs brought about by human experience.

Let me note that I write the word meta physical as two words to signify that this term can no longer be applied to the often hypothetical philosophical digression of the past, but on the contrary, today refers to a branch of physics resting on experimental proof and doing obeisance before the highest impartiality of the facts.

Under this new approach, can one seek to recapture the classical formula of Descartes: "I think, therefore I am"?

To think: that is to receive from space to act in time. It is, from the *subjective* point of view, to have received information which has communicated knowledge; from the *objective* point of view, it is, by means of the same information, to increase order, that is to say, to have organized or even made *organismic* this knowledge.

To be: that is to perceive the present and to be integrated into it. The present being the limiting notion between two variations, it becomes the awareness of a circumstance which tends to disappear within the very moment it is reached, that is, with the energetic movement (*momentum*) which carries it away.

158

If to think is to know, to be is thus to acknowledge. And being is going to insert itself between the two functions of thought, between information and action at least to the extent that one cannot artificially dissociate them as we have in this analytical discussion, or as happens spontaneously in mental illness, when functional troubles appear in the dynamic function of the brain.

Thus, the conception of Descartes, "I think, therefore I am," can be translated functionally: "I know, therefore I acknowledge." Can one go still further cybernetically and add to the formula of Descartes a *temporal functional* corollary, formulated thus: "I think, therefore I am; I am, therefore I persist"?

This pronouncement is not so simple nor so evident as it seems here, and the fact that it can be proved subjectively and superficially does not give it profound epistemological value. But if it can be *demonstrated*—and we are going to try to do this through an examination of the consequences—then, but only then, will it take on a practical explanatory and eventually therapeutic value.

To do this, let me state again some definitions and some conclusions from the preceding chapters.

According to Wiener, "A message is a series of continuous or discontinuous measurable events, distributed over time." This is to say that the information perceived by the sense organs, in particular by the visual and auditory sense organs, as I have described, will absorb this spatiotemporal sequence and communicate it electrically to the cerebral cells, in a conscious or an unconscious manner (which, does not yet matter).

More important, as Ernest Huant[1] has demonstrated, this information can take on, beyond its quantitative value, a qualitative value, linked in part to the variation of the energy (more or less) during its transmission, and in part to the fact that from the time of the transfer of energy this sensory information can be augmented by conceptual information, which is added to it or sometimes even substituted for it. Therefore, the summation of information and knowledge constitutes an essentially negentropic condition under the following circumstances: if it augments the presence of order, which is relatively static at this stage, but prepares for and makes

---

[1] Ernest Huant, "Sensorial and Conceptual Information Within the Bio-Electric Activity of the Brain," *Progress in Brain Research,* Vol. 2 (Amsterdam, London, New York, American Elsevier Publishing Co., 1963).

possible a secondary order, this one dynamic, which is the basis for the command for action and execution.

It is interesting to recall, parenthetically, the enormous discrepancy which often exists between a weak information signal and strong actions or secondary reactions. To take only one example, a visual reaction, which is in the last analysis dependent on a chronological displacement among photons emitted by an object frequently distant from the retina [1]—for example a glimpse of a tiger can release a violent secondary muscular reaction of flight. This reaction in successive chains of nervous impulses is no different, in its mechanism, nor in its lack of proportion, from phenomena which can be released by a simple electrical contact, for example, as it turns on a powerful motor—or even explodes an atomic bomb.

But let us return to our subject. We have seen (Chapter 9), while studying the mechanism of recording, that it is the very function of information, acting on the central nervous system, which creates the memorizing function, almost independent of its structure and localization. One proof of this is that this functioning and this function can be altered by humoral alcoholic or mescaline intoxications, without any structural modification.

We have seen therefore that the memorizing function is the essential dynamic function, the most comprehensive, the one on which depends imagination, intelligence, motivation, language, in one word —the personality. Inversely, in the amnesic psychoses, there is a loss of perception and of a notion of the present as well as of the self.

Then it is possible to say, remaining within the limits of authentically proven facts, that consciousness is only, at the onset, recognition of the "traces" which awaken in memory the "previously perceived" and that this recognition, in the exercise of its differentiating function, discriminates the newly conceived from the already proven, from the previously received. It should be added that the essential quality of this consciousness, born of memory, resides in its power *to distinguish in time* the new perception from the old, to *discern what has changed.* A crucial point, because *it is at this level that one can observe the release of mind beyond matter, as well as the enlistment of the self in duration.*

---

[1] I have indicated (Chapter 7, p. 70) that the eye is sensitive to 100 quanta of light, 90 per cent being absorbed through the milieu of transmission and convergence and only 10 per cent striking the cells of the retina.

If we consider memory to be recording and hysteresis, that is, the remains of "traces," understanding which springs from it is going to be synthesis and progress, that is to say, reliving and unfolding. *The junction between matter and mind is made through exercise of the electrical function of the brain in time.* And the self is only affirmed, that is to say only exists (in the proper meaning of the term), through this live internal sensation which causes the ego to partici-pate in duration, including it and actualizing it within time.

Using physiological and psychological terms, verified by the coun-tertest of psychiatric observations, Costa de Beauregard (*cf.* Chap-ter 5) advances beyond a purely physical point of view when he says that the relationship between negentropy and information places "the hinge between the objective and the subjective, between matter and mind." The value of his assertion is increased by the fact that it rests on a double verification: on the one hand, it is verified physiologically, within the evolution of man between infancy and adulthood, by the development of the temporal notion during the growth of language, which symbolizes and exemplifies all of the mechanisms; on the other hand, inversely, the involution produced by age or by illness initiates disintegration and a progressive dissolu-tion of memory, of conscience, of self, and of the notion of time.

These diverse data permit us to utilize electronic models to study the variations in the brain's functions which, as I have noted, are fundamentally electronic, even if they are apparently electrochemi-cal (we have seen above that in reality an electrochemical phe-nomenon can be reduced to an electronic phenomenon). The physical proofs of Costa de Beauregard, as well as the psychiatric and psychobiological verifications given earlier, permit the utilization of electronic models [1] to compare the profound mechanisms of hu-man thought to the electronic artifacts: temporal and functional cybernetics is justified by the manner in which the understanding develops from similar circumstances, from brain matter and from the functioning of the brain's electrical network with its relays. In brief, the electrical mechanisms common to these disparate phe-nomena justify a functional comparison, even though this com-parison does not imply an identity in substance and can only help in the explanation of their processes.

What is more, the study of the biological functions will permit

---

[1] *Cf.* Chapters 3 and 15.

us in return to build more perfect computers and to ask them more pertinent questions. For example, our observations will permit us to appreciate better the relationship between the function and the junction of space and time, from the psychological point of view. If the function is exercised within time as a movement in space, one might say that since the external movement is only that of space traversed, the internal time can perhaps only be a fulfilled function, in the last analysis an energy which is consumed, a force which is spent. A force which, when one considers it as attached to matter, can consume it, but which, when one thinks of it as attached to energy, or even as pure energy, is transformed, that is, persists and "endures" (in both senses of this last word).

By these "round trips" in the observation from the electronic machine to man, we will arrive at the study of the functional mechanisms, to vary them systematically, to see what is possible, probable, or on the contrary, impossible. That the structures may be very different does not constitute an obstacle, since as I have already stated, for both the human brain and the electronic computer the *structure is important only to the extent that it permits the exercise of a certain electrical function.* There is a temporal and energizing common denominator which seems to perform in an identical manner, beyond the modalities of structure or of substance,[1] and thus gives complete validity to the functional comparison.

If up until now it has been primarily men who have perfected the electronic machines, one can hope that the day is not far away when electronic machines can teach us, if not how to perfect the extraordinary electronic functioning of the human brain, at least to prevent its disturbances, to augment its productivity, to evaluate it, or even to repair its difficulties in psychiatric disorders. None of this is impossible, because it is precisely in the psychoses, and in particular those wherein the individual loses his memory, that is, his understanding and his idea of time, that illness through the very systematization of his psychosis brings him closer to the electronic machine. The psychotic individual barely conserves his essential activity; he has lost the activities of choice, exercise of desire, and of free will: his very activities have become *"mechanical."*

But having examined all the similarities between the electronic machines and the electronic functioning of the nervous system of

---

[1] *Cf.* Chapter 15.

man, I must now point out some essential differences which correspond to the reality of man. Even to state the problem may seem a little ridiculous, and any complete statement will be devoid of the humor so characteristic of mature man, who is capable of exercising his critical powers objectively on his own behavior and of correcting it, thanks to this autocritical effort! The cyberneticists claim, however, that the perfected electronic machines are also capable of autocontrol, of the equivalent of autocriticism. They can perceive when they are in error, signal this, stop, eventually recognize the trouble, and start off again in the right direction. This operational correction amounts to the equivalent of a change of behavior.

"Ridiculous discussion" the philosophers will reply: it is unthinkable to want to compare the mineral and metallic elements which make up electronic computers with organic matter, above all with living matter, capable of suffering and reproducing. To this the extreme cyberneticists have again a reply. They say that the perfected "computers" can repair a defective circuit, "cicatrize" it in some way, or even completely create a replacement circuit. What is more, an electronic machine can print out all of the electronic circuits of a "daughter machine" and condition it to be like itself. Finally, the machine can apparently be made to suffer: if its circuits are blocked by contradictory orders, it imitates the anxious hesitations and repetition-with-procrastination "reflexes" of the animals that Pavlov and Masserman made anxious by giving stimuli which contradicted the conditional factors previously established.

But let us close this discussion which can become trifling and go on to bring together fundamental differences and similarities.

I have already said in the course of this work (but it is important to repeat it here) that one of the essential differences lies in the simple fact that when one cuts off the current that feeds the electronic computer, the apparatus returns to rest, ready to start off again when the electric current is re-established. For man it goes otherwise: when the current is cut off, when the vital nervous impulse is interrupted, death follows and is irreversible.

If the above comparison shows man to be the inferior of the machine (only in that respect), he is clearly seen to be superior at any stage of activity, by the sole fact that he *can escape determinism through the exercise of his will*. Not only because through his will he chooses to invent, to build, and to ask questions from the electronic computer, but also because, through the exercise of free choice, he

163

can in a certain measure escape from the blind determinism of causality; thus, will saves man from the "programming" of necessity, which, in appearance at least, is teleological.

This much-discussed and crucial meta-physical point must be examined in detail, and especially in its temporal aspect which is the object of this essay.

From an epistemological point of view, we must first ask: what is the difference between external space-time of the physicists and internal psychological time which develops from it?

The fact that this psychological time is an internalization of the former does not mean that it cannot be *very different:* no more and no less different than are afterimages of the colors developed from electromagnetic waves or the sonorousness from the vibrations of mechanical waves. To use a simple comparison, let us try to grasp the essential point which differentiates two types of electrical communication such as telephonic communication and nervous system communication: we immediately perceive that, in the first case, it will be primarily the message of the *sender* which provides information to the listener; while, in the second case, that of an organ of perception communicating information across synapses and nerve fibers, it is, on the contrary, the cerebral *receiver* which will give the message its value.

If the comparison is simple, the explanation is not, inasmuch as the normal tendency of the mind is to pose the problem in reverse, which makes it insoluble. This is one of the errors in reasoning made particularly by Kant,[1] which Bergson perceived in his very first books,[2] then ingeniously resolved in a work published at the end of his life: *La pensée et le mouvant.*[3] I will recall the solution he gave to this crucial problem and pay homage to his memory as well as to his talent, by adding here the precise details and experimental proofs which were accomplished after his death, but which in every way confirmed his argument.

Bergson begins by remarking that the first cause for confusion comes from the fact that the terms designating time are borrowed

---

[1] I. Kant, *Kritik des reinen Vernunft.*

[2] Henri Bergson, *Essai sur les données immédiates de la conscience* (Paris, Presses Universitaires de France, 1946) and *Matière et Mémoire,* Chapter IV.

[3] Henri Bergson, *La pensée et le mouvant,* Second part (Geneva, Albert Skira, 1946).

from the vocabulary of space. Second confusion: it is a function of intelligence to mask mobility, whether it be in movement or in variations, and hence to mask duration. Everything happens as if the intelligence considered only immobility, in order to facilitate its action. Thus, he says, "the moments of time and the positions of the mobile are only instantaneous views (snapshots) taken by our understanding about the continuity of movement and of duration." And he says further, "What a *laissez-aller* attitude of intelligence has brought about, an effort of intelligence can defeat." Most remarkably, moreover, intuition, that is, the enlivened sensation of the original communication, "gives us the very thing which intelligence only grasps in its spatial transposition, or only in its metaphorical translation."

What then is this "thing," if it is not what I described at the beginning of this chapter (p. 160) as the enlistment of the self in duration, in the acceptance and the awareness of becoming? To enlist the self is to grasp or recover possession of the internal life of perception and sensation, of pure emotion; emotion meaning motion, the movement which constitutes this becoming and which thus identifies the substance of the self and of duration all in one.

The temporal and functional corollary of the sentence of Descartes, "I am, therefore I endure," thus takes an intuitive value of necessity, paradoxically greater than its conceptual value of choice, because this is only one consequence, while the other constitutes the reality of the self, felt in time and put to the test within the lived duration. This is why, in building a bridge between natural external phenomena and the nature of man, *the temporal factor will always occupy the key position.*

The external world appears as "relatively" immobile, and the objective time of Minkowski-Einstein as spread out in its fixity as space. Therefore, the relative variation in time sensed by the individual, comes from the intuition of the self, which, feeling only the variation of becoming, applies to psychological time an internal directional arrow and thus provokes the sensation of before and of after. Nevertheless, it is not, as is customarily said, the past which swerves away from us nor the future which approaches us, *it is we who, through becoming, feel that we swerve away from the past and that we go towards the future.*

Why, in opposition to every physical and mathematical conception, do we have this sensation of the relative immobility of the

165

external world? Because of the functioning of our sense organs. And why, on the contrary, do we try at all costs to give a temporal orientation to a message from the exterior, which more often than not is lacking this orientation, if not because of our intuition of the internal growing of the self? As Spinoza once said: *"Tempus non est affectio rerum sed merus modus cogitandi."*

Can one go still further in these explanations and try to perceive why man tries to assure himself pragmatically? Proceeding from "I think, therefore I am" of Descartes, I have already expressed the functional corollary: "I know, therefore I acknowledge." Whence follows the temporal consequence: "I am, therefore I endure." Now through comparison, evaluation, and sometimes entropic and cybernetic opposition, we are going to try to grasp the concept which flows from these: "I endure, therefore I wish to continue to be." Information, sentiment, desire, or concept—one sees them in every possible degree and their real blending in the single statement of this sentence.

All that I have said, particularly in Chapters 4 and 15, about entropy and cybernetics, can be reapplied here, and the two concepts can be reunited with respect to their functional value. Given their importance, I am not afraid of certain repetitions,[1] which will only stress, with more precise detail, research on more profound correlations between physical and psychological phenomena.

As Arthur Eddington[2] remarked, the idea of entropy probably constitutes the greatest contribution of physics to the development of scientific thought during the nineteenth century. Thanks to it, for the first time physics departed from the almost anatomical tendency to seek, through division and ever finer microscopic or ultramicroscopic dissections, to isolate entities, and, on the other hand, to cling almost physiologically to the evolutionary qualities of a system, considered in its evolutionary and functional entirety, as though physics were dealing with a living organism, beyond the details of structure. This way of thinking paradoxically permitted a more

---

[1] André Gide, from the work, *Retour de l'enfant prodigue:* "Everything has already been said, but since no one listens it is always necessary to begin all over again."

[2] Arthur Eddington, *The Nature of the Physical World* (Cambridge University Press, 1928 and Univ. of Michigan Press, Ann Arbor Paperback, 1958).

166

pertinent view of the over-all dynamic of phenomena (above all when large numbers were concerned) than of their statical details. But from the time when the entropy of a physical system was considered as a disorder of this system linked to a lack of information, study of the nature of any phenomenon in its general evolutive tendencies improved. Curiously enough, the mere fact of knowing accurately the initial and final stages of a reaction, in other words to analyze, *i.e.*, to dissociate in time, the ordinance of a phenomenon helped a lot for the appreciation of its precise nature —not only its nature, but also its measure, since the latter appears also to be connected to further information, and to timing, which is the order of development of the reaction, and the possible appreciation thereof.

Be that as it may, we have seen that the first cybernetician of power and action in "wishful thinking," was the all-powerful "demon" created by Maxwell. Whatever this demon wished, the electronic computers have realized, thanks to modern cybernetics. Cybernetics constitutes the great functional discovery of twentieth-century physics and as well the complement and answer to questions raised by entropy, especially because it diminishes if one furnishes it with information.

I send the reader back to the remarkable exposition of O. Costa de Beauregard[1] for the description of the reciprocal practical convertibility between information and negentropy. He emphatically states that there is a direct transition of negentropy → information corresponding to the process of *observation,* in which information signifies the *acquisition of knowledge.* He also states emphatically that the reciprocal transition of information → negentropy "schematizes the process of *action* or organization, where the word information this time signifies the *power of organization.*"

The ideas developed previously from the works of Clausius, Boltzmann, Brillouin (*cf.* Chapter 5), from the purely physical point of view, should be reunited here with those of Bergson,[2] in their dynamic aspects. Our point of view thus differs according to

---

[1] O. Costa de Beauregard, *Le second principe de la science du temps* (Paris, Editions du Seuil, 1960).

[2] Henri Bergson, *L'évolution créatrice,* Paris, 1940; *Creative Evolution* (New York, Modern Library, 1944).

whether we are dealing with matter or with the mind of man: As Bergson sums it up, "All our analyses show us an effort in life to reclimb the slope which matter descends."

In effect, what is the slope along which matter descends, if not the unavoidable diminution of energy (linked to the principle of Carnot, of delayed actions and of the determinism of causality), which is consequently associated with an increasing entropy, that is, with a decreasing negentropy? Conversely, what is the slope which is reclimbed by vital effort, if not a constant living opposition, "antimaterial" and "antiphysical" in some way, therefore opposed to these very diminishing tendencies: a means of surmounting them by the mind (despite the fatal diminution, as well, of the body material and even of the brain itself) and through the combined strengths of memory, intelligence, and will, exercising a free choice of action. In this process information as well as knowledge is increased. Let me repeat here that the very act of functioning, that is, the *functioning of the central nervous system, creates and develops the function, organizes it, makes it organic in an incomparably superior order.* In the last analysis, the central nervous system victoriously resists the decreasing negentropy of the external world, and, on the contrary, increases the existence of internal order, thereby also increasing internal negentropy. It is this function which sums up the superiority of man over nature. It is the directional arrow of our time by which our perception of things is linked to our initiative for possible action. It is the function which gives us the awareness of existing in time, of being and of acting, that is to say, also of becoming within duration.

This is what Bergson meant when he said,[1] with a kind of foresight, in one of his first books, *Matière et Mémoire:* "The truth is that memory does not consist at all of a regression from the present to the past" [which would be opposed to the directional arrow of time], "but on the contrary of a *progress from the present to the past.*[2] . . . In enabling us to attain within a unique intuition the multiple moments of duration, it disengages us from the flow of things, that is to say, from the rhythm of necessity."

Thus it appears that it is the characteristic of man (in spite of

---

[1] Henri Bergson, *Matière et Mémoire,* Conclusions (Paris, Félix Alcan, 1896); *Matter and Memory* (New York, Humanities Press, 1962).
[2] My italics.

the material nature of his body and even of his brain) to resist through his mind the decreasing negentropy of the world of matter. Thought, which is incorporated in matter, detaches itself like a hertzian wave from its material sender and conserves a nondecreasing message; that is, the inherent mental information persists. The difference is that a *hertzian radio wave propagates and sends its information across space, while the information conserved by the cognitive structure is exercised essentially within time.* This is why one may learn through experience and one never forgets *if one acts in time,* that is to say, in the immediate time when this action is still possible.

But here again, the substance of the self is confounded with its own duration. Why, given this continuity of internal time, and consequently its indivisibility, is it nevertheless possible, at least apparently, to forget? I say "apparently," since in the course of certain dreams, of certain pathological states, or of the electrical excitation of certain cerebral cells (Penfield),[1] one can bring the past back to life, reactualize it to the point that it seems to be relived, even though one "felt" that it had been forgotten. The trace of memory is always there. Then why is it not always evocable?

Let us again take up the comparison with the tape recorder. Everything is recorded on the vinyl tape, but there is no recall or reactualization if one does not unroll the tape, if one does not play back. It seems to be the same for human memory. Fortunately, to avoid functional hindrance, the remembrance only reappears when we need to *replay* it within a present action, when it will be brought to awareness again by means of a watchful concentration, meaning the attention and interest stemming from actual need. The mind, like the electronic computer, is made up of dynamic organizations, *conditioned in view of action and released by this very action;* this accounts for the appearance of automatism and explains also the facilitating influence of repetition to create habit. In the intervals between action, the potential activities—information (bits), remembrances (traces), images, symbols, concepts—rest in a virtual state, unconscious or unapparent, ready to become conscious and apparent, that is to say real, as soon as the action programmed externally or internally puts them back into play, that is, reactualizes them within the ride of duration.

---

[1] See Chapter 4.

For an electronic computer, the programming is there because an engineer put it there; for self-taught man, internal language conserves the code words which he has programmed himself. At all times "this program" is ready to be played or played back on the stage of life, *i.e.*, in the course of the performance of becoming, in the theater of duration.

In this psychological explanation, over and over again, I have had to add to the expressiveness of words through analogies or even metaphors, the latter being more precise than purely denotative language in describing the continuity of movement of psychological time. The term metaphor contains, etymologically, the idea of transfer and of transport, of movement or of duration. It is to the word what the algebraic function is to the arithmetic function: a functional derivative (even by definition) of the evolution of numbers and of values within their coordinated succession.

Having said this to apologize for my form, I return to the metaphysical basis of my argument to see how it is directly tied to physical, biological, and pathological considerations which I have just called into play. First, before explaining my experimental, synthetic, and biological views which have been furnished through my experience with humans in sickness and in health, I will sum up in a brief analysis the opinions of various other authors about the problem.

Chapter 17

Essay on the Interpretation of the Nature and Measurement of Time

Actually, it is necessary to begin with a classification of different times. Because, although using the same word, mathematicians, physicists, philosophers, and physicians often consider very different things, according to whether they refer to the measure of time or to its nature, and according to whether the latter is considered from a macroscopic point of view or from a microscopic, ultramicroscopic, biological, or psychological point of view. If we return to the preceding chapters, we may now synthesize as follows:

—For Newton, the universe was considered as a harmonious relationship of things; the creation and the limitation of absolute space and absolute time are, by definition, only a means of studying the relationship of these things. This is a restricted *physical* expression, even though it developed into something fruitful.

—For Minkowski and Einstein, the universe was considered to be a group of relationships originally set forth in space and time. Time is only a fourth function of space. (The word "dimension" as generally used leads to confusion.) The theory of relativity is a theory, actually, of the absolute relationships in a universe relatively empty of matter. Thus it is a *mathematical* expression of time, the practical consequences of which no longer need to be demonstrated, after so many brilliant proofs.

171

—However, as Bergson has remarked, commenting on the Einsteinian theory to say, "Restore independent time and you restore things," is to accept these things implicitly if not explicitly. The Bergsonian position is a *philosophical* expression of macroscopic time.

Another remark by Bergson in *L'évolution créatrice:* "Every preceding consideration raises the question of determinism, of causality, of finality, since radical finalism and issues of causality are substantially identical in that, for them, everything is given and nothing happens."

In order for something to happen, it is necessary that it be approached in microscopic, electronic times, that is to say, on a subatomic scale, with the quantum theory of Planck and the kangaroo leaps of Bohr's electrons, jumping each time from a quantum orbit to another orbit and another quantum, in their elliptical path around the nucleus of the atom. This quantal transition by its very discontinuity "transcends the spatiotemporal limits."

The work of Louis de Broglie has reconciled the formalism of restricted Einsteinian relativity with quantum theory, not only through study of the cinematic transformations of the "spin" of the electrons, but also through superquantification which adds an essential element to the evaluation of the interrelationship and interaction between waves and corpuscles. Thus de Broglie has permitted, again, *a physics from which the becoming, that is to say time, is not excluded.* As this author ingeniously remarked, historical order influences our manner of considering and describing phenomena: "Because Fresnel preceded Einstein and because Perrin preceded Davisson, physicists hold the impression that light is more undulatory than corpuscular and that the electron is more corpuscular than undulatory."

To this Costa de Beauregard gives a pertinent reply in his first book on *La notion de temps:* [1] "Every measurement in quantum physics is a wave as long as it appears as a question, a number of occupation (corpuscular) as far as it appears as an answer."

This is to say that if a question is poorly phrased, and if we should share Heisenberg's pessimism about a certain indetermi-

---

[1] O. Costa de Beauregard, *La notion de temps, equivalence avec l'espace* (Paris, Hermann, 1963). Again, we refer the reader desirous of becoming better acquainted with these physical discussions to this author whose power of discrimination and talent for exposition and for invention place him among the top-ranking physicists of this generation.

nation, then, for reasons already described above (in Chapter 3), how can we know at the same instant both the position and velocity of a particle? At this level, we find ourselves, seemingly, face to face with a relative negation of determinism, to the extent that the probability of large numbers and statistics is going to replace eventual precise causality. Exactly as Heisenberg notes: "The question of knowing if a complete knowledge of the past permits one to foresee the future cannot be asked, because a complete knowledge of the past implies a *self-contradiction.*" He goes on to say that at this scale *each increment of knowledge can only be acquired at the price of an increment of ignorance.*

To sum it all up, it is difficult to draw from the well of temporal truth with a bottomless bucket, that is to say, a bucket opened in space!

However, let us not forget at this stage that the human mind can, through its own mechanism, as we have seen earlier, and by means of its own functioning, relatively dissociate the idea of pure duration, even though this idea was originally received from space during childhood along with perceptual information. The recording of memory and the persistent "trace" of information, constitute, as we have seen, the *operational intermediary between space and time.* Although they were associated primitively, the mind has the privilege of being able to dissociate them by its own activity, and we have seen that memory can dissociate itself from space and insert itself with the self in pure duration. Briefly, by putting *the self as the abscissa and time as the ordinate,* one can construct the curve of psychological duration, this time springing from the *interior,* which is superimposed on the vital curve. And that holds true whether this self and this psychological time are exerted through their internal activities or whether they are exerted by their external actions in space. This is a possible and contingent consequence which remains independent of space, to the extent that space no longer intervenes in the becoming of the self, nor in the development of the internal temporal phenomenon.

We have experimental certainty—through the study of the formation and evolution of the temporal function, as well as of its involution with age or mental illness—that a *cybernetical-biological estimation of the idea of time* can bring great light to bear on the nature of psychological time and its relationship with the time of the physicists. It is well to say this in most ample detail, because the physicists, mathematicians, or philosophers whose names

173

I have just mentioned, being human, act in accordance with the very principles I have described when developing their concepts and their theories.

We must not attempt to force the facts, and to conclude that because the brain is matter and its function is electric and because it is thus linked directly by means of its function to the microscopic time of the physicists, the psychological (mental or internal) times that develop from it are necessarily similar in their essence. The contrary seems true, if only because the "personal" opinions developing from these common electric mechanisms are often individual and different.

As opposed to the peripheral nervous system which is activated only by an excitation stimulated from the outside, the brain constitutes a mass of nervous tissue whose networks are constantly and spontaneously energized by electrical (or electrochemical) nervous impulses which are exercised throughout the life span. We have seen that the order of magnitude of these networks is ten billion cells, neurons, and synapses. Thus there is a sort of reaction engine in constant activity with billions of possible times, continually pulsated by the stimulation of electric nervous impulses. And this is so during the operation of information on recording, of symbolic programming on intelligence, of communication of activity upon action (voluntary act), or inversely of the reaction of the action upon activity (conditional reflex). As Pavlov has demonstrated,[1] in the intervals between activities action continues, and *these intervals of activity (which are only apparent) constitute in themselves a specific and measurable conditional stimulus.* (As in a theatrical performance, the interludes were part of the play!)

These extraordinary circumstances make one think of the words of Einstein: "It is far from right to say that nature always plays the same game." *Functional mental times are different from anatomical cerebral times.*

To H. Weyl's expression, "The objective world is, it does not become," I can reply, *"The subjective world is, only to the extent that it is becoming."* I know very well that in this statement born of observation, the word "becomes" implies the development over time; but this word has been adapted to the extent that it cor-

---

[1] Ivan Pavlov, *Lectures on Conditioned Reflexes* (New York, International Publishers, 1941).

responds to the placing in opposition of objective external time and of psychological subjective internal time.

In summary, to the objective spatiotemporal spreading out which appears more or less discontinuous, if only because of the electromagnetic (visual) or the piezoelectric (audition) fractionation imposed by our sense organs, we must oppose the subjective mental-temporal continuum. This latter constitutes for man the only true continuity, because the becoming of the self, alone, inserted in the curve of time can induce the feeling of what one could call *persistence without space*, that is to say the intuition of pure duration.

We have seen, along the way, that these phenomena can be evaluated according to their nature and measured in a valid manner without having recourse to space. We are approaching a *rapprochement* between functional entropic physics and the physiology of mental time. There are in effect two common denominators, one negative, the other positive, which give this analogy considerable epistemological value. For both, in effect, space does not intervene and remains an invariant factor; on the other hand (and above all, the following represents the positive element) this function is exercised in time, without being measured by an independent external time. For the psychological time of the self, as well as for the duration of the thermodynamic entropic phenomenon, it is the *time of this very action or reaction* which constitutes the isolated duration and becomes identified with it, in its irreversible purity.

May one see not a begging of the question, but a dynamic definition of time expressing itself in the function of pure duration, that is, *capable of being superimposed on the operational curve of the self* and being blended with this curve within its existence and by means of its very existence! That is why the common expression "We pass our time," is incorrect; in fact, it is *time which passes and we who pass with it.*

The unidirectional characteristic of the arrow of psychological time and its superposition on the essential curve of the self are easily verified by the following explanations: from the conception and the birth of the individual until his death, biological processes, even if one considers them only on a cellular scale, are progressive and relatively irreversible. Certainly, they are equally as irreversible as the thermodynamic process in Boltzmann's idea of entropy, which is primed in a certain direction in a closed system. There, the order of the molecules is superimposed on the direction of time of the reaction. In both cases, it is a question of *time internal to the system and linked to the very action or reaction.*

I should remark once more that these times, whether they be physical or physiological, *are similar in their functional character:* they are linked to what takes place or to what happens unexpectedly. They are *operational* times.

In this, they are fundamentally opposed to time spread out in advance, such as that of the relativistic mathematicians, who only consider *"frozen" times* to the extent that they are given in advance. Thus, the relativists deny, through convention, the existence of the past, present, and future. But, to offset this, it is not contrary to relativism to consider the system of reference of a particular man who observes or of a factor capable of recording the *before* and *after* of an action or reaction. And this same fact does not trouble us in naming or in interpreting any given functional physical and psychological time. Nor, it must be recognized, does it bother the relativists in the interpretation of their calculations! Moreover, as Reichenbach [1] remarks, the theories of special or general relativity do not take complete account of the role of time, even in physics. We have seen that the physicists themselves, following Louis de Broglie [2] and Costa de Beauregard [3] particularly, have had to introduce or reintroduce into their considerations and their calculations a functional time from which becoming is not excluded. Certainly the addition of the "spin" of the electrons and the intervention of superquantification in the interpretation of temporal phenomena constitute a functional element. Thus, the physicists have approached the time of the philosophers and doctors, that is, *"operatory"* and *evolutionary* times on the human scale. If as we have seen, psychological times approach macroscopic times by the irreversible character of their unidirectional arrow, they differ from ultramicroscopic subatomic

---

[1] Hans Reichenbach, *Direction of Time* (Berkeley, University of California Press, 1956).

[2] See p. 172 of this chapter.

[3] O. Costa de Beauregard and Charles Goillot, *Mise en évidence d'un phénomène nouveau: l'effet inertial de Spin sur corps d'épreuve ferromagnétique.* Report made to Académie des Sciences, Paris, 24 August 1964.

times where this factor does not enter. (*Cf.* Chapter 6.) On the other hand, biological and cerebral times approach subatomic times in that, in both cases, the law of large numbers must come into play and considerations from statistical probability must intervene. We know that the phenomena of destruction when particles and antiparticles meet, as well as the phenomena of quantum mechanics, permit us to foresee only the distribution of *certain possible future events*, and with a certain functional coefficient of indetermination, the latter being expressed by the plural of "future events." This thing is important, because it accounts on the atomic as well as on the human scale for the fact that *temporal fatality can only appear retrospectively*.

Given all these considerations about the nature of time, one can judge at what point it differs from the nature of space, even if, in certain cases, it can, according to the relativists, seem to be assimilated for measurement as a coordinated fourth dimension. Nevertheless, the fact that it is possible, through a number of experimental proofs, to despatialize, properly speaking, and completely in certain cases, the temporal function, does not justify the Bergsonian exaggeration of considering this function as inexpressible in mathematical terms, because these particular cases cannot be expressed geometrically.

On the contrary, I think that just as according to Einstein we have found a unity of space (linked to the speed of light), we will be able some day to accept a unity of minimal time, beyond which time will be indivisible, but not at all infinite. At the moment, the minimal limit reached seems to be the chronon, calculated from the spin of electrons and protons. Based on the fact that the smallest physically measurable length is that of the diameter of the electrons and protons (of the order of 10^{-13} cm), it is possible, by correlation, to calculate the unity of minimal time by division of this length by the speed recognized as maximum: that of light in a vacuum (3×10^{10} cm/second). Based on this calculation, the order of magnitude of the chronon would be 10^{-24} seconds. This figure is analogous to that which Heisenberg found when, studying the principle of indetermination, he calculated the time of minimal precision of a "subatomic clock" struck by a photon of light.[1]

---

[1] Coefficient of precision $= \dfrac{h}{mc^2}$ (h: constant of Planck; c: speed of light; m: mass of the proton of the order of 10^{-24}).

It is also analogous to that described by Bunge [1] when he described a time for the electron arrived at from the algebraic sum of extrinsic and intrinsic times (t) and linked to the rotation period (spin) of the electron (τ), that is, $t \pm 10^{-21}$ seconds.

Thus we can envisage the existence of a unity of time, the *chronon*, capable of playing for the interpretation and measurement of time the same role that the *photon* plays for the interpretation and the measurement of space. Moreover it is possible that this unity does not yet constitute the minimal definitive unity. To say that in the present state of the science one cannot measure a smaller unity, does not mean that, theoretically, one cannot conceive of a smaller unity; [2] indeed, the important thing *is* to conceive of the probable, plausible, and even possible existence of this unity.

In effect, one can foresee that this unity, drawn from the very nature of observed raw matter, could contribute to the measuring of it internally, within its innermost functional behavior, within its constitutional *becoming*, that is, its duration. In sum, we could realize for nonliving matter what we have proven in the study of man, where the mental becoming of psychological time can be studied by means of the intelligence attached to the gray matter of the brain but nevertheless detached from slavery to this matter.

With this goal in mind, I shall not dwell here on the mechanical pendulum or spring clocks [3] where in the end the measurement of time, however precise and fractionated it may be, is only a precise division of a movement, a measurement of the length of a space traversed. I will be content to remark that this behavior contains

---

[1] M. Bunge, *Nuovo Cimento* (Rome, 1955). Period of "spin" of the electron calculated by the formula $\dfrac{h}{4\pi m c^2}$ (h: constant of Planck; m: mass of the electron).

[2] G. S. Whitrow, *The Natural Philosophy of Time* (London, Thomas Nelson, 1961). "Theoretically, the shortest length can be constructed by use of the three fundamental constants: g, h, c (gravitation, Planck's constant, speed of light). It would be $\sqrt{gh/c^3}$, that is to say, of the order of 10^{-32} centimeters. In fact, lengths shorter than 10^{-13} do not seem to correspond practically to an actual scientific context."

[3] Results of the magnificent works of Huygens after the discoveries of Galileo and of Newton, and notably of the law of isochronism of small oscillations—the period of the pendulum $T = 2\pi\sqrt{L/G}$.

an anticipation of *periodic times, as compared to the continuous times* of sundials or hourglasses of antiquity.

On the contrary, I shall concentrate on the statistics resulting from study of the natural oscillation of an atomic electric field, or the periodic decay of radioactive substances, or even the exponential discharge of a condenser. In these instances the irreversibility of time appears from the onset as indisputable, and the idea of space does not intervene (at least officially and directly) in the production of the phenomenon or in its measurement. These are, in a word, nonspatial and non-"temporal" measurements of the time function, similar to the entropic modifications which allowed us to measure the temporal evolution of a transformation towards thermodynamic equilibrium in a closed system. Since the works, today classical, of Henri Becquerel (1896), we know that the radioactive substances or their isotopes disintegrate spontaneously through the emission of alpha or beta particles, or more rarely gamma, and that their disintegration follows an *exponential* curve. As J. J. Thompson has shown (1912), when there is a mixture of substances, they can be isolated in the form of ionized vapors by submitting them to an electric or a magnetic field or mixed electromagnetic, by means of a mass spectrograph. The deviation, for each ion, is indeed inversely proportional to its mass.

Thus once one possesses a pure radioactive element, it is easy, according to the simple formula of E. Rutherford,[1] to determine for every moment of the existence of the radio-isotope the duration of its half-life, and then to measure precisely the time of the disintegration of its particles. By means of radioactive metals with very slow disintegration (lead, strontium, rubidium), one can estimate retrospectively the duration of the early ages of the earth; analysis of the radioactive carbon contents of prehistoric relics yields a measurement of the ages of geological layers where these specimens have been found. The decay of radioactive substances and their isotopes constitutes only one particular measurable case of the decline of universal entropy over time, that is, "within time."

With the atomic clocks built today by man, one can arrive at measurements which, if they do not yet attain the precision of the

---

[1] $Nt = No.—0.693\ t/T$. No: number of initial atoms; Nt: number of atoms after a time; t/T: interval of time when the number of atoms is half the number of that of the initial atoms $(No/2)$.

chronon described above (10^{-24} second), nevertheless are getting closer and closer to it. Such are the cesium clocks [1] where the magnetic field produced by an oscillating electric current is synchronized by the vibration of the cesium atom. This is possible because these atoms have only one electron in the outermost layer of their electric "shell" and because the interaction between this unique electron and the atomic nucleus is capable of producing a frequency of 9,200 megacycles per second (corresponding to a wavelength of 3 cm). The precision of this "chronometer" thus exceeds that of any astronomic determination. The model at the United States Naval Observatory has a precision of the order of two parts for one hundred billion, which corresponds to a possible variation of one second every three hundred years. [2]

In the same order of ideas and of magnitude, the Laboratory of Marine Research in Washington [3] has produced a system of three digital electric computers which simultaneously record the piezoelectric oscillations from a quartz crystal. If the count of the oscillations from one of the electronic computers does not correspond to that of the others, it signals the error and stops to permit a repair while the other two continue their temporal recording. This clock attains a precision on the order of the microsecond, that is to say of a millionth of a second.

But the most precise of the atomic clocks functioning today (May 1964) has been established by three Harvard physicists [4] who have developed a gaseous maser [5] permitting the recording of the pure frequency of liberated hydrogen atoms. The frequency of this atomic clock is that of 1,420,405,751,800 cycles per second + 0,028 cps. The precision of the hydrogen maser is so great that, for a control, it was necessary to build an identical apparatus in order to compare the results. The experiment proved an agreement of frequency of the order of a trillionth.

---

[1] Dr. L. Essen, National Physical Laboratory (London, 1955–57).

[2] Since the writing of this work, the 12th General Conference on Weights and Measures, meeting in Paris in November 1964, has adopted as unity a time of one second as measured by means of the relationship of the resonance frequency of cesium 133.

[3] Donald J. Jones and Douglas A. Venn, Naval Research Laboratory, Washington, Patent No. 3 130 297 (April, 1964).

[4] Donald Kleppner, Norman Ramsey, Stuart B. Crampton, *Report to the Annual Meeting of the American Physical Society,* New York, February, 1964.

[5] Maser: Microwave Amplification by Stimulated Emission of Radiation.

If I have dwelt at length on the ever-greater precision in the measurement of time, it is naturally not because that precision has a practical interest of some kind for the daily life of man, nor even because these measuring apparatuses have great interest for astronomy as well as for astronautics. But these measurement apparatuses on the subatomic scale touch the *very nature of time within the functioning of the electron.*

Innumerable experiments and applications are foreseeable, not only with the maser, but with the laser.[1] It would be beyond the limits of this book to enter into all the details of experimentation with lasers. But I must emphasize the fact that, for the first time in the history of man, he is given the possibility, with *natural resonators,* of producing strictly monochromatic and coherent light waves, and, consequently, whatever the intensity of electromagnetic waves, to measure and cause to vary their phase as well as their polarity. Dwelling here only on the phenomenon of phase, which touches at the heart of our subject, I can state that:

First. In an ideal monochromatic field, the amplitude of the vibrations at some fixed point or other is constant, while the phase *varies linearly with time.*

Second. In a wavefield produced by a true source, the amplitude and phase are subjected to some irregular fluctuations, of which the rapidity varies with the breadth $\Delta\nu$ of the spectrum.

Third. The interval of time $\Delta t = 1/\Delta\nu$ corresponds to the *time of coherence.*

Fourth. For a monochromatic source, if one considers two electromagnetic vectors at two points P_1 and P_2 of an undulatory field, such that the distance $SP_1 - SP_2$ is small in comparison with the wavelength λ, the fluctuations at P_1 and P_2 will be the same.[2] Consequently in studying the electronic modifications, one can define the *regions of coherence, as well as the times of coherence.*

To cite only one recent example of the application of the laser, let me point out the experiment made by a group of physicists [3] from the Massachusetts Institute of Technology, who have reproduced

---

[1] Laser: Light Amplification by Stimulated Emission of Radiation.

[2] Bela A. Lengyel, *Lasers* (New York, John Wiley & Sons, 1962): "Moreover, one can expect that a certain correlation persists even for a separation greater than that of P_1 and of P_2, provided that the size of the difference does not exceed the length of coherence: $c \Delta t \approx c/\Delta\nu$."

[3] T. S. Jaseja, A. Savan, S. Murray, C. H. Towny, Massachusetts Institute of Technology, *Physical Review* (March, 1964).

with great simplicity and with "three times more precision" the classic experiment of Michelson-Morley, that which in 1891 had served as a bridge between the classical physics of Newton and the special relativity of Einstein (1905). Using two lasers of neon and of helium gas mounted at right angles on a revolving plate (resistant to any shock), the MIT physicists observed, in making the plate turn at 90°, a weak variation in frequency probably caused by the influence of the earth's magnetic field, but, more important, they verified the constancy of the speed of light and its uniformity in all directions, thereby confirming the soundness of the theory of special relativity.

Thus, with the maser and above all the laser (which is only an optical maser), we possess the instrument which finally permits us —with an intense electromagnetic sheaf of weak diffraction, of great monochromatic coherence—to study all the variations of photoelectric effects, to stimulate at will individual atoms to study their variable properties, according to whether their electrons are in a state of energetic excitation or, on the contrary, of semirepose.

Moreover, the laser is an instrument of junction between wave or corpuscular statistical mechanics and special relativity. It is an experimental process which proves and justifies the reconciliation made earlier by Louis de Broglie.

But what is more, because of the measurements it makes possible, the laser increases our information about space and time and is going to bring about an advance corresponding to that brought about by cybernetics (in the quality of computers and thus in the models of brains).

If there were doubt that certain phenomena, which are in appearance authentically temporal, because of their apparent autonomy should be separated and isolated from space, the functional electronic subatomic physics made more precise by the laser reestablishes their connection and their intimate correlations and verifies their quantistic mechanism by stimulating them experimentally. The proof is imminent, if not already made, that the generation of monochromatic light by the stimulated emission, using natural resonators, of atomic crystals or gas, throws *new light (psychological this time) on the physics of "becoming,"* that is, on the functional physics which includes human duration.

Chapter 18

Heuristic Point of View of Research on Determinism

So far, after partaking of diverse ideas about time, such as are offered by the philosophers, the classical physicists, the relativists, the anatomists, the physiologists, and even the cyberneticists, I have asked myself to what the nature of internal time corresponds and what its relation is with the mind of man.

In studying the various theories as objectively as possible, I have sometimes repeated, sometimes contradicted myself, by changing my point of view according to the discipline involved; sometimes I have even been deceived, taken in by appearances. The truth or the approaches to it are sometimes disguised in an attractive cloak of lies, glittering with scientific ornaments.

One important error, for example, has been from the beginning to hold, along with numerous philosophers, that within a material world of relative discontinuity, human thought constitutes the only element of continuity, if not through the individual, then at least across the human species. The fact that this error is widely distributed does not diminish its gravity. Like many other authors, I should have been able, when I had changed my opinion and acquired the proofs of my error, to turn back and correct the first pages of the manuscript. I preferred not to do this for two reasons: (a) An experimental study has value only if it shows its processes in detail and shows the negative and contradictory results as well as the positive and confirming results; (b) This hypothesis has been fruitful to the extent that, knowing what I was seeking, I was far from foreseeing what I was going to find!

For what purpose, otherwise, to pass ceaselessly from the machine to man, from the well-functioning to the ill, to study time and space of matter, than times which are in appearance at least dissociated from space and matter? For what purpose should I interest myself in the gaseous lasers, estimating time at a millionth of a second, while trying to approach still from afar the unity of theoretical time, the chronon of 10^{-24} seconds? Does it matter whether in the actual state of the science one can demonstrate that this unity exists or whether it will remain indivisible? Finally, why have I dwelt so insistently on psychotic subjects affected by temporal alienation, for whom time no longer exists? It has been my goal, at all times, to test the facts not only by their statistical value, but to try to estimate the *values of behavior*, that is, the dynamic functional value of temporal variation, in physiological behavior, as well as within its pathological "eclipses."

Within each of these diverse phenomena, I have sought a common denominator, a unifier of the idea of time. And if, having come almost to the end of my study, I seem to bring forth an idea of time which is probably univocal only for man, is that to say that its nature must remain equivocal with regard to the universe of matter? I do not think so.

However, without exceeding the limits of the facts duly stated, I must try to synthesize more precisely what the analysis of physical, biological, and mental phenomena has furnished me. Yet even when I make an appeal to the mind, I forbid myself to use any generalization appearing to be meta physical, however tempting it may be. I write this expression in two words, in order to signify that today it constitutes a branch of physics and one of physiology, each inclusive of the other. It is only in this way that meta physics can conserve an epistemological value, and acquire a pragmatic value for research.

To recognize ignorance, or the limit of knowledge, actually appears more important to me than to propose, by extension, a false knowledge which would limit my power of investigation.

Niels Bohr [1] found himself confronted by a similar problem when

---

[1] Niels Bohr, "Biology and Atomic Physics." Address at the Physical and Biological Congress, in Memory of Luis Galvani (Bologne, October, 1937).

he tried to apply the laws and measurements of classical physics to the study of subatomic phenomena at the quantum scale. That, with the boldness of his genius, Einstein had grasped the correlation between the photons and their emission of quanta, greatly facilitated the understanding of the problem faced by Bohr, but not its solution: "The quantities which, in classical physics, are utilized to describe the state of a system have been replaced, in the formalism of quantum mechanics, by symbolic operators limited in their commutation by the laws inherent in the quantum." This is what Heisenberg came to express mathematically in his feelings of regret about indetermination.[1] Bohr, the great observer, expressed similar feelings when he added: "While the deterministic description of classical physics rests on the assumption of an unrestricted compatibility of the space-time coordination and the laws of the conservation of energy, we are confronted here by the problem of knowing if, to the extent that this concerns atomic objects, such a description can be retained."

In fact it could not be, and the deterministic individual description had to be replaced by a prediction of a functional statistical character.

Moreover, it became necessary, in a *complementary* manner, to change the instruments of measurement: "Although in classical physics there is no difference between the instruments of measurement and the objects under investigation, here the situation is essentially different."

Bohr implies, by this sentence, the importance, beyond the structure, of the study of the function, which we will again find necessary in biology and which justifies cybernetic study. In another talk given in Copenhagen at the end of his life, Bohr [2] came to recognize this expressly. Coming back first to the principle of complementarity, he says: "This is not a renunciation of the usual physical explanation, it is an idea which refers directly to our posi-

---

[1] "The chain of cause and effect could be quantitatively verified only if the whole universe were considered as a single system—but then physics has vanished, and only a mathematical scheme remains. The partition of the world into observing and observed systems prevents a sharp formulation of the law of cause and effect." Heisenberg, in the *Physical Principles of the Quantum Theory* (New York, Dover Publications, 1930), p. 58.

[2] Niels Bohr, "Unity of Knowledge." Conference given in New York for the bicentennial of Columbia University, October 1954, in *Atomic Physics and Human Knowledge* (New York, John Wiley & Sons, Science Editions, Inc., 1961).

tion as observer, within a domain of experience where application without ambiguity of the concepts used to describe the phenomena depends essentially on the conditions of observation."

To what an extent would not this notion be particularly applicable to biological phenomena in general and to cerebral ones in particular? "The irreversible character of biological phenomena implicates this complementarity, and an inherent temporal direction in the function of organisms is evident, in a striking manner, in their utilizations of previous experiences to reply to the subsequent stimulus." That is to say, as we have stated many times in this book, that the very irreversibility of a reaction shows its existence in time, in *a time internal to this reaction and contemporaneous to the transformation which takes place*. During this transformation, space plays only a contingent role, in every case invariant, while the temporal element, itself, is covariant, dependent, functional, operatory. *Mechanism and finalism are neither contradictory nor mutually exclusive for the human mind:* but in the observer's effector system of communication, recording of the memory plays a complementary role, which must be taken into account for observation, as well as for the interpretation of phenomena. If the observing subject takes himself as an object and becomes observed, his self is going to be confused with the impression of lived-through duration. All the while losing his experimental objectivity, he exercises the temporal function on himself, that is to say he becomes aware, he becomes *conscious*.

Given the complexity of the phenomenon involved in the study of psychological time and the fact that the observing instrument remains the human brain, it is desirable to find an external instrument, sufficiently complex to be adapted to the extraordinary complexity of the cerebral mechanism and conditioned in such a manner that, through a different structure, the cerebral functions can be imitated in an analogous way, but nevertheless dissociated from the time factor. This last would then be no more than an independent variable rather than by necessity dependent, a relatively contingent element rather than a given determinant.

The cerebral functions can be imitated by the cybernetic function of general electronic computers, which are both digital and analog.

I have attempted (Chapter 15) to show the development of this science and also its possibilities of application, not only to the neurological phenomena, which the pioneers (Norbert Wiener, Walter Grey, Ross Ashby) had noted, but also to the study of psychological and psychiatric phenomena. What remains to be done here is to clarify the epistemological value of the cybernetic process and its exact position as the reproducing instrument of that human thought from which it has sprung.

Before going further in this discussion, I shall ask the reader to concentrate his attention on Table V below (p. 188), which outlines the extent to which, in the development from simple to more complex machines, one can see the progressive organization, and even the "organicization," of the interaction of effects on causes.

For machines as well as for men, the servomechanism necessary for this reaction of effects on their own causes usually consists of a retroactive circuit or "feedback" which limits the intensity of the effects, while acting on the causes which produced them. A further degree in the refinement of the mechanism, and of the "feedback" will be the addition of a "feed ahead" circuit, one which foresees the action, a kind of real preaction circuit. With it, the releasing cause itself will be adjusted in advance to limit its effects, even before they act retroactively on it. This capacity to predict, this anticipated modification gives *the machines every appearance of intelligence and makes up part of the real mechanism of intelligence in man.*

Table V, to reflect on it a minute more, also immediately shows on the one hand that there can no longer be opposition or mutual exclusion between mechanism and finality, and on the other that the problem of determinism must be modified in these terms. The finality of a complex system (mechanical or organic), whether it be apparent or real, is of little consequence in the end; since, to employ a current but scientifically pertinent expression, *it will always be for the requirements of the cause.* But in fact those requirements are *seen by the effects and in view of these very effects!*

And this leads us to understand better and redefine functionally automatisms and more complex systems of equilibrium of the homeostatic type.

"Automatic" is a term that means a reaction or a system of reactions so determined (established by man or by nature) as to induce an equally determined corrective action and *released by this very contingency.* A simple illustrative example: the safety valve of

TABLE V: Classification of Automatisms and of Their Progressive Improvement

Apparent Structure	Real Nature	Causal Determinism (at least apparent)	Resultant Effect (provocative interaction in view of the effects)	Feedback	Consequences	Temporal Function
Parts adjusted in view of the action	Machine tools	External in view of determined actions	Coordination of actions	0	Manufacture	External to the system
Simple organization in view of the action	Semi-automatic machine, i.e., sprinkler system, sensitive to rise in temperature	External, conditioning a reaction or a system of predetermined reactions	Limited by intentional specialization	0	Autoregulation of the cause	External to the system
Complex organization established in view of a system of reactions	Simple cybernetic models (James Watt's ball regulator)	External, but stabilized by its own interior effects	Automatism	+	Autoregulation of the effects	External to the system

188

Autoregulatory organization	(a) Ashby's homeostat (b) Cannon's homeostasis (sympathetic)	Internal to the system (a) established by man (b) established by nature	Equilibration, often of several effectors (appearance of finality)	+ +	Interior equilibrium	Covariant to the reactive system
Pseudo-organic machine	General electronic computer, digital and analog-complex cybernetic models (Uttley H. Blum)	External programming secondarily interiorized and registered	Appearance of adaptation	Feedback constructed by man + + + addition of anticipator feed aheads	Equilibrium in view of stable action; appearance of the intelligence and will	Invariable
True organism	Nervous system of man, electro-chemical computer of the human brain	Programming from exterior and interior; code self-formed and conserved in memory	Reality of adaptation acting on the internal and external causes	Feedback self-formed + + + added regulating systems (either procrastinating or anticipatory)	*Mobile* equilibrium of *life* Reality of intelligence and free conceptual choice	Covariant, *inherent* to the system, is blended with reality of the ego

the boiler of a steam engine [1] is established for the purpose of correcting an excess of pressure and is released by this same hyperpressure, which opens the corrective caretaker mechanism by means of excess steam. In the more complex case of an intelligent or pseudointelligent equilibrating adaptive mechanism, it is necessary to add to the preceding definition a modifying limiting element.

As equilibrium (established by man or self-developed in man) is approached, there is more than one automatic corrective action, a constant modification and correlation of causes and effects (through the intermediary of feedback), which, in its maximum adaptability, amounts to the permutation of causes and effects. A simple example: a thermostat is preset to reach a certain temperature. The raising of the temperature releases the corrective mechanism which shuts off the heat, a limiting mechanism; *vice versa*, the lowering of the temperature releases the restarting of heat, a secondary corrective mechanism.

For the phenomena of organic equilibrating self-regulation, such as those described by Cannon under the name of homeostasis, one can restate the above formula in the following manner:

In physiology, it is not only the mechanism to be corrected which specifically excites the corrective mechanism; there can be an inversion, that is, the mechanism which was formerly to be corrected becomes the corrective mechanism.

A simple example is arterial hypertension (mechanism to be corrected) which is the specific instigator of the hypotensive releasing mechanism (corrective). In arterial hypertension brought on by the excitation of the medulla oblongata, the sympathetic hypothalamic nuclei, the carotid ganglion, etc., a superficial peripheral vasodilatation and a profound splanchnic vasodilatation lead to a diminution of vascular resistance, thus to a hypotension. When hypotension becomes the mechanism to be corrected, it, in turn, through inverse stimulation of the same centers, will produce the vasoconstrictions, both superficial and profound, tending to elevate tension and to re-establish a normal arterial pressure.

It should be remarked that in all the actions and reactions described above the temporal function does not intervene: it remains external to the phenomena, and at the most an independent covariant, not taking an integral part in the systems of action or of

---

[1] James Watt (1788), "The Flyball Governor." See Chapter 15.

reaction involved. The above reactions, one might say, are exerted within time, time accompanies them, can serve to measure them, but it is not the essential instigating functional element.

In considering the last column of Table V (p. 188), one sees that there is only one case where the temporal function is exercised in a manner inherent in the system: that is in the functioning of man's brain. And it is evidently upon this unique exception,[1] which constitutes the temporal function of living beings, that we must now dwell.

In going from the simple to the complex, certain preliminary remarks must be made:

First. As Raymond Ruyer[2] said, when one addresses oneself to a living being, whether it be simple or complex, one must consider its form, that is its structure or anatomy, "which is arranged within time as well as within space, the anatomy of the adult being only a segment," at a selected moment. He describes as "potential, the form or more exactly the explicit scheme, to the extent that it controls not only the structure at a given instant, but the coordinated succession of structures which appear over time."

Second. Ruyer pertinently adds that "without the idea of a transspatiotemporal form of potential, one would not be able to understand that the organic form must be organized within time as well as within space."

Third. It is a classical notion that the embryological development reproduces, within a fixed time for each species, an ontogenesis which recapitulates phylogenesis.

Fourth. For a living being the adaptation to temporal survival precedes its birth, whether it be an amoeba, fish, bird, bear or man. Before the temporal function is fully developed, there is already in the structure of the genes (ribonucleic acid RNA or deoxyribonucleic acid DNA, imprinting on the protein molecule a specific form), a pattern of adaptation which reacts both to the eventual external environment and to its internal becoming, that is to say its duration.

It is important to remark here that unicellular beings such as amoebas or white corpuscles, which are only a mass of protoplasm,

---

[1] See Chapter 15.

[2] Raymond Ruyer, *Eléments de psychobiologie* (Paris, Presses Universitaires de France, 1946).

with one or more nuclei, surrounded by a membrane, already live and endure in an *autonomous time*. They are without organs, digestive tube, lungs, or nervous system. Without a doubt, they can be conscious of neither space nor time, but, even so, they can *behave*. They can move themselves by means of their pseudopodia, surround and swallow up foreign substances menacing them, and maintain by means of electrical osmosis across their semipermeable membrane a constancy of internal environment, adapted for survival in the external environment. The unicellular life is already miraculous and already tends towards self-actualization and autonomous endurance, as opposed to the constant disintegration of the external physical world, although it must adjust to the latter in order to live . . . and survive.

At a higher degree (considerably higher!), and omitting the intermediary stages which are outside the limits of this book, we come to man, pluricellular being that he is, with highly specialized organs and functions.

Compared to the amoeba which lives in an aquatic environment, human cells have "internalized" their external environment, and as Claude Bernard [1, 2] remarked a long time ago, one of the vital necessities of this organism is to maintain the constancy of this environment become internal. But a spatiotemporal external space also exists for this organism which must not only adapt to it, but at the same time protect itself from it to survive.

It is useful to recall these well-known facts here in their simplicity, because one often forgets by what extraordinarily complex and highly specialized mechanisms the human organism maintains its unstable adaptive equilibrium. To repeat the words of Claude Bernard, "Life is stable only because it is unstable."

We have seen that the equilibrium of the internal environment is maintained by the mechanism, so well described by Cannon,[3] of homeostasis, a word encompassing all of the glandular automatisms and all of the peripheral sympathetic and central hypothalamic autonomies. These unconscious and probably innate phenomena es-

---

[1] Claude Bernard, *Introduction à l'étude de la médecine expérimentale* (Paris, Baillières, 1868).

[2] Claude Bernard, *Leçons sur la physiologie et la pathologie du système nerveux* (Paris, Baillières, 1868).

[3] Walter B. Cannon, *The Wisdom of the Body* (New York, W. W. Norton, 1932).

cape from the realm of voluntary control, and in short deal with our *inner world*. It remains to establish how the connection with the spatiotemporal external world is equilibrated, thanks to what I shall call a *second homeostatic system:* dealing this time with relations with the *outer world*.

This unusual term is justified in my eyes because it seems to me that this second system, without a doubt conscious and modifiable at will (at least to a certain extent), is no less indispensable to the survival and to the development of man. From an anatomical and physiological point of view, it has been masterfully studied by John Carew Eccles,[1, 2] during a lifetime of research which is summed up in his book, *The Physiology of the Synapses*. And Leo Szilard,[3] in an article published two months after his death, drew from it the probable and possible consequences for the mechanism of memory.

The reader interested in the experimental details is referred to the original works; I outline here only certain consequences useful to our demonstration, concerning the nature of the temporal function and the way it is exercised in what I have called the *homeostasis with reference to the outer world*.

A preliminary general remark should be made: just as one of the essential functions of memory is apparent *forgetting* (*cf.* Chapter 5), one may say that, within the electrical functioning of the brain, its electrical constancy shows itself as much, if not more, through its *inhibiting* functions as through its stimulating functions. We shall see further on that it is probably by means of these inhibiting functions that the brain exercises its selective function to the highest degree: everything happens as if, at a given moment, a moment created by itself (in the most authentic sense of this temporal word), the brain isolates itself from external communication and retires within itself to compute, that is to think, to choose, before acting or not. These functional delays, these inter-

---

[1] John Carew Eccles, *The Physiology of the Synapses* (New York, Academic Press, Inc., 1964). A book where the reader will find all the details and possible references.

[2] John Carew Eccles, P. Andersen, C. McC. Brooks, "Electrical Responses of the Ventro-Basal Nucleus of the Thalamus," *Lectures on the Diencephalon Progress in Brain Research*, Vol. 5 (Amsterdam, London, New York, American Elsevier Publishing Co., 1964).

[3] Leo Szilard, "On Memory and Recall," *Proceedings of the National Academy of Sciences*, Vol. 51, No. 6 (Washington, D.C., June, 1964).

ruptions, true temporal pauses, seem to play the same role in the central nervous system of man as retarding circuits in the electronic model of Albert Uttley (*cf.* Chapter 3).

If the result is analogous, the mechanism, nevertheless, is noticeably different, in fact considerably more complex and perfected, primarily because, instead of being purely electrical, it is electrochemical. Whence, theoretically and practically, come three essential advantages: (a) The stimulations, as well as the inhibitions, can be exercised with more selectivity and precision; (b) In spite of the extraordinary multiplicity of the neurons (of the order of ten billion), these phenomena of excitation and inhibition are not likely to become confused, since they are separated by a physical-chemical refractory period when the neuron is unexcitable; and (c) The electrochemical residual modifications of the synaptic proteins will constitute "residual traces," capable of being more permanent and more highly systematized than the purely physical remnants of hysteresis, recorded on our electromagnetic models (*cf.* Chapter 15).

Actually, we know that the connections between neurons are made essentially by contiguity, by means of relays which constitute synapses. The anatomic fissure between two neurons at the level of a synapse, verified by the electronic microscope, is on the order of 200 angstroms, that is to say 200×10^{-17} millimeters. But this anatomic hiatus is closed up functionally by electrochemical potentials which are exercised on both sides of the synaptic membrane. The latter constitutes the crucial functional point of the mechanism of the myelin fibers of the central nervous system, the one also where the *essential point of its temporal function* is exercised. This membrane acts as a unidirectional *valve* with a forcible threshold, permitting the "all-or-none" passage of nerve impulses, and thus of action, according to whether or not it attains a level of energy sufficient to leap over the threshold.

It is the behavior of this electrochemical energetic level within the membranes of the synapse which we must now consider more precisely, because on this level the future of pre- and postsynaptic neuronic conditions depends. Their associations within cerebral space and their direct or indirect temporal connections, in retroaction (feedback) or in preaction (feed ahead), also depend on this level.

The chemical intermediary which transmits presynaptic excita-

194

tion is acetylcholine, its proportion being noticeably greater as the exciting intensity of the electric discharge is stronger. This acetylcholine, diffused at the level of the contiguous postsynaptic membrane, is destroyed in the vicinity of this membrane by an enzyme, choline-esterase. Given, according to Eccles, that the resistance of the fissure is about 100 ohms/cm and that of the surface of the membrane is 500 ohms/cm^2, the *interrupter which constitutes the electrochemical synapse* effectively interrupts the continuity of electric current which, without the synapse, would have the tendency to flow as if across a cable from the presynaptic region to the postsynaptic region. Through the electronic microscope, one can see the vesicles containing chemical substances accumulating within the presynaptic and subsynaptic regions of the membrane. The flux of ions, sodium, potassium, and accessorily calcium and magnesium,[1] accompanying the rupture of the liquid from the vesicles within the fissure, fills it up functionally if not anatomically; thus it permits the transportation of the nervous impulses and, by means of "ionic pumping" (Hodgkin and Huxley), the progressive restoration of the initial state (*cf.* Chapter 3). According to Eccles, there is *"like a quantic liberation of the transmitting substances* during the synaptic period of activity." Elsewhere, Koelle [2] has demonstrated that acetylcholine released within the presynaptic terminals acts in an important way like a *positive feedback,* producing an increase of acetylcholine secretion, but at the same time playing the role of *an amplifying* factor at the same level as the system of interruption and of transmission.

The above discussion gives only a very restricted glance at the extraordinary mechanism of nervous transmission. The mechanism of purely electric synapses is much simpler. Transmission is accomplished by means of the depolarizing action of the current from nervous impulses. The electric potential of the membrane of the synapse acts as if it were an electric rectifier which gives the synapse the role of a valve allowing the passage of the nervous current in one direction. This simplified valve is very effective al-

---

[1] Bernard Katz, "Mechanisms of Synaptic Transmission," *Biophysical Science—A Study Program,* J. L. Oncley, Editor (New York, John Wiley & Sons, 1959).

[2] G. B. Koelle, "A New General Concept of the Neurohumoral Functions of Acetylcholine and Acetylcholinesterase," *S. Pharm.,* Pharm. 14 (London, 1962).

though less complicated than the electrochemical synapses. These alternatives of discharges and depolarizations or, on the contrary, of refractory state with hyperpolarization, have primarily been studied in the crayfish, where the synapses are more dissociated and of greater size than in man.

However, Eccles succeeded in studying, within the brain of mammiferous animals, great fields of inhibition produced by the pyramidal cells of the cortex, which, acting in synergic adjustment with connecting neurons, form recurrent *circuits of inhibition,* associated either with the thalamus or with the hippocampus, or with the genicular ganglions. Some of these phenomena of inhibition can lead to extended and prolonged reactions (of the order of 100 milliseconds) from potentials of the postsynaptic membranes, while other recurrent phenomena of inhibition intervene within the setting off of the cycles of discharge, such as are recorded in electroencephalograms: alpha rhythm (cortical-thalamic inhibitions) theta rhythm (cortical-hippocampic inhibitions).

It seems, according to Leo Szilard,[1] that there exist two functional varieties of behavior and of neuronic specialization in the central nervous system: (1) the *congenitally determined* neurons; (2) neurons that can be *"imprinted"* in order to construct memory. Szilard suggests that membrane proteins or those of the nerve cells and synapses can be compared with the antigens: both have a certain specificity of constitution and of response. Just as an antigen and antibody combine, and, by allosteric action, become capable of combining themselves with the complement, so "the specific proteins of membranes" from two nerve cells having affinities could combine through allosteric action and could unite themselves with the complement choline-esterase, which would be destroyed at once. This theory has not yet been demonstrated, but Szilard applies it fruitfully for the construction of a memory and cerebral organization system, based on the synchronizations of conditional stimuli of the Pavlovian type.

The theory, certainly ingenious, takes account in a heuristic manner of a great number of details of the memorizing function and even suggests the possibility of autoimpression of the code of a certain nervous impulse, depending upon the definitive modification which it would leave on the proteins of specific membranes.

---

[1] Leo Szilard, *loc. cit.*

The models of Szilard, which are in effect his scientific testament, are sufficiently precise to be programmed in a general (digital and analog) computer, and probably would be in large part verifiable. This would be the experimental demonstration of what I consider an acquired human behavior, that man himself imprints his neuronic electric circuits, according to the functioning of his nervous system, that is, his experience and his needs: to adapt, create, and maintain simultaneously his "secondary homeostatic" system.

If we have dwelt in detail on these extraordinary mechanisms of the human brain, complex, compact and efficient, it is to highlight the many possibilities of these mechanisms which experience verifies.

1. So far as we know at present, the cerebral cells exercise an action, apparently electrical and continuous, but in fact electro-chemical and *discontinuous*, by means of *quanta* of energy transmitted by neurons and rectified by the *synaptic membranes which augment these discontinuities.*

Thus is realized an *autonomous temporal element of the central nervous system,* the behavior of which is analogous to that which we have encountered in microphysics when we studied the discontinuous jumps of electrons in their elliptical orbits about the nucleus of the atom. In the work of Planck, Bohr, and Einstein, which is also on a subatomic scale, we have found an irreducible autonomy and independence of electronic times which are opposed to the spatiotemporal external continuity. In spite of illustrious suggestions of ways to unite these different time systems, the formal quantal irreducibility remains.

Of course, this comparison between the discontinuity of the functioning of the central nervous system and the quantal phenomena of mineral matter is apparent to many authors whom we have cited (Eccles, Ruyer, Huant). But they seem to be astonished by it, while I think that it is better to marvel at it. I see it in effect not only as a phenomenally fortuitous similarity, justifying a comparison, but, on the contrary, as a unique law of nature, applying in a similar fashion to mineral matter and to living matter, the ultimate common denominator being precisely, in both cases, the *discontinuous electronic phenomenon.* That this mechanism is purely electronic for mineral matter and electrochemical for living matter does not constitute a difference of essence, even if it is applied to different substances. The ionic action of metals which produce the phenomenon, as well as sodium or calcium, or the inhibitors like potassium or

197

magnesium, all can finally lead to pure electronic reactions, according to the laws of the quantal mechanisms of Planck and Bohr.

Briefly, it appears that both mineral and living matter, beyond their immobility and their apparent continuity, conceal a "prime mover" of quantal and fundamental electronic discontinuity, which takes account of their peculiar qualities as well as of their functions.

2. Like every electric medium functioning in order to receive information, the brain has above all an *inhibiting* and procrastinating role. If not, how could it be selector and detector?

Let us, for a moment, compare the brain to a simple receiving apparatus of radiotelegraphy. In both receivers the frequently weak signal would be covered by an intense parasitic "noise" if there were no reductor circuits or selectors also acting as detectors, because of their semipermeable character. The same terminology can be applied to both the semipermeable membrane of the membrane of a nerve cell or synapse and to a germanium transistor or to a semiconductor diode, and for a simple reason: the element to dissociate is in both cases electronic. It is only after the original selector stage that amplifications, transformations, and secondary interpretations are permitted. I have previously described perceptrons and maximum amplitude filters, which can imitate neurons and their functions. The extraordinary and almost unbelievable difference is that the brain "imprints" the majority of its own circuits in proportion to its needs. What we have seen with respect to the study of memory in particular is also true, from a general point of view, of the cerebral mechanism: it is *the functioning itself which creates, which organizes the possibility of the function.*

3. This last fact alone would make it possible to see no opposition between the electrical mechanism of the brain and its finalistic behavior, if this finalism had not already been given authority, as Lecomte du Nouy [1] and Teilhard de Chardin [2] call to our attention, by many millions of centuries of evolution, of progressive selection, and of successive perfectioning, and by the fact that it is by means of the mind itself that this evolution of man is pursued and affirmed.

---

[1] Pierre Lecomte du Nouy, *Le temps et la vie* (Paris, Gallimard, 1936); *L'avenir de l'esprit* (Paris, N.R.F., 1941); *Human Destiny* (New York, David McKay, Inc., 1947).

[2] Pierre Teilhard de Chardin, *Le phénomène humain* (Paris, Editions du Seuil, 1962; New York, French & European Publications, Inc.)

The preceding observations, as well as the behavior of man's nervous system, permit us to consider the brain as an essential organ for survival and for action. That this survival may be limited for the individual, if not for the species, changes nothing about the problem; it is an incidental point, as long as the action remains possible within time.

It seems that this action is made possible by the two mechanisms which I am about to describe: (a) Electric discontinuity of the quantal type; and (b) The phenomena of inhibition and retardation.

If one combines these two orders of phenomena, as they actually are combined in the natural function of the brain, one will immediately perceive certain new advantages.

Psychological experience verifies, for example, that in order to think, it is necessary for the individual to isolate himself from the multitude, even if it is necessary to join it in order to act. This fact from current observation could be strongly revealing of a more general functional necessity for the innermost mechanism of the conceptual function of the brain.

Let us take, from among the phenomena already studied in this book (Chapter 7), visual perception. *A percept is never simple.* I have already mentioned that it is selectively transformed within the three layers of the retina, the deepest layer being, anatomically and physiologically, like an outpost of the cortex. We have also seen that to every perception of light a complicated sequence is attached. This sequence requires coding, symbolization, imagery, recording, before the idea of form, color, or distance can be usefully evaluated. Obviously, it is desirable, not to say indispensable, that at some point the brain be able to shut itself off from the luminous information in order to confirm, communicate, grasp the relationships, establish useful information for a plan of behavior, choose and begin an initiatory action before acting, or refuse to act, which is also an action. In brief, all of the informative perceptions from the sense organs, communicated to the brain, will be useful only insofar as selective disconnection from the external world interrupts their communication sufficiently that the signal can be distinguished above the parasitic "noise." This can happen only in introspective, selective, and interpretative isolation.

In the same manner, the slowing down and delaying phenomena will prove to be just as necessary for the human brain as they were

199

for the "learning model, by trial and error" of Albert Uttley, and for the same reasons. Procrastination gives the brain time to perceive, to compute "its sight" *internally* this time, to conceive, to manage its ideas, images, and words.

This having been done, *what it has accumulated as potential becomes actual.*

This point is crucial if only for the fact that we must apologize at once for having called it a point, when it is only a passage and transformation. However, the words "potential" and "actual" do not betray me. They have both, fortunately under the circumstances, a double meaning which is going to help me describe the phenomena under consideration: *the birth, that is to say the exteriorization, of the internal temporal function of the brain, characteristic of man.*

"Potential" means either potentiality (virtuality) or power, particularly when it refers to a charge of electricity. Actual means being in existence at the present time or revealing action.

In fact, the cerebral mechanism, as we have described it, makes it possible to consider both words *in their double sense,* as the most authentic illustration and the most pertinent characterization of what happens when the brain exercises its temporal function: *its potential becomes actual, that is to say presentified and energized.*

That it is an act due to an electrical mechanism of the brain will facilitate our interpretation. It will also illustrate, in a simple manner, what we have proposed in the preceding chapters.

The actual could be considered as an a priori concept, if the actualization of the action does not make it authentic as far as the present. Only time remains, if one so wishes it, an idealization which is superimposed on this action. Considered from this angle, for the organism as well as for the brain, *from the temporal point of view the present alone exists, to the extent that it is expressed and within this finds its act.*

From the functional point of view, the past, as it is defined in ordinary language, is only a heresy. If the brain bases its action on that which it has previously recorded and which has left a potential trace, it re-creates this record anew when it actualizes it within the present action.

The future, as it is described in ordinary language, also constitutes only fiction for the functional brain. For the future is like a remembrance of the yet-to-come, and *mutatis mutandis,* one can apply to it the commentary of the preceding paragraph. What are usually called past and future are, for the functional brain, only some *actual representations*, that is, present each time they are thought about, and active only if the brain decides to play them or to replay them. This functional thesis does not deny, as I have already said (Chapter 17), that these phenomena can be grouped as preceding or following a determined action. And to reject the terms past and future is not simply a play on words; it is a rejection of the ideas which they represent in order to have a clear comprehension of the exercise of the present temporal function of the brain.

This is an even more important conclusion than those which have preceded it, because within this actualization, in the double meaning of the *presentification and of the action, awareness finds its act and the self its existence.*

One might object that after I have rejected, from the functional point of view, the ordinary notions of past and of future, I demonstrate an extraordinary indulgence, if not naïveté, in accepting with double meaning the word actual, a useless synonym for the word present! Raymond Ruyer [1] furnishes me with a first reply by remarking "that if there were only one being in the world, and a unique passage from potential to actual, there would be no reason at all to use two words to designate the same thing, to call the present the actual and to manufacture a linear time composed of past, present, and future." But as this author has remarked, and as everyone knows, if time is an idealization, it represents a very large number of actualizations which must be taken into account simultaneously!

Besides, psychological, cerebral, individual time, which we are considering, has nothing to do with linear time; the complex psychological functions of the brain defy any attempt at linear interpretation or representation. What counts, for the function of the brain, and for the body which bears it, is the energetic transformation from the potential to the actual; presentification merely situates the function in the casual spatiotemporal framework of other men and in eventual "synchronization," equally accidental, with common astral time, the external time which has only practical and administrative importance.

In this sense, we interpret the words of Einstein that "the present has no meaning" outside of the *interaction of actuals,* since a de-

[1] Raymond Ruyer, *op. cit.*

TABLE VI: Scheme of the Four Functional "Dimensions" of the Mind

Circumstantial Variety	First Dimension	Second Dimension	Third Dimension	Fourth Dimension
Degree	Unconscious and instinctive	Conscious and informative	Conscious and voluntary	Consciousness itself acting
Origin	Inborn, congenital	Acquired, informative	Acquired, progressive	Acquired, pragmatic
Principal anatomic localization	Peripheral sympathetic and central—hypothalamic region and basal gray nuclei	Sense organs, inputs and afferent pathways, cortex with its reticular, thalamic, cerebellar, etc., connections	Cortex: -interhemispheric association pathways -recurrent connections with hypothalamic and glandular regions -the entire diencephalon and mesencephalon -efferent output fibers	Cortex and its vast system of connection with feedback and feed ahead

202

Original essential functions	Homeostasis and maintenance of constancy of the internal milieu for vital essential functions	Perception Selection Symbolization Definition Code Image—plan Idea Registration Memory Internal language	Association of ideas, of code words, computation by matching, *i.e.*, comparison or contrast, establishment of relationships, intelligence, judgment, choice, free will Initiative of the motor act External language	Constituted mind: Internal temporal function in full exercise and activity -knowledge of the virtual has become real -behavior: former potential has become actual -the "ego" is included in the actual -consciousness is this double recognition of the ego in the present
Action of sleep	Liberated in the dream	Inhibited in sleep	Liberal inhibition in the dream	Notion of time disappears; that of space persists
External spatio-temporal relationships	Indirect, adaptive through vasomotor, respiratory, sympathetic, systems, etc.	Adaptive adjustment	Tentative action on this external space	Internal psychological time is dissociated from it
Derived functions	Automatisms of adaptation and survival	Constitution of subjectivity	Constitution of objectivity in view of the action	Junction of subjective and objective; the potential has become actual in view of the mental creation

termined simultaneity without a possible signalization (that is to say, interaction) means nothing.

In the electrical function of the brain, it is evident from the very fact of its quantum electronic activity, that there is constant oscillation, and thus signification of the potential and actual alternations of energy. If these alternations constitute the only present, the action of the present is a theatrical representation, for which the individual awareness is the only true spectator and the "self" the only "author-actor." Let me add, to complete the comparison, that the play has been written by the brain, within the electrical background of the synapses, perhaps having received impressions from the outside, but certainly inspired by its own internal creative concepts within the solitude of its temporary periods of isolation, inasmuch as they are discontinuous.

If this play ceases to be actual, it is because the man is dead: for this "author-actor" there is no intermission possible; he must play morning and evening every day of his life; his only repose is at night when he is permitted the energetic recuperation of sleep between performances. He is for himself, through his awareness, his own audience; therein lies his slavery. But he is also his own judge; therein lies his greatness.

I have outlined in Table VI the different "dimensions," that is, the various functional systems encountered in the course of this research and growing out of the electrical mechanism of the brain. The order of the table is not haphazard, since it is determined by the very nature of the integrative processes, and their natural order of increasing complexity.

In looking at this Table VI closely and comparing it with Table V from this same chapter and with Table IV of Chapter 12, one will be not so much astonished by the frequency of psychological malfunction, as by its relative rarity. This is due without a doubt to the *extraordinary possibilities of substitution* that the very abundance of neurons permit. This fact has been verified by cranial traumatisms, in which great losses of cerebral substances, particularly in the region of the frontal lobes, nevertheless permit the possibility of extraordinary functional recovery, even after extensive lobotomies.

In the last column of Table VI, that of the fourth dimension, where, having been prepared within the second and third dimensions, the mind asserts its personal and temporal authority, one will

204

see that *from the functional point of view, consciousness is not the opposite of unconsciousness, in the usual sense of the word.* Unconsciousness is not, in functional terms, the absence of awareness; it is the *absence of the actual, that is to say, the presence of potential.*

There are those who say—and this is important—that contrary to the usual etymological definition, we have some awareness of our so-called unconscious, and that it is probably through laziness, cowardice, or lying with regard to ourselves, that we eventually refuse to transform this potential into the actual.

But then it is necessary to re-evaluate the interpretation of the process of psychoanalytic investigation, and above all to re-evaluate its therapeutic effectiveness or ineffectiveness, according to the circumstances.

From the functional point of view, the repressed turns out to be only the voluntarily and consciously suppressed, and forgetfulness is always "voluntary," as Freud humorously said, and as I must repeat here with seriousness and precision. Freud compared the forgetfulness called "voluntary" to the involuntary loss of objects, attached by association to an "emotional taboo." Here it is necessary to clarify each term and to avoid playing hide-and-seek with the truth. This great genius, Freud, could permit himself an apparent contradiction, because always talented in managing the paradox, he was never fooled. But for the ordinary man, "unconsciously voluntary" constitutes a false and deceitful assertion. The will—being by very definition the awareness of the choice and the initiative of the act, or else preceding the action—cannot be unconscious. The will prepares and leads to the actual, as opposed to the potential. The slight beginnings of will can refuse to pass from the potential to the actual, but even in this case of velleity the will is conscious and knows what it is refusing to do.

The numerous examples which we could give on this subject would constitute a sort of functional corollary of the temporal alienations described in Chapter 13. We shall retain only one, borrowed from the clinic, which illustrates what the analytic "transference" can realize, and the means by which the treatment can act within the functional and temporal concept described above.

Let us suppose an anxious patient, whose cerebral circuits, according to the description of Table VI, are obstructed by some fixed ideas which, by their very persistence, can become obsessional and produce, according to the classic expression, a "block." This blocking prevents contact with present reality and inhibits action, then justifies the fear and the risk of losing the object of this action.[1] The psychoanalyst will try to lead this patient to unblock these circuits, that is, to accept the present, by creating the present anew through the transformation of his accumulated potential energy, which will tend to renew relationships with the object, or even with another object! The role of the psychiatrist is found then to be much more that of inciter of new action than of investigator of forgotten remembrances! In most cases of authentic anxiety, the patient does not know the reason for his great distress: he invents some excuses in order to eliminate this distress, to explain it, and so to find himself not guilty of his inactivity and of his lack of interest in the object, which, nevertheless, he dreads to lose!

The fact that according to Freud, beyond these false excuses, the great distress is always to be united, appropriately or not, to a sexual element, changes nothing in our interpretation of the eventual therapeutic process.

The important thing, from the therapeutic point of view, is to suppress the "block," and experience proves that even if the patient and the doctor ignore the precise cause, this inhibition will disappear from the moment that its effects are acted upon, that is, when the anxious patient becomes cerebrally active, liberates his potentials under the pressure of anxiety in order to actualize them and to make them present as real energy. I emphasize the point that the reestablishment of activity must be cerebral, because the anxiety-ridden often escape into a substitute physical activity of a compulsive character, which can only camouflage their cerebral blocking. We shall see further on that the "tranquilizing" drugs for anxiety, or the electric shocks applied in the obsessive cases, act in a liberating manner analogous to the functional approach just described, which is sufficient in most cases.

Thus, it appears that in anxiety the marvelous mechanism of cerebral regulation, with its system of retroaction (feedback) and of preaction (feed ahead), is blocked. With the fundamental inhibiting recurrent system no longer functioning, the electric circuits of these patients remain perpetually excited, thus obstructed, thus "anxious" or "obsessed" by a potential incapable of being realized within action and of reaching its objects.

---

[1] *Cf.* Chapter 20.

Chapter 19

Other Purely Physical and Psychological Responses to So-Called Metaphysical Questions

I do not pretend, in the synthesis below, to bring up revolutionary ideas, but only to place a value on certain consequences, so much neglected that they may appear to be new. If they have remained in the shadow, it is because, in my opinion, the role of the temporal factor has been omitted or poorly interpreted or minimized with regard to its operatory function in the mechanism of the central nervous system and therefore with regard to the psychological behavior and activity of man.

From the explanations which have preceded, I shall extract relatively simple facts, and if the reader has the impression that I am repeating myself, that the facts now seem evident to him, I shall have attained my goal, because to say "evident" means that the truth has taken you over and integrated you into the reality of observed phenomena.

All the times which I have considered in this work can be grouped into three fundamental varieties:

First. External space-time of the classical and relativistic macrophysical mechanics;

Second. Electronical subatomic material time of quantum microphysics;

Third. Organic internal time, cerebral or psychological.

I have spoken of the first two in order to explain to what extent these times are comparable or opposed to the times of living matter, and to what extent they intervene within the formation of the temporal function in normal man and within its deformation in psychotic man.

Here I shall concentrate solely on the last category of *internal psychological times.*

A first point, on which no ambiguity should exist, is that there is no essential difference for us among the different names: internal time, cerebral time, psychological time, mental time, or even the word "mind" which abstracts, integrates, and adds the crowning achievement in the exercise, as well as the superior action, of the temporal function in man. That is why in Table VI (p. 202), I have outlined the functions of the central nervous system, with regard to their mechanism of progressive cerebral integration, under the term of "fourth spiritual dimension."

The first homeostatic dimension, necessary to maintain the humoral constancy favorable to the functioning of the brain, is no less indispensable than the others. The proof of this is that if the equilibrium of the first dimension is artificially modified by such disturbances as acute alcoholic or LSD intoxications, chronic progressive glandular modifications with glandular insufficiency, suprarenal insufficiency, or intoxication by the simultaneous action of cortisone on the suprarenal and the pituitary glands, then the functioning of the mind is altered, insofar as it loses complete awareness in the exercise of all its successive dimensions, including also the fourth temporal dimension.

Briefly, the first dimension permits the exercise of the second and third functional dimensions of the central nervous system, which themselves only constitute preparatory stages for the ordering activities of information, organization, organicization that permit the coming of awareness, *as well as the exercise of the self constituted within its supreme function: the fourth dimension of the mind*—that function wherein the self makes contact with itself and actually recognizes its own existence from the point of view of creation and action.

How are these processes synthetically possible and actually realized?

And first, how can one reconcile the facts of the functional anatomy of the central nervous system and the discontinuous character of its electrochemical functioning with the continuous functioning of the brain, its constant rhythmic activity in the form of sinusoidal

208

waves recorded by the electroencephalogram, in the state of wakefulness and in sleep? Millikan [1] remarks that it is evidently necessary to take into account the law of large numbers, since we are dealing with ten billion cells, axons, and synapses. For an individual cerebral cell, or for an axon, or an isolated rectifying synapse, Brink [2] and his pupils have verified that the passage of electrical nervous impulses definitely takes place in a discontinuous manner, with intervals of time of the order of 6, 12, or 18 milliseconds. The fact that these intervals constitute whole number multipliers of six milliseconds suggests the possibility that they are not necessarily linked to an electrical blocking of the permeability of the membranes (such as I have described according to Bullock, Eccles, Huxley, and Hodgkin),[3] but perhaps to an absence of pulsated energy. Millikan considers, along with Brink, that an isolated microscopic process of this order can be considered in a way corpuscular, electronic, quantal, discontinuous; but when one views simultaneously ten thousand, one hundred thousand, or more elements functioning together, the phenomenon becomes *continuous* and of the *undulatory type, without changing its nature.*

We have seen also (Chapter 18) that if this temporal energy of the nervous system, expressed by means of electrical frequencies, is not regulated within its rhythmic pulses in the same way as electronic material apparatuses, this is due to the equilibrating and retarding influences from the ionic phenomena and from the respective equilibration of sodium-potassium and calcium-magnesium in the constitution of *refractory periods.* If I emphasize this retarding phenomenon here, it is because the delays are necessary, as we have seen, for the learning mechanism [4] and the formation of judgment. McCulloch and Pitts, [5,6] as well as von Bonin, have dwelt on the

---

[1] R. A. Millikan, *Electrons (+ and −), Protons, Photons, Neutrons, and Cosmic Rays* (Chicago, University of Chicago Press, 1947).

[2] F. D. Brink, W. Bronk, M. C. Larrabee, *Physico-Chemical Mechanisms of Nerve Activity* (New York, Academy of Sciences, 1946).

[3] *Cf.* Chapters 4 and 18.

[4] In the Albert Uttley electronic "learning models" (*cf.* Chapter 3) the retarding circuits, whether of mercury or of crystalline quartz, made the electric current pass from the speed of light to the speed of sound, that is, they reduced its speed in the proportion of 100,000 to 1.

[5] W. S. McCulloch and W. Pitts, "A Logical Calculus of the Ideas Imminent in Nervous Activity," *Bulletin of Mathematical Biophysics*, Vol. 5 (1943).

[6] W. S. McCulloch, "Modes of Functional Organization of the Cerebral Cortex," *Fed. Proc.*, VI (1947).

fact that these synaptical delays especially permit an understanding of how, within the nervous network, the *"output"* can be very different from the *"input"* current. We shall see that this is one of the important characteristics of the functional mechanism of the brain, in the exercise of its temporal and mental function, and consequently of the total function of the brain in the constitution of the personality, as it has been described in terms of the spatiotemporal models of Adrian,[1] or the spatial and especially temporal configuration of Teitelbaum.[2] For this last author, as well as for von Bonin,[3] what counts in the last analysis is not so much the quantity of energy distributed as the degree to which it has order. This depends directly on the negative entropy linked to the quantity of homologated information.

In fact, in a living organism, entropy is always diminished, never completely negative. As Hoogland[4] points out, "The form and the function of living cells maintain them in a state of dynamic stability. Only some dead cells could be in perfect thermodynamic equilibrium with their environment." For the brain, the alternations of chaos and of order, so characteristic of vital instability, ceaselessly renewed and re-evaluated, constitute its strength.

If we consider the exercise of the constituted temporal function in order to evaluate it, it is necessary to discern precisely what happens in two very different circumstances: whether it is applied to the external world, or *whether it is applied to itself,* that is, to the internal world of thought.

In relation to the external world, one can, as Adrian C. Moulyn suggests,[5] distinguish certain characteristics according to whether or not the temporal function is applied to a movement. For contrast, let us take a very simple case of inert matter moving in a spatiotemporal space: a dead leaf falling from a tree by the action

---

[1] E. D. Adrian, *The Physical Background of Perception* (Oxford, Clarendon Press, 1947).

[2] H. A. Teitelbaum, "The Rhythmic Activity of the Nervous System," *Philosophy of Science,* Vol. 20 (Baltimore, 1953).

[3] G. von Bonin, *Essay on the Cerebral Cortex* (Springfield, Ill., Charles C Thomas, 1950).

[4] H. Hoogland, "Rhythmic Behavior of the Nervous System," *Science,* CIX (1949).

[5] Adrian C. Moulyn, "The Functions of Point and Line in Time Measuring Operations," *Philosophy of Science,* Vol. 19, No. 2 (April, 1952).

of its weight, caught by a whirlwind which carries it off at the whim of aerial currents that make it turn over and over. If one knew the totality of causes which make the molecules of air and the molecules of the leaf, one could foresee all the effects, and the temporal relationships would correspond in a precise manner with the before and after of the tumble of the leaf.

But let us go on to consider a paper kite, still inert matter, but matter to which we transmit, by means of the intermediary of our will and of the string attached to it, an intention and an actuality of resistance to the wind: the kite will remain in the air as long as our wish and the wind will keep it there; loosen the string and the problem is reduced to the preceding one: intention is cut off, the paper kite falls. Even in this intermediate example intention appears, the voluntary finality of man transmitted to inert matter, to regulate its movements in time and external space. But when we look at a living being, such as a bird flying, what happens analytically?

Through its conditioned reflexes, innate or acquired, the bird resists the aerial currents, surmounts them, uses them, masters them, governs itself. Faced with inert matter, it surmounts by means of its will, its instinct, its desire for food, the ensemble of sensorimotor reflexes, already harmoniously conditioned by experience, and achieves automatism in its flight; but, beyond this, the bird commands its behavior in the atmosphere. It is very necessary to add that when the observer of this bird is a man, he becomes identified through his personal time with the movements of the bird in space and time and projects onto it concepts and goals, which a bird perhaps does not have. It is probably content to fly in order to be, and acts through pure reaction to the currents in space.

However, when a man changes his place in the spatiotemporal external world, i.e., walks, another factor (which he can only project onto the bird) necessarily intervenes: that of his will and of inherent psychological time. I allude not only to the superficial phenomenon of modification of external time, according to the rapidity of movement instilled in the muscles by which man changes his place in space, but also to his *internal psychological time*, which makes his attitude vary according to circumstances. Thus, a path is established, if not the first time, at least the second, and a memory is created, thus a knowing, a habit which can already facilitate action. This is what makes it possible for us to understand that the

211

present psychological time of the walker will be subject to discontinuity and variability with relation to the spatiotemporal external continuum for which present and past, before and after, extend in an almost unlimited manner, lost from view, and lost from time, if the reader will permit me this expression.

Most authors attribute three characteristics to present psychological time, this time that Clay [1] calls the specious present, William James,[2] "a saddle which straddles the past and the future," and Adrian C. Moulyn,[3] the valuable present. All these expressions can perhaps be summed up in that "phantom space" with which Bergson [4] said the reflective awareness is obsessed. But whatever we call it, we come to the fact that there are three essential characteristics of psychological time:

1. In opposition to relatively unlimited and determined, inorganic, external time, psychological time cannot be defined by a linear equation, to the extent that it is contingent, limited, undetermined.

2. The psychological temporal function is capable of learning, thus improving in the course of successive experiences.

3. The psychological temporal function is linked to the emotional life in that, when it exerts itself in the present, it tends to become detached from the fringes of its past and forces itself to act in order to obtain, that is . . . to attain the affirmation of persistence, thus assuring its future welfare. It is in reduction of a situation of "stress" in the present that human fatigue, linked to effort, is initiated.

To these three classical characteristics, we shall add a fourth which appears fundamental to me:

4. Whatever may be the apparent finality which subtends the desire and intention of man, *the temporal function totally escapes from external causality.*

This assertion does not mean that we should refuse within the makeup of our memory and of our judgment information which we may have previously received primarily from our sense organs, nor

---

[1] E. D. Clay, *The Alternative* (London, Macmillan, 1882).

[2] William James, *Principles of Psychology,* Vol. I (New York, Dover Publications).

[3] Adrian C. Moulyn, "Time in Relation to Neurophysiology and Psychology," *Philosophy of Science,* Vol. 19 (Baltimore, January, 1952).

[4] H. Bergson, *Essai sur les données immédiates de la conscience* (Paris, Presses Universitaires de France, 1946).

deny the accumulation of observations and experiences which constitute the personality. However, when we wish to utilize this awareness, that is, the perspective which the self has of external reality, this knowledge and this self may impose their "point of view" on this external reality when from potentials and in reserve they set out to externalize themselves within an actual action.[1]

Whence this corollary to the fourth characteristic of psychological time:

In many cases, if not all, external causality constitutes only an appearance and an artifact, to the extent that the temporal fixation of our internal attention distorts reality. The projection of our awareness into the external world of phenomena runs the risk of transferring to these a borrowed human logic, in brief, of adorning them with a temporal dress of lies which is only human truth in disguise.

This distortion, or deformation, has relatively serious consequences; therefore it is necessary to consider them in detail for a moment.

A preliminary remark is called for: The constitution of the nerve circuits described in Chapter 18—the "servomechanisms" of retroaction or of preaction, their cortical-thalamic, cortical-limbic, corticohippocampic, corticocerebellar anastomosis,[2] and the entire system of recurrent fibers, which assure a first-class system of "feedback" and of "feed ahead"—this very constitution makes clear the possibility that for the autonomic functioning of the brain causality has no significance. If the causes anticipate the action of the effects, and if conversely the effects act on their so-called causes in order to self-limit themselves, this efficient miracle of organization *closes a circle of interaction which is self-sufficient: causes and effects lose their autonomy as well as their reason for being.*

This having been said, we can go on to external reality. We know that from the teleological point of view, two essential varieties of causes have been classically distinguished: (a) "Transeunt"[3] or extrinsic causes; (b) "Immanent" or intrinsic causes.

---

[1] This repetition is intentional and is meant to underline all of the interfering force of the self, when it is presentified within the course of external phenomena, by its unwarranted totalitarian interference.

[2] Karl U. Smith, *Delayed Sensory Feedback and Behavior* (Philadelphia and London, W. B. Saunders, 1962).

[3] Also called transitive causes.

213

Extrinsic causes are spatially separated, at least at the beginning of the process. When they enter into interaction, it is only *our internal psychological choice* which applies to the *contemporaneous* phenomena the notion of cause and effect, according to our interest. The examples which Walter Fales [1] chooses are excellent in their simplicity; we borrow them from him. If one puts a cold spoon in a hot cup of tea, one can choose the chilling of the tea as the effect and the elevation of the temperature of the spoon as the cause, or, *vice versa,* choose to say that the heating of the spoon is the effect and the warmth of the tea the cause. As time does not intervene in the interaction, the simultaneity permits us to choose, according to our pleasure, the effect which interests us more; and if, for example, our interest is to cool the tea, we "shall reduce" the time of the reaction by putting ten cold spoons in the cup instead of one.

This is the evidence, but one readily forgets it. In fact, even the most complicated phenomena with chain reactions, to the extent that interactions or external systems of interaction are concerned, can be divided into phases, thereby simplifying the problem and bringing it back to the preceding terms.

This is not true for the phenomena of immanent or intrinsic causality, where the interactions are separated by an interval of time internal to the system. Moreover, one can change many of the phenomena of extrinsic causality to intrinsic or immanent causality, precisely by the introduction of the factor of time, *but the reciprocal is not true:* one cannot transform an immanent causality into a system of transitive causes. Having said this, I go on to say that it is the function of immanent causes to take account of changes in the interior of a closed system within time. But here again it is necessary to avoid the fallacy of *post hoc ergo propter hoc* which is far from being necessary. The intervention of man must still be taken into account, if only in the choice of the intervals of time; if the interval of time is reduced to zero, one sees that the so-called cause disappears. Briefly, one cannot say that the past must be the cause of the future. The child precedes the man, but he is not the cause of the man. It is necessary for us to mistrust our involuntary anthropocentric interpretation of events which has a tendency to cover the depth of our ignorance concerning the proven alterations in an

---

[1] Walter Fales, "Causes and Effects," *Philosophy of Science,* Vol. 20, No. 1 (Baltimore, January, 1953).

interval of time. We invent a bridge of causality which overhangs the precipice of interaction. Leaning on the bridge, we look from "time to time," mistakenly feeling ourselves masters of the phenomenon, if only through our understanding of it, like Maxwell's demon acting in the course of a thermodynamic reaction.

Newton, in the *Principia Mathematica*, spoke of forces which pulled, resisted, attracted, held on to, repulsed, etc., without seeming to be aware of the fact that these expressions are contaminated by our human psychological impressions. Only few allusions are made to the causes of phenomena which he observes and describes ingeniously. However, he confesses to consider causes as having a metaphysical nature, and when he says to ignore the cause of gravity, he is content to refer it to God.

Einstein was perhaps the first physicist to realize the necessity, at some point, of looking for a system of references *external to man,* and independent of him, in order to observe absolute phenomenal interactions and the relativity of our knowledge. This realization permitted him to develop the idea of the electromagnetic origin of mass and to identify the mass, inertia, and energy of a system, by eliminating mass as an independent concept. This is a marvelous illustration of what the genius of man can do when it is abstracted from himself, to the point of imagining what would happen if he were deplaced like a photon with the speed of light, that is, if he ceased to be a man in order to become a recording instrument.

But this discussion only puts back the problem without solving it, because many of the so-called causes continue to be ignored, and even if they are temporarily viewed in their true nature, the question remains: As Hume said, "What is the cause which provokes the cause to act as a cause?"

This problem naturally did not escape Kant,[1] who decreed that it was the human mind, not nature, that was the origin of all causes. But he went too far when he raised causality to the rank of a category, in the absence of which all rational intelligence cannot be exercised. The fact is that, through its perceptive experience, the human mind has a horror of emptiness and has *a tendency to cover its ignorance by means of a problematical causality.* In the absence of such causality, one sometimes finds the telefinalistic hypotheses,

---

[1] Immanuel Kant in Emil Ungerer's *Die Teleologie Kants, und ihre Bedeutung für die Logik der Biologie* (Berlin, Bontraeger, 1922).

satisfying to the great mystic mind of Lecomte du Nouy. But without this mysticism, the telefinalist, as well, can only displace the difficulty. Voltaire's humorous remark might be taken as an answer to the telefinalists: "If God made man in his image, he gave it back to him plentifully since." Here again is the story of the spoon and the cup of tea: If God is the cause, man is the effect; if man is the cause, God becomes the effect. It is this that Freud tried to demonstrate through sublimation of the superego, and through the instinctive need for refuge within the personification of a protective father figure.

I do not pretend to resolve these questions, but in avowing my ignorance, to show how and why the problems are raised and will continue to be raised.

What has happened? Through the formation of his mind and because of his "temporal fourth dimension," of his self-constituted internal duration, man has a tendency to feel himself independent of the fourth dimension of space, that is to say, of the external time function of this space as well as of its "depth." In that he is correct, but he is wrong to feel himself both "eternal" and capable of being a judge. When he considers the nature of external phenomena, he has the tendency through the search for causality "at any price," to forget that his so-called impartial observer is also the observed: he forgets that he is both "judge and jury," that he has implicated himself, but that this does not explain him.

Introspection constitutes an important part of awareness, above all to the extent that it tends to prevent deceit with regard to oneself, even though this would be only through indulgent and convenient omission. Well directed, introspection permits one to capitalize on potential knowledge and, through a plan of action, to transform the energy of the potential self into a present and creative actuality.

But introspection is not "an article for export." In contact with external reality, it changes its form with a bias which it is necessary to acknowledge and to take account of in our calculations, our estimates, and our interpretations of phenomena exterior to the internal consciousness.

Chapter 20

The Temporal Element, Fourth Dimension of the Mind Considered as a Means of Evaluating the Active Behavior of Man in Health or in Mental Illness

Having arrived at this stage, after a discussion of many physical, neurological, psychological, psychiatric and medical facts, I must first question why the intervention of internal time, so integrally constitutive of all the phenomena observed in man, has not been perceived sooner. Why has no one recognized the value that it merits as a unifying and explanatory factor of the specific constitution of man and of his differentiating active behavior?

The reason is doubtless to be found in the historic manner—mythological before being religious, philosophical before being medical—in which man has been educated to participate in the "eternity" of things and accustomed to feel himself eternal. The concept of eternity is *an absolute denial of this time which is exercised in him.*

Most occidental civilization, particularly that around the Mediterranean basin, submitted to the influence of Greece. The great Pythagoras,[1] in his *Creed of Man,* abstracted in his famous *Golden Verses,* describes the three progressive stages of preparation, purification, and perfection, which tend to constitute the man par excellence. Nevertheless, he ends his poem with this line: "Amidst the immortals, you will be a god yourself." The reward for perfection in human conduct was to be associated through the μῦθος (myth)

---

[1] Fabre d'Olivet, *Les vers dorés de Pythagore* (Paris, 1816).

217

with the gods or heroic demigods who, according to tradition, sojourned among men, εξω μεταξύ (without an intermediary), thus without differentiation from men. The men who associated with the gods were therefore also able to possess the privilege of a temporal identification: participation in the eternity of the cosmos!

When the gods ceased to inhabit the earth, different myths, rites, religions, traditions, made man emigrate into the skies in order to permit him participation anew in eternity. Even in the seventeenth century, Descartes, in spite of his scientific thought as a mathematician, dissociated the body from the soul in order to permit the latter to survive.

Today, there are numerous people, irreligious or atheistic, who hold on to astrological superstition and attach their fate, thus their eventual survival, to constellations, paying, without realizing it, silent homage to unknown gods, an attitude which they maintain in conformity with tradition, negating the time which would limit their duration.

Given these traditions and influences, it is not surprising that, for a long time, physicians themselves have remained faithful to the dichotomy between the mind and the body. The study of psychology was left to the philosophers, the study of psychiatry considered a branch so much apart from medicine that it did not, if I may say so, make a part of it. Even in our day, in many countries, asylum doctors are not ordinary doctors, the administration being "stubborn" in confirming the duality of the medicine of the mind and the medicine of the body. Even neurologists are not always psychiatrists. What is more, a solid knowledge of psychology is not exacted of doctors.

However, besides what modern science has discovered, common sense tells us that the patient, as well as normal man, forms an indissociable psychological and biological unity. In order to evaluate a man within his totality, at a given moment, it is necessary to be able to see his body and his psychic structure as one. Patients know it well, above all those who suffer from functional diseases and who are obliged to go to the specialist in order that their "emotional balance" may be taken into account, and made indissociable from their symptomatology, even physical. An attempt has been made to palliate the difficulty by renewing the term psychosomatic medicine, but it is a poor term which only makes the past duality between the body and the mind more official. The fact that special courses have been instituted to teach it seems to constitute a further proof! The term cannot be justified in any degree, since all medicine is psychosomatic, and the so-called normal man is a psychosomatic being! In the active behavior of normal man, the brain is no less indispensable than the heart or the lungs, and the rhythm of his mind is no less hierarchically important than the rhythm of his respiration or of his heartbeat. However, mental rhythm is neglected: so far as we know a book on the "disturbances of the rhythm of the mind" does not exist!

From psychology to psychiatry there are only some imperceptible transitions, and this is why it is not an exaggeration to say that the pioneers of modern psychiatry were philosophers. To cite only some: Pierre Janet, Henri Bergson, John Watson, William James, Wilhelm Wundt, Ernst Mach, Charles Peirce, John Dewey, etc. However, I owe it to the truth to say that some psychiatrists were also philosophers, and it is without a doubt because of this "supplement" that they became great. Here again, I will cite only some of those among the departed and by alphabetical order: Baillarger, E. Bleuler, P. Broca, J. Charcot, C. Child, E. Dupré, J. Flourens, S. Freud, A. Forel, D. Henderson, D. Hume, T. Huxley, J. H. Jackson, C. Jung, E. Kraepelin, P. Marie, C. Mercier, A. Meyer, H. Müstenberg, I. Pavlov, W. Russell, T. Salmon, E. Southard, C. Strong, C. Wernicke.

The testament that the pioneers have left us is that every medical doctor should be a psychologist and instructed in psychiatry, this latter constituting a fundamental branch of *general medicine* if one wishes to study the activity of man within his total behavior.

Having said this, I shall remain, as I have done up to now, within the domain of observed facts with an experimental rigor, carefully avoiding any generalization, any reification, any sublimation. In order to test the pragmatic value of what I have observed until now of the temporal function personal to man, I will show more precisely in what way it intervenes within the active behavior of man during his lifetime, accepting with simplicity that this function ceases with death.

Life can be defined in effect by means of activity. *Every animal organism lives in the design of action and acts in the design of life.* This gives his behavior the appearance of having an instinct of conservation which it is perhaps not necessary to pose as a postulate, since it is not demonstrated in every case. Even the higher animals live without knowing that they live, and they react *immediately* to interventions by their sense organs, without intervention of the temporal function other than that which is included within the conditioning of their reflexes; but man is quite different: he constitutes a unique phenomenon within the animal nature, because not content with *being* a body, he knows that he has a body, and that all of his actions and reactions will be *mediated*, thanks precisely to the exercise of his internal temporal function.

It is to this last study that I shall limit myself, but noting, as I have done since Chapter 3, that from the beginnings of the human condition, the creation of this differentiating temporal function has formed a part of human behavior from infancy to manhood. In this "behavioristic" study, we observe the *action of time during the time of action,* and go from the simple to the complex, from the normal to the pathological.

I do not fear the apparent repetition in the sentence above, because the dynamism of this activity constitutes the essence of man's life to the extent that he is a thinking animal and a symbolic animal: it is precisely the exercise of this temporal function which subtends the "sequence" of his intelligent acts, to make a connecting link between his intention and his realizations.

Behavior always has a goal. The precise goal is the object of voluntary action. This is not an interpretation, but a fact of current physiological observation. For example, in the simple exercise of taking an apple from a plate and bringing it to the mouth, we do not think of all the flexor or extensor muscle groups which come into play, nor of the correlating and limiting temporal sequence of the action. In fact, *what we execute is an intention.* Previous descriptions of the anatomy and physiology of the nervous system and of the imitative cybernetic models permit us to accept, before a fuller description of this mechanism, the theory of Rosenblueth, Wiener, Bigelow,[1] which is that intentional behavior is recapitulated in a negative "feedback," whereby it is the effect itself which limits the moving of the hand to grasp the apple, then to reach the mouth. This constant control within the time of the effective action to realize a direct intention puts into play a large number of regulatory systems, retarding and equilibrating. To cite only one, the cerebellum retards, moderates, and controls muscular coordina-

---

[1] A. Rosenblueth, Norbert Wiener, S. Bigelow, "Behavior, Purpose and Teleology," *Philosophy of Science,* Vol. 10, No. 1 (Baltimore, 1943).

tion; every lesion of this center (as in multiple sclerosis) produces a lack of coordination of the voluntary movements which become oscillating and go beyond the desired object without attaining it, at least on the first try.

Now let us take an example a little more complicated: that of the hunter shooting at a bird. To take advantage of his previous experience, he must call upon his memory and estimate, according to the speed of the bird in the wind, his distance, the speed of his shot, and the degree more or less to which his gun is "choked," the point where he must aim in the flight of the bird. The behavior of the hunter is remarkably complicated. It involves a cerebral mechanism analogous to a radar system mounted in a jet aircraft for the purpose of regulating gunfire at another jet aircraft, by a rapidly executed estimation by an electronic computer.

In both cases, the intentional or pseudointentional behavior, which has the goal of obtaining certain effects, is well conditioned by these effects (feedback), limited by them (negative feedback) for the purpose of making them more efficient. Let us remark in passing that this is not a case of true causality, but only an inter- action for the purpose of attaining a goal. That is to say that teleology is not opposed to determinism, but that the contrary of determinism is simply nonteleological. As we have seen in the preceding chapter, within external nature the relationships between objects and events depend on multiple interactions, variable and contingent, and causality is only introduced by human intervention, to the extent that it is induced by our intention to exercise our ac- tive power over a *thing, which becomes object through this very same intervention.* On this subject, Kurt Lewin[1] has remarked that our intention can even alter the degree of our perception of eventual objects: he says, for example, that when we have put a letter in a mailbox, our action being achieved, we no longer record the ex- istence of other mailboxes; they have become "without object" as current usage would put it, wrongly inverting the formula (one should say: *without a subject* who considers them!).

This being so, one will realize at the outset that in order to study the activities of the behavior of man in their complexity, it is first necessary to define how the plans of action are elaborated,

---

[1] Kurt Lewin, "Intention, Will and Need," in David Rapaport's *Organization and Pathology of Thought* (New York, Columbia University Press, 1951).

how the symbols are born which feed the images and schemes of action,[1] before these actions can be exercised.

Miller, Galanter and Pribam,[2] with the sense of humor that characterizes their excellent monograph, note that it is necessary to be unduly optimistic, not to say simplistic, to see within the Pavlovian theory of conditioned reflexes a sufficient explanation of the behavior of man and its intentional character, which is often exercised not after a stimulus, but before this stimulus, that is to say in anticipation. Between the stimulus and the response, it is necessary to make the symbol intervene. Adolph Meyer dwells on this in his lessons on psychobiology.[3] These symbols are both substitutes for and complements of reality. They are the result of the previous experience of the individual and of the intervention of his memory, and physically of the existence of retarding circuits, which I have dwelt on many times and which, in this particular case, permit a delay in execution, a *temporal reflection*, before the constitution of a plan of action.

For a description of this plan, it is better to compare the brain, as Tolman [4] has, to a map room rather than to a telephonic switchboard, as is often done. The information coming from the outside (perceptions) or from inside (symbols) must be considered and controlled, before one can choose the map, the plan of the route to follow, that is, of the action to be effected. This plan, which will indicate the intention of the subject and the choice of goal, will finally be elaborated in a hierarchical process and a temporal sequence of operations to be accomplished, with all the details of a total strategy and particular tactics.

Since this plan is elaborated and coded by means of language, it becomes homologous with the programming of an electronic computer, and the initiative of the act appears clear, before the action results.

During its execution, the action will always be controlled by

---

[1] Frederic C. Bartlett, *Remembering: A Study in Experimental and Social Psychology* (Cambridge, Cambridge University Press, 1932).

[2] G. Miller, E. Galanter, K. Pribam, *Plans and the Structure of Behavior* (New York, Holt, Rinehart and Winston, 1960).

[3] Adolph Meyer, M.D., *Psychobiology. A Science of Men* (Springfield, Ill., Charles C Thomas, 1957).

[4] Edward C. Tolman, "Cognitive Maps in Rats and Men," *Psychological Review*, 55 (New York, 1949).

the image of its present execution, combined by means of "feedback" with the knowledge of previous experiences, similar or opposite, which have proven efficient or, on the contrary, turned out to be failures. That is to say that within the constant oscillations between the plan of execution and the image of action within the imagination, memory necessarily intervenes. But in this instance, it is short-term memory functioning in a closed circuit of subcortical neurons, perused by the nervous impulses pulsating within the "reverberation" circuits. Elsasser [1] compares this phenomenon to the active memory of electronic computers—"circulating memory without delay lines"—as contrasted with passive memory—"long-range memory"—interposed in the magnetic cores of the computer or of man's synapses.

This last observation provides a supplementary explanation of the systems of action, the schematic diagrams of Head and Bartlett.[2] The latter objects to the term "schematic diagram" as being both too precise and too vague: too precise, because it suggests a persistent but fragmentary mode of arrangement; too vague, because it does not take into account the essential characteristic of permanence within the execution of the blueprint for action, where "something must be effective at all times." If there is a schematic diagram, it is therefore a constantly *operatory* schematic diagram, which can be accounted for perfectly by the circulating memory described above, in the brain as well as in the "computer," and verified by experiment.

In studying what man gains in the carrying out of his active behavior, it is necessary to render homage to John Dewey, who inferred, with extraordinary foresight,[3,4] fifty years ago, what all the "behaviorists" demonstrated in the years that followed. In the experience of an action, he differentiates that which "acts" from that which is "undergone." If the action is very easy, if there is

---

[1] Walter M. Elsasser, "Reformation of Bergson's Theory of Memory," *Philosophy of Science,* Vol. 20, No. 1 (Baltimore, 1953). It should be noted that since the appearance of Elsasser's works, many computers carry, even in their circulating memories, *retarding* circuits.

[2] Frederic Bartlett, *op. cit.*

[3] John Dewey, *Human Nature and Conduct* (New York, Modern Library, 1930).

[4] John Dewey, *Experience and Nature* (New York, Dover Publications, 1925).

no temporal retardation in its execution, the experience is less fruitful for the self, for the creation of consciousness. He dwells on the point that the significance of the pursuit of the objects is acquired through active behavior, and not only through the passive recording of experience.

To sum up, a human organism acquires more or less significant experience according to the manner in which the ego is involved and asserted in facing obstacles which must be surmounted in order to achieve its action.

It is not only obtaining the result which counts, but the retardation which permits reflection and the enrichment of the consciousness in the perfection of the act. The harmony between what the subject does and endures is important in the experimental assertion of the self. Let me note in passing the double meaning of the word "endure"; on the one hand, lasting, on the other hand, suffering. This double meaning takes into exact account the phenomenon described. Alfred de Musset magnificently expressed it when he said: "Man is an apprentice, sorrow is his master, and he cannot know himself until he has suffered."

One step further in the execution of action, and we will see the *temporal function constructing the symbolic bridge which leads from action to abstraction.*

To abstract, that is, to choose from an object that which serves one's designs for action and enterprise, is a symbolic and characteristic choice of man. Etymologically, the word symbol comes from συν βαλλειν, throwing together. What links together then is precisely the bond created when the acting subject submits the object to his personal use. This is indeed the connecting intention planned in the act. This is also what Bergson was referring to when he said of abstraction that it was "a similitude felt and lived . . . a similitude which automatically would become action."

When action is being executed, the intentional abstraction of the plan becomes actualized; the object, instead of merely persisting, becomes *existent,* since it inserts itself temporally within the anticipated plan. But in the course of this execution, a fatal interaction is established between the object and the subject: *if the action is creative through the intervention of time, it is going to react upon its creator.* This Goethe [1] says in a different way: "Man is only the sum total of his acts."

---

[1] J. Wolfgang von Goethe, *Dichtung und Wahrheit* (Berlin, 1829).

This analysis is worth slowing up for, because if one thoroughly grasps what happens in normal man, one will better understand the disorders of the behavior in the psychotics.

The mechanism involved is of crucial importance, since at the very moment of action there is an integration of internal time with the external time of the object, and eventually with social time of other people, in short, an experimental confrontation of the internal world by the external world. In other words, the subject performing an act imagines, within the goal of the execution, a *temporal perspective* where he himself becomes the participating object. This is what we have described in Chapter 16 as the engagement of the self in duration. But here this engagement is put to test: this temporal perspective forces a revision of the potentialities, through the present prediction of future possible actualizations. We are objectively carried away from the perspective intent of time by means of the development of action, to become *prospectors of time*. From being subjective authors of desires and intentions, we have become through the necessary development of action, participating actors, objects ourselves. It is perfectly normal to accept the resistance of objects, the disorganization of plans of action, the unexpected temporizations, the eventual checks, the vain pursuits. It is necessary to have considerable self-confidence to prefer to lose a pursued object than to lose oneself, a choice which must be clearly discriminated, avoiding the always possible confusion, since the subject himself has become an object.

Two corollary remarks are of importance here, because they suggest ways to increase the efficiency of man's time within the conduct of his acts:

First. Practice increases the chances of success, if one knows how to capitalize on the data *observable within the present*. This present, in effect, not only integrates the acquisitions of the past, it also permits an eventual correlation of future possibilities, in the same manner that the well-stated premises of a syllogism contain its future conclusions. The temptation is to predict, but the wisdom is to act, in order to understand and to be more, that is, to become more. The initial plan, the temporal route, remains unknown; it can only become real during the path of the action: it is by means of the walk that we trace our route, within time as well as within space.

Second. It is not necessary to restrain goals and activities. Human behavior is much more significant if it is established with

225

a view to a comprehensive goal and a continuous becoming, than if it tends towards a final and limited goal. Gordon Allport [1] notes that man has a tendency to formulate durable plans which facilitate the conservation of life, rather than an ephemeral achievement. This fact, he says, is ignored by the majority of psychologists who think that behavior strongly implies definite goals. This remark of Allport's seems doubly important to me, on the one hand because it refers to an acquired behavior, the exercise of which can simulate the so-called instinct for self-preservation (assumed, but not demonstrated), on the other hand because it justifies within time a *raison d'être*, sufficing man through action. Man is conservative of himself as subject; the *means become its end*. Even if the result of his action does not obtain all that he wishes from external objects, the pursuit cannot be in vain, if the pursuit creates man and justifies him within time, beyond time. *The pursuit becomes the goal.*

As counterproof and in anticipation, let me say now that inversely, within neuroses and psychoses, we observe a restriction of goals, a reduction of times, an impoverishment of the personality, an anxiety about disintegration when the subject, become his own object, abandons his pursuit, thus, all in one, losing himself, and abandoning his own ego.

We now possess all of the necessary elements to try to interpret broadly the behavioral psychoses, the fifth syndrome in our Table IV (p. 124), to which the reader should turn again.

But first, in order that the differences be most clear, we shall recall what actually constitutes the personality of normal man within the exercise of his temporal function and within his active behavior. The concept of personality will soon bring us again to the temporal element, the fundamental element within the mechanism of man's activity, without which his potential would not know how to actualize itself, nor his ego assert itself as far as being a real person is concerned.

It is true that on this point my views are opposed to those of some psychoanalysts who accept retrocession as possible. For me, the arrow of time lived through is unidirectional: the vital process cannot go backwards in time. Therefore, the so-called regression cannot correspond to the reality of the facts: among

---

[1] Gordon Allport, *Becoming: Basic Considerations for a Psychology of Personality* (New Haven, Yale University Press, 1955).

the neurotics and even among the psychotics, *nothing is undone, even if everything ceases to be done.*

The normal subject has established, thanks to experience maintained by his interest and his needs, satisfactory temporal relationships between himself and the objects of his choice; these active interrelationships confer security on him from the fact that he feels himself to be stable because of this very engagement in active duration. Inversely, in psychosis, poverty in demeanor, reduction of the activity of the self destroy, by a mechanism the reverse of the preceding, temporal perspective and the security which is attached to it.

This simple statement, the facts that I have described at the start of this chapter—and more particularly the fact that the temporal function of man makes the juncture between his unique symbolic nature and the possible choice, equally unique, of his active behavior—state within what measure my concept, without being oposed to that of Freud, exceeds its too narrow limits. My hypothesis in this way comes close to that of some existentialists and to the hypotheses of Gordon Allport [1,2] and Ernest Becker.[3] The latter author, in a remarkable book, exposes the modern psychiatric revolution, and I shall cite it further on. Let me say here, in order to avoid any subjective misunderstanding within an objective critical evaluation, that I subscribe completely to his judgment about Freud: "The place which Freud occupies within the history of science is as assured as that of Newton. And if we now depart from his conceptual system, it is because we are on the threshold of entering into a period as flourishing as the Einsteinian reaction was in relation to Newton."

But let us come back to normal man, as Allport and Becker saw him.

Allport remarks that, from the start of life, the infant is moved by his *interests* more than by his instincts. Later, when the infant becomes a man, his motivation has transformed his interests into perceptions which systematize his plan for life ("design for liv-

---

[1] Gordon Allport, *op. cit.*

[2] Gordon Allport, *Explorations in Altruistic Love and Behavior* (Boston, Sorokin, 1950).

[3] Ernest Becker, *The Revolution in Psychiatry* (London, Collier, Macmillan Ltd., 1964).

227

ing"). "This design—not his hypothetical instincts—is the dynamic force in his life. Each time he is confronted by an adjustment, he will adjust himself to it with his *present* equipment—with his prejudices, attitudes, and feelings of the moment."

This hypothesis comes very close to mine, in that, within the dynamic actuality of adaptive behavior, it makes present with potential power the prejudices, attitudes, and accumulated perceptions and readies them to be exercised.

With a very similar perspective, even though under a different form, Becker gives a simplified but dynamic view of what he calls "the triad of action" of the normal personality: (1) perception and awareness of objects; (2) the object considered as a point of application for possible actions, whether towards this object, or by taking the object as a model; (3) the activating power that this awareness of the object has on the subject actor, and the increase in value and of self-value (self-esteem) which results in the behavior of the subject. And Becker's conclusion, of crucial importance in my opinion, is that "these three aspects of each act are *inseparable*.[1] This fact cannot be emphasized too much."

Is it necessary to say that I subscribe completely to Becker's hypothesis, to which my interpretation adds only the fourth temporal dimension of the normal human mind, because this is what constitutes the bonds which make possible the continuity of action during Becker's "three-act play"? As we have already seen in Chapter 13 in discussing the temporal alienations, and again in the study of the behavioral psychoses, *action and temporal function are made and unmade together.*

We should not be astonished at this, since this is what all of our study leads to: the future exists only virtually and potentially within our present plans. The fourth temporal dimension of the mind is only the actual interpretation of the personal past, acquired experience re-created within the present for the requirements of

---

[1] The word "inseparable" is not italicized in the original text. If I have taken the liberty of italicizing it here, it is because, as we shall see further on, at the time of the interpretation of our Table IV (by means of Table VII), psychosis is charged with dissociating and separating this "triad of action" in an almost experimental manner of great pathogenic, if not sometimes pathognomonic, value.

immediate action, as well as in anticipation of future wishes, *all in one.*

Thus, action is the practical expression of this fourth dimension, that which makes possible the affirmation of the self and its assertion in the present act, that which *realizes the contact with external objective reality, affirming itself through and upon this reality.* It is through the exercise of this fourth mental and activating temporal function (even by means of its retarding processes) that the personality affirms itself, becomes *existent within action,* in place of passive submission, without reaction, which would be mere survival.

Briefly, and as a practical illustration of what we have conjectured in Chapter 16, let us say that this is the action which *engages* both our internal time and our self within the external world of things, and it is the development of this very action which simultaneously releases the keen internal feeling of *being* alive, over and above the ineluctable fixity of space and of external duration. The "I think, therefore I am" of Descartes should be expressed and translated as: "I act, therefore I am, therefore I must endure." It is mobile time, inherent in human action, which gives frozen (Einsteinian) time the appearance of flowing and of flux. It is man who becomes and passes; nature persists.

Everyone knows this. And if one does not feel it, it is because one has become in some manner "schizophrenic," to the extent of losing the idea of internal time.

This is what Table VII tends to verify.

This table, very much abridged, deliberately incomplete, makes no pretense of outlining all psychiatry in four pages! It has only the goal of demonstrating that beyond the "officially" recognized temporal alienations described in Chapter 13, the internal temporal function is *constantly altered,* "officiously" modified, or in extreme cases suppressed, in the behavioral psychoses (*cf.* V of Table IV).

What I have proposed at the beginning of this chapter can be verified by the facts of clinical observation: the internal temporal function (fourth dimension of the mind), the self, and the possibility for action lose strength and disintegrate together.

This conclusion can have considerable diagnostic and prognostic value.

If the physician limits himself, as in the past, to considering only

229

TABLE VII: Temporal Patterns in Behavioral Psychoses

Reaction Types	Mental Disorders	Plans	Symbols and Language	Ego	Behavior Towards the Object	4th Dimension of the Mind and Variations in Temporal Function
1. Depressive Reactions	Melancholia Cenesthopathies Depersonalizations	Conceived but limited because they appear useless and doomed to failure	Paucity of symbols. Diminution of internal language. Tendency to mutism and self-accusation	Impoverishment of ego. Loss of security and self-esteem, probably an initial phenomenon	Loss of significance of the object. Asocial or antisocial attitude; in any case eventually negative, eventually becoming aggressive	Attempt to justify refuge in the past. Present hopeless because dissociated from continuity of duration
2. Reactions of Excitation	Mania Hypomania	Impractical due to total lack of a scale of values. Vain repetition of plans	False exaggeration of certain symbols, false depreciation of others. Repetitive verbosity	Uncoordinated stimulation centered upon itself	Object seems out of reach. Object is blamed, is made responsible and, for this reason, hated	Patient makes plans for the future rendered impossible by refusal to construct a present

3. Cyclic Reactions	Cyclothymic constitution, with alternations and "swings" between excitation and depression	Alternation between 1 and 2. Suppression of plans that never materialize	Alternation between 1 and 2 in various combinations	Progressive weakening in course of the alternations	Patient regards excitation as an inspiration of "genius," depression as a "living death." Objects lose their significance. Patient retires from all participation in society	Progressive loss of time function with each alternation
4. Obstructive Reactions	(a) Confusion	Incoherent, consequently no plans	Symbolic chaos. Verbosity alternating with mutism	Impoverishment. Stupidity. Range from torpor to dreamlike agitation	Irritation or indifference towards objects	Temporal chaos. Confusion of the potential and the actual
	(b) Anxiety	Fear of unknown prevents making of new plans and forces abandonment of plans of proven worth	Fixed upon an old symbolic framework that cannot accommodate the present situation. Patient cannot verbalize and thus reduce pressure	Loss of identity and of confidence. Narrowing and restriction of ego	Loss or threat of loss of object, aggravated by loss of significance of object and ensuing inaction	Blocking of time function which nothing can stop gives patient the impression that time has turned back in a vicious circle without escape

TABLE VII (Cont'd)

Reaction Types	Mental Disorders	Plans	Symbols and Language	Ego	Behavior Towards the Object	4th Dimension of the Mind and Variations in Temporal Function
5. Escape Reactions	Hysteria Pithiatism	Altered perceptions and absence of normal communication deprive patient of the formative elements of a plan	Symbolism impaired and chaotic, absence of a code; conversion phenomena, substituted for language, are inappropriate but are often abundant	Enfeeblement of ego. Neither means nor aims. Alterations of judgment and critical ability. Split personality	Object is without significance. Patient is incapable of action worthy of the name	Loss of contact with temporal reality, which falls apart through the impossibility of living in the present. Emotional traumata are slow in taking effect
6. Reactions of Dissociation and Disintegration	Schizophrenia Dementia praecox Hebephrenia	Plans impossible despite a sense of omnipotence and transcendence. Religious and political megalomania alternating with depression, hebetude and negativism	Internal symbolization bears no resemblance to action; it constitutes a protective shelter. Safety-valve language that no longer has meaning as a code and	Ego disconnected and enfeebled, without emotional response, therefore without identity, therefore with no capacity for criticism or self-criticism	Object without significance; complete incapacity for behavior and thus for action. Conscience disconnected from objects. Total absence of	Complete disconnection of internal and external continuous time. Patient's only present is his feeling of immortality, superiority, transcendency,

	Increased symbolization detached from reality. "Reasoning 'folly'."—delusion existing only in thought. Profuse language associated with debased, ridiculous, incoherent ideas	is drained of ideas, is stereotyped. All action is symbolic, theoretic, and fantasmic, but barren	initiative to act. Catalepsy with or without catatonia	eternity, thus displaying the destruction of the temporal function
Paranoid psychoses	Apparently logical reasoning based on false assumptions, from which plans are often detailed but ridiculous and delusional	Ego disorganized without self-critical power; valuation of ego is often exaggerated, always overrated. Often violent, due to frustration of aims	Chaotic behavior. Incapacity for action. No appreciation of or contact with object; everything takes place in thought; no possible concentration on the object	Temporal disconnection always marked; often appears as the initial phenomenon

the self and the active behavior of a psychotic subject, he will have a relatively static view of his patient. On the contrary, if he adds to this an estimate of the patient's temporal function, he will have a more objective and dynamic view. The patient's condition in its eventual "becoming" towards external, as well as internal, reality can be better defined. In order to make a psychological chart for a patient, one should therefore systematically examine him from three aspects: that of the ego, that of action, and that of time.

The internal time of behavior fixes the normal subject in active and efficient relationship with the object, thus giving him security and confidence. In illness, as one sees in Table VII, different clinical varieties do exist: sometimes the self is impoverished and becomes disintegrated first and the attenuation of temporal perspective follows; sometimes, on the contrary, it is the temporal notion which first becomes disintegrated, bringing in its wake a vitiation of relationships with objects, a loss of contact with reality. Whence the allusion of Meerloo [1] to a truly "schizophrenic temporal experience" in which, from the onset, the temporal perspectives with regard to objects are completely changed: the future seems to be farther away; the past seems to come closer; the present contracts, is limited, loses its meaning. Along with the desire for action, the initiative for the act disappears and the patient is plunged into the negativistic stupor of hebephrenia. In its most advanced stage, it is "a living death," and nevertheless quite often the patient feels himself to be "eternal," that is to say, without time!

In contrast, let me say that the security of the normal individual, wherein he finds and justifies his identity, must surpass the contingent and variable field of his present action. In order to strengthen and integrate the self within a relatively constant duration which provides this security, man tries to assert and to justify himself at the same time. Through the exercise of his internal temporal function, he *retrospectively* constructs a past which is appropriate to him, a past if not of causes and effects, at least of intentions, plans, goals, and the results of preliminary interactions. He is not necessarily aware of this during the course of action; it is

---

[1] Joost A. M. Meerloo, *The Two Faces of Man: Two Studies on the Sense of Time and on Ambivalence* (New York, International University Press, 1954).

then useless, as Bergson [1] has remarked. But when the action ceases to be present, its retrospective *fatality* appears to be a retroactive necessity, to the extent that it allays the individual's fears about his own fate, in relation to the multiple hazards of what could have been. Thus, justification for his inclination as well as his destiny is found in the consolation of and the conformity to a linear destiny which must continue to be accomplished, since it has been accomplished up to this point, within the "personality profile." This linear destiny seems indeed doubly reassuring: on the one hand it justifies the identity through the straight line already existing in the *actualized past;* on the other hand through its mere continuation in the same direction it contains the promise of a *personal future,* the certitude of tomorrow beginning today.

This *present apperception,* which integrates duration and identifies the time of internal life with a justifying coherent action, outlines the daily *adaptive* effort of normal man to his existence. In this sense the "struggle for life" finds its act within the actor, and within the action of time the justificative support of a strengthening performance, even within the short intermissions filled up by active memory.

It is stating an obvious fact to remark that the internal temporal mechanisms of man, of which I have tried to give an account, have been implicitly assumed since antiquity by all the creators of myths or the founders of religions. An advantage that all religions have in common and one of their greatest attractions is that of suppressing for man incertitudes, anxiety, and even the necessity of playing the game of life well in order to be sure of being on the right "temporal" . . . or "spiritual" road. The author (God) is solely responsible for the play and the game of the actors, and always promises them continued employment in the theater of duration.

The power, called "spiritual," of every religion and of all churches is based upon this necessity for internal temporal constancy, allaying the fears of man; it permits the churches to exercise what they themselves call their "temporal power," and this with a truth and efficacy much greater than generally imagined. In this sense, the

---

[1] Henri Bergson, *Matière et Mémoire* (Paris, Félix Alcan, 1896); *Matter and Memory* (New York, Humanities Press, 1962). See Chapter 4, p. 36 of this book.

temporal power of the churches is only an authentic and unavowed prolongation of their spiritual power.

The temporal power of the churches is exercised over the generality of men and is addressed to the masses. It is on much rarer occasions that, more "evolved," more "spiritual," and more courageous, a man chooses within the solitude of his brain to exercise fully the privilege of the fourth dimension of his mind, that is to say "temporalizes" in some manner his "internal space" and in an autonomic manner tries to justify his existence through his belief, and his belief through his action.

Chapter 21

Consequences

Consequences, not conclusions.[1]

Consequences, postconceived ideas formed after observation of nature in its dynamic activity, after discussion and as much documentation as is available, and after a constant going back and forth from the machine to man, from anatomy to physiology, from psychology to psychiatry, from the exception to the rule.

Nevertheless, given the complexity of the subject and the law of large numbers, we can only arrive at probabilities.

We cannot count on causality, since we have demonstrated that because of man's intervention, it is contingent and artificial in character. To refer to it would be to mask our problems, without increasing our certitude.

On real finality we cannot depend much more, since it involves only an apparent determinism, leaving the voluntary choice of possible actions within the sphere of control of the retroactions, the feedbacks which constitute and regulate their own effects.

---

[1] If a reader "impatient" to find out just what I am getting at begins at the end of this book, let him stop reading here: his internal time will not permit him to understand it. A book on internal time implies and demands that one must follow with continuity its unidirectional arrow, the time sequence, before being able to appreciate the range of its consequences. The mystery of psychological time is not unraveled in its results, but in its process and its functioning.

This means that the consequences stated below have an *interrogative* basic structure, if not an interrogative form, similar to that adopted for the preconceived ideas, the ideas abandoned progressively along the way.

We should not be surprised at this; nature is complex, and although man seeks to simplify it, after the more than a million centuries of existence it preserves many accumulated secrets. In attempting to imitate it by means of a "tentacular" electronic machine similar to the brain from which it sprang, we are approaching the code which will allow us to pose more and more intelligible questions to the sphinx, and fewer and fewer false problems. No doubt the sphinx will answer these questions as it always has, by uncovering other questions. For the process of science represents the sphinx of today; and nature will continue to keep its secret.

This means that *man's internal or psychological time appears to us as a function of a function* in the relatively closed system of the human brain, which is open to perceptions only by eclipses, since it stores them away, codes them, transforms them, symbolizes them, gives them names, gives them the quality of ideas, and then closes itself back over them. The brain folds back on itself, in order to think before acting. Acting is its true goal, but because of the thought process, being may seem to be its objective, a fact which has made room for many errors of interpretation concerning a so-called instinct of self-preservation.

To recapitulate, in a relatively closed system like the brain, the various internal states, induced by the phenomena of electric nervous influx, develop functionally (through their reciprocal interactions and their anastomoses) in a curve which implies succession, and hence *time as function of an active function.*

First corollary. Succession solves and sums, in its twofold meaning, the terms of the differential equation in which time and action are the unknowns, the dependent variables to be integrated. The first meaning of the term refers to the success and achievement of the action, that is, to the transformation and actualization of what was potential. The second meaning of succession *integrates* time and explains duration in the exercise of the reaction itself, that is, in what the reaction transforms and *actualizes.*

Second corollary. For a relatively closed system, for an internal action, time is the equivalent of what space is for a reaction external to the system: *it is what permits the action to develop.* In short,

238

time can be differentiated as a function derived from action, and *vice versa* can be reintegrated variationally in the action, that is, in functioning.

Third corollary. Internal time, operating electrically by the mechanism of nervous impulse, is not necessarily irreversible by nature; [1] it only seems *irreversible in practice* when it is *applied* to a structure whose functioning is irreversible. As we have seen (Chapter 18), the structure and the function of the central nervous system are both doubly *unidirectional,* by the constitution of the synapses and the neurons, and by the way in which the thresholds and refractory states operate under the electroionic, chemical influence of the glands. The nervous impulse can only be propagated in *a single direction,* and the psychological time which accompanies it and externalizes it is therefore irreversible and, like it, unidirectional in its directing arrow.

Fourth corollary. The memory for recent facts seems to contradict the preceding corollary, insofar as it seems reversible. This is only apparent, however, and derives, in part, from the facts of anatomy: the memory is diffused through many billions of cells and constitutes the geometric location of all the recurrent anastomotic systems and of feedback.[2] Also, the memory is *constantly circulating in the present* in its active period. This is what allows it to be faithful and at the same time to seem reversible. While it circulates, like the active memory of an electronic computer, it is *constant in time,* that is to say, *in reality irreversible.* An important consequence of this last fact: *time does not "operate"* for this memory; [3] it, time, can operate with it! This is also what happens with the active and circulating "memories," called "volatile," of electronic computers, for which time does not "operate" either, that is, it *does not count.*

Fifth corollary. The memory for old facts retains, even in appearance, its conformity with the third corollary. Like the inactive bits of recorded information of electronic computers, these memories are isolated (in "storage") in the crannies of the cortex, are probably attenuated and hence blurred by the polarity of inaction. They

---

[1] When the mechanisms of inhibition and the normal connections of the central nervous system are functionally suppressed during sleep, we know at what point internal time becomes, on the contrary, reversible!

[2] *Cf.* Chapter 18: primarily cortical location.

[3] The opposite may be produced in sleep and in dreams. See the sixth corollary.

will only be reawakened from their apparent oblivion by the depolarizing influx from a long fiber, when the intention of a new action fixes new electric "attention" on these "forgotten" cells. In the same way, they can be reawakened, if they are located on the surface of the cortex, by an artificial electric excitation in the course of surgery.

Sixth corollary. During sleep, these phenomena are inverted, following functional disconnections, the attenuation of the recurrences, and the suppression of cortical inhibitions, all of which liberate the autonomous, automatic systems of the base of the brain. The volatile circulating memory ceases to circulate, enters a period of rest; in short, the memory, instead of being constant in time, becomes discontinuous, inconstant. The point at which these phenomena are inverted in the dream is known; time, being liberated (having thus reduced its intervals of possible variations), plays with the memory and indeed plays abominable tricks on it, combining present, past, and future all in one. Even the distant memories, by an occasional discharge of association, may be "reawakened," if that is the right word, during the dreams of sleep.

Seventh corollary. Keeping a "trace," a virtual modification of the perceptions received and of the images or ideas already experienced, without change over time, represents the constituted memory; time only intervenes during the original constituent action of learning behavior and in the secondary reactualization, mistakenly called evocation, although it is in fact *re-creation.* Evocation implies a recognition, a contingent quality that is not at all necessary to the *action* and to the creative or re-creative actualization, *which alone engages the ego in duration.*

Eighth corollary. Thus, it is the coherence and the cohesion of *the ego,* of *action,* and of *time,* and their reciprocal interactions, that create by a sort of "synchronization" the fourth dimension of the mind, by which man asserts psychologically, with his own *identity,* his personal internal time, ready to *act* on the outside world and to *be* to the extent that he reacts. Or rather, he exercises his temporal function and his ego combined in an action that reveals both his own existence and duration. This twofold recognition defines the consciousness.

Ninth corollary. The "exception that proves the rule." Every alteration of the internal temporal function and every reduction or inflation of the ego, whether separately or in association, will on the

240

one hand prevent the action from being carried out, and on the other hand will disconnect man from external objects, will make of him a foreign subject in his internal behavior and a foreigner to external reality, "alienated" in the true sense of the term.

Tenth corollary. The old conception, relatively static, of the memory does not take into account the exercise of this dynamic internal temporal function which is attached to it. The memory is indispensable, just as the accumulator battery is necessary to the function of the automobile combustion engine; if it is a four-phased engine, these internal times are indeed connected to the electric spark of the plugs fed by the accumulator, but they are "independent variables" in the exercise of their own function and their "personal" action, with regard to a determined goal. This comparison is intended only to clarify the meaning of the following corollary.

Eleventh corollary. Organized finality or organic finalism can give an appearance of determinism. For man, however, real determination of the will ought not to be confused with the apparent determinism of fate; it is man who chooses to accelerate or to brake the engine of the motor car, or his own thoughts, or his own actions, in his behavior as the driver, having his own judgment and carrying out his own plan of life. *The exercise of this active behavior implies the putting into play of the temporal function.*

Twelfth corollary. Intelligence, for electronic machines just as for men, is essentially the function of manipulating bits of information in order to establish relationships among them that allow them to be turned to account. Thus, it can be said that *man's genius* lies in the fact that he is essentially a *reducer of entropy, a creator of order.* This establishment of order is asserted primarily through *the exercise of his internal temporal function,* which allows him successively (a descriptive term that strongly implies time) to choose among the mass of phenomena, to judge what will permit him to establish a voluntary personal relation with the object which, by this very choice, he isolates from chance.

Thirteenth corollary. The choice that makes the object makes the man more of a subject as well, insofar as he, in return, "communicates" his own potential energy, actualizes it in making use of the object rendered present by this ascendancy. The creator of order, man, has *engaged himself in duration* by the conquest of the object; his genius will only really be exercised in time if he can possess this object, that is, enjoy it, but *without losing himself* in the conquest.

241

And this means, in the final analysis, *disengaging* himself from duration, which he makes use of to his ends, *without forgetting himself!*

From this angle, man cannot "lose time," but time may lose him if he does not know how to make use of it through action, by being always the master and never the slave, in other words, by making time count to the point of not counting. In that sense alone, that of his internal time which he dominates, for man to live is to act, and to *act is already to become,* since tomorrow is foreshadowed in the present action today, action which includes this time . . . always. *Always* marks the becoming of time and signifies that this becoming is superimposed on the evolution of action, and thus on the becoming of being.

In the relativity of the human "system of reference," man must keep absolute account of the exercise of his internal time in order to take pertinent advantage of his behavior in action, and to evaluate the coefficient of error of his reactions with regard to his own observations. If this is true of observations bearing on the outside world of facts, it is all the more so of observation bearing on himself in the realm of ideas and imagination.

To correct the "aberrance"[1] of this "intellectual lens," it is necessary to bring in the corrective "parallax" of the fourth dimension of the mind, which actualizes in man's own time his vision of the real, at the moment when he seeks to believe rather than to know, or to hope rather than to act.

---

[1] In classical optics, the term "aberration" is more frequently used.

Epilogue

by Olivier Costa de Beauregard

In this excellent book which you have just read, a prominent researcher sums up the over-all concept which comes out of his immense information and his multiple investigations in the field of neurology and medical psychology. I cannot better characterize Dr. Robert Wallis' leading idea than in the following formula: either the functioning of the brain (prolonged by the nervous system) and psychic life, reverse and obverse of a same entity, will be thought as *essentially temporal*, or *nothing* will be understandable. This new manner of approaching the problems of health and disease of the nervous system and of cognition processes entails an inevitable corollary: the utilization of the cybernetic notion of *information*, and the assimilation of the human organism to a cybernetic machine (incredibly complex and perfected). Dr. Robert Wallis thus places himself in the very axis defined by Norbert Wiener, the ingenious father and sponsor of this new discipline. Examining the collection of synoptic tables assembled at the end of this work, one will be able to acknowledge to what extent the representation of the numerous phenomena of neuromental diseases becomes more intelligible, when one resorts to classifications and explanations of the cybernetic type.

As the reader may not immediately comprehend the necessary link which exists between Robert Wallis' two leading ideas (and

243

which are, I repeat it, proper corollaries) a few words of explanation will be useful.

Twentieth-century physics is, as one knows, an essentially relativistic and an essentially quantistic physics; these two qualifications, which had for a time appeared as heterogenous towards one another (and even hardly reconcilable) are today "reconciled" in their formalism, in a way which is altogether satisfactory. But it so happens that this physics, at the same time so relativistic and quantistic, *cannot* consider matter other than *actually developed over space-time's four dimensions*. To refuse it would be at the same time to transgress against *geometrical covariance* (since the former Newtonian disjunction between past and future is replaced by *Minkowski's trichotomy* between *past, future* and "elsewhere"); to deny the understanding of particle-antiparticle association (Stueckelberg-Feynman); and to deny solving Einstein's and Schrödinger's "paradox of correlation after scattering" (1935). But then, one will say, *where* is becoming?

To this, the relativistic answer has always been, in the observer-experimenter's psychism. Without enumerating Minkowski's and Langevin's implicit ideas, and those of other prominent relativists, I could, to make this point clear, quote Hugo Bergman's striking text (1929). But, since one has to be short in an epilogue, it is from Whitrow (1961) that I will borrow the sesame-sentence: "We ought to concentrate all our attention upon the fact that the brain, being a material object, exists at the same time in tridimensional space and in time, whereas the mind, such as it manifests itself in conscience, only exists in time: mind is a 'process' it is not a 'thing.' As a consequence brain and mind can only interact in time, and it follows that this interaction can only take place mentally. *Mind is essentially temporal through its own nature.*" Dr. Robert Wallis has applied word for word Whitrow's prescription as a theoretical physicist, and as Whitrow requested, he found out at the end of his analysis that mind does not constitute a "thing," but a "function."

And why then, does the perceiving and acting mind have to be bound to explore without pause or drawback the fourth dimension of the cosmos displayed in space-time? Boltzmann, the illustrious founder of statistical mechanics, felt it intuitively when he postulated that life is bound to explore the curve representing entropy as a function of time in the direction where entropy increases, and not in the opposite direction. But what, then, is entropy?

Entropy, this "prodigiously abstract" notion, following Henri Poincaré, had been invented by Clausius in his reformulation of the Carnot principle, which was reinterpreted by Boltzmann as the *logarithm of probability* of a physical state. Entropy, therefore, increases when disorder increases, which constitutes the tendency of inert or "passive" matter: sand piles disperse themselves into the wind, and the shuffling of cards destroys their previous order. But the tendency to disorder is *also* and *indissolubly* the tendency to *information loss:* after shuffling the cards one *does not know any longer* the position of a specific card whose initial location was given, and the needle disappears very quickly in the hay stack, if it is not picked up at once. We thus catch up in the very act the subjective and objective aspects of the notion of *physical probability.* Being freely schematic in summing up subtle analysis, one can say that the *objective* or *entropic* aspect appears in the law of *frequency* attached to *great numbers,* and that the *subjective* or *informational* aspect appears before and after an *individual* "test."

It is to recent cybernetics that we owe this interesting precision of the concepts which (as we can see today) existed implicitly in many classical problems. In this way, L. Brillouin enunciated the "generalized Carnot Principle," following which, in an isolated system containing observers, the sum *negentropy + information* constitutes essentially a nonincreasing dimension (by negentropy, an entropy with reversed sign is obviously meant). The deep justification of Boltzmann's above-mentioned postulate thus appears at once: if to live, in its biopsychological meaning, consists essentially in receiving from the cosmos an information flux, then necessarily, subjective time is bound to "flow" in the direction where entropies appear on the increase. This is a very sophisticated way of saying that one learns through experience. . . .

This being said, let us come back to Dr. Robert Wallis' fine book. "It is true," as he says at the beginning of his third chapter, "that it is not the *mind* that originally conceives space and time; but [physical] *space and time fashion and condition the mind.*"

I, for one, wrote that "the arrow of biological and psychological time represents an adaptation of life to the conditions of the four-dimensional cosmos." It seems to me, that if Dr. Wallis in a new book which we would like him to write, would draw out the philosophy of the rise of the human cybernetic machine through phylogenesis and ontogenesis, as he did here through its autoeducation and

245

through its multiple possible disturbances, he would have the good fortune to be confronted with problems still more fundamental than those that he so lucidly examined here.

This is no small problem and Wallis realizes it perfectly. At the beginning of Chapter 5 he writes: "The comparison [between an electronic computer and the human nervous system] . . . acquires all of its epistemological validity only if it is not forgotten that the electronic computer was built and programmed by a human brain. Even admitting the objection that one computer can program a second one and that the human brain in the course of evolution was itself programmed from the outside only serves to put off the problem without resolving the essential difficulty; the difference of essence, though not of mechanism, remains untouched." If, indeed, in an isolated system, the sum negentropy + information can only decrease, one can well conceive that a machine of high "structural negentropy" could train itself in an order of problems defined by the conceiving engineer, or even create for itself a lineage of machines provided with analogous qualities. But the "emergence" of a series of more and more perfected machines raises a formidable problem, for which I cannot personally visualize any possible solution, except through nonexperimental sources of information. Would it not be the very expression of psychism, and at the top of psychism, of conscience? Wallis suggests it on several occasions, when he writes (p. 34) that "electronic registration is certainly an assessment, but assessment is not memory and does not deserve the name," and that in dreams "conscience is disconnected," and finally, that (p. 43): "If the study of the parallel functioning of electronic machines and the brain is capable of shedding light on the latter mechanism and its intimate functioning and, more specifically, on the functions of the human nervous system, on the other hand it cannot solve the problem of the profound nature of the *mind*, a phenomenon peculiar to man, a characteristic incomparably superior to any machine, however perfected it may be." One example, which we find on p. 160: it suffices to receive very little light energy to acknowledge the presence of a tiger and to answer it by flight triggering a big expense of energy. The problem of building up and programming a machine capable of such a performance, without confusing a false tiger with a true one, is in principle not insoluble. But could it be solved without the cybernetician engineer? "This capacity to predict, this anticipated modification gives *the machines every appear-*

246

ance of intelligence and makes up part of the real mechanism of intelligence in man." (Page 187.)

And now, dear reader, you have instructed yourself, as I did, by reading Dr. Wallis' fine text. You have found out how clinical study experimentally confirms this new truth of relativistic physics, as well as this old truth of introspection: that as Pavlov said, "Psychologic facts are only thought in terms of time." You have found out how cybernctical interpretation demonstrates the pre-eminence of *the trouble of the function* (which is temporal) over the perhaps minute *lesion* which induces it (and which is spatial). You have found out finally how this essentially temporal conception of the mind interacting (as Whitrow says) with the organism which is at the same time spatial and temporal, allows a new classification of mental diseases which, I believe, will be of interest to physicians.

As far as philosophers are concerned, it seems to me that this remarkable work of philosophy of science will give them ample matter for reflection.

Translated from the original French text of Olivier Costa de Beauregard.

TABLE I: Structural and Functional Comparison Between

ELECTRONIC COMPUTER

A. *Reception of Information and Code*
   1. Arising from the external environment
   2. Receptors of a programmed code
B. *Transmission Mechanism*
   3. Input conductors
   4. Communication networks
   5. Valves, amplifying or selector relays, tri-electrode tubes or semi-conductors, transistors, diodes, capacitors, and eventually luminescence
C. *Registration of the Communication*
   6. Conservation of magnetic impulses
      Hysteresis
      Polarization at level of semiconductors; ferromagnetic coils, electromagnetic tape
D. *Association Networks*
   7. Interconnected circuits

      Eventually, feedback
   8. Means to avoid overload of circuits
      Depolarizing (erasing) heads
      Leakage or stochastic process
      Electronic safety valve
E. *Internal Handling of Information*
   9. Alternation between polarization and depolarization
      Circuit resonance

   10. Study of conditional probability by procrastinating circuits and delay stages; mercury, piezoelectric quartz. Computer can profit from previous experience, to select and "learn"
      (a) 1 or 0 (binary digital computer)
          "on" or "off"
      (b) employed to compare functions, and to integrate and develop them (analog computer)
F. *Action of Communication*
   11. Electromagnetic reactivation of registration by a special current capable of restoring hysteresis
       Emission through depolarization
   12. Emissive circuit (output)
G. *Retransmission of the Communication*
   13. (a) external: automatic models
       (b) internal: correctors, substitute and restorative calculations

   14. Character of action appears voluntary but is in fact predetermined

Electronic Computer and Human Nervous System

HUMAN NERVOUS SYSTEM

A. *Reception of Information*
 1. Arising from the external or internal environment
 2. Sense organs already code-programming
B. *Transmission Mechanism*
 3. Afferent nerves
 4. Anastomotic networks of neurons
 5. Synapses or junction plates, basal gray nuclei, cerebral cells, membrane potentials, single and selective electrochemistry (refractory states) and eventually catalyzers and hormones
C. *Memory*
 6. Conservation of impressions (traces) *Cf.* Chap. 15

   Polarization at level of cerebral cells of basal gray nuclei (sympathetic)
D. *Association Networks*
 7. Anastomotic interconnection of nerves (interhemispheric, thalamo-cortical, hypothalamic, hypophyseal, etc., fibers)
   Feedback
 8. Forgetting
   Relative depolarization through action of time elapsing
   Selectivity between old memory (long fibers) and recent memory (short fibers)
E. *Internal Handling of Information*
 9. Probable alternation between polarization and depolarization
   Electrochemical equilibration
   Adjustment of chronaxies
 10. Procrastination, permitting perception of relations, simultaneous utilization, in parallel or in series, of comparisons, contrasts, relationships, memories
   Summation of impulses often necessary to avoid the "nothing" and admit everything; yes or no
   Awareness, reasoning

F. *Communication of the Action*
 11. Recollection and *evocation,* re-creation by symbolic reactivation of image or idea of code word

 12. Efferent nerves (output)
G. *Transmission of the Command*
 13. (a) external: striated muscles, inclusive of language words
   (b) internal: basal gray nuclei, thalamus, cerebellum, sympathetic nervous system, viscera
 14. Character of action appears to be from free-will choice but is perhaps unconsciously determined

H. *Connecting Systems*
   15. Replacement and substitute circuits, servomotor automatisms, *autonomous*, interior to the system, with feedback and feed ahead

   Linkage of binary computing systems, digital and analog

I. *Acceleration in Retransmission*
   16. Apparent automatic "habits"
       Reaction of action on the very activity of the internal system, leading to a sort of conditioning of circuits

J. *External Expression*
   17. Can trigger and direct any other mechanism or even program another computer, either arithmetic (digital) or logarithmic (analog)
       Source of new information and communication
K. *Disconnection of Internal Motor*
   18. Current remains connected but tapes do not revolve
L. *Current Cut Off*
   19. Temporary arrest

H. *Connecting Systems*
 15. Extraordinary multiplicity, even redundancy of replacement circuits, linkage to *autonomic* nervous system (sympathetic), electrochemical "instinctive" automatisms
 Tournade's law, servomotor equivalent:
  the mechanism to be corrected constitutes the specific stimulant which triggers the correcting mechanism
I. *Acceleration in Retransmission*
 16. Actual unconscious habits
 Reaction of activity on the functioning of the nervous system, facilitating secondary action
 Conditioned reflexes (Pavlov)
J. *External Expression*
 17. Can trigger and direct (through intermediary muscles) another mechanism, especially the voice—through an initial programming code, the word-concept now becomes pragmatic
 Source of new information and communication, especially social
K. *Sleep*
 18. Static "activity"; dream
L. *Current of All Neural Impulse Cut Off*
 19. Death

HUMAN BRAIN

A. *Exterior phenomena:*
electromagnetic or material
B. *Information received by*
—sense organ: In this category the inner ear, retina, cutaneous receptors, and olfactory receptors
—preselective: *cf.* basilar membrane of the cochlea
cf. rods and cones of the retina
—electric or piezoelectric
C. *Transmission*
—electric or electrochemical by central core of the afferent nerve fiber
—across synapses, relays which selectively change or amplify as needed

D. *Storage*
Pseudohysteresis by electrochemical "residual magnetism"
—by polarization in cerebral cells, both cortical and subcortical
(Possibility of forgetting through depolarization with the passage of time or by electric shock treatment)
E. *Recall*
—by depolarization of nerve cells creating electric currents in the efferent nerves

—released by
(a) an analogous or identical external sensation calling forth a stimulus current or return of activity,
(b) internal emotion provoked by association (similar or opposed), thought, visual image
code word producing intentional or pseudointentional program
(c) internal language, word codes activated or as a reaction to the electric current of thought
F. *Communication of action*
—by the intermediation of efferent nerves·
—accessory circuits with effective or selective "feedback," "affirming" the choice following synaptic relays and reflex releases, and recurrent association fibers
—exterior manifestations
—by neuroelectric muscular motor plaques, provoking movement and notably speech and language according to the quality of the incoming electric nerve impulses and the choice of means of execution

G. *Examples of difficulties in functioning*
—Confusion of efferent and afferent circuits:
confabulation and delirium of hallucination: constituent memory and constituted memory confused; the past is taken for the present
—Information is received, thought is possible, action or language impossible, a variety of motor aphasia

* Translator's note: Hysteresis is used here to denote the residual magne-

the Brain and a Tape Recorder

TAPE RECORDER

A. *Exterior phenomena*
   electromagnetic or material
B. *Information received by*
   —microphone or photoelectric cell

   —preselective: analytic pickup through the electromagnetic head

C. *Transmission*
   —electric or electromagnetic by input electric circuits
   —by means of transistors or diodes which limit or amplify as the case
   may be
D. *Storage*
   Hysteresis *
   —by polarization on plastic tape or electromagnetic ferrite
   (Possibility of demagnetization with the passage of time or by depolarization by electric current)
E. *Recall*
   —by depolarization and unwinding of the tape, this time generating
   an electric current for the electromagnetic original analyzer, which
   becomes now a playback head; *i.e.,* a synthetizer
   —released by
   (a) re-establishment of an electric current, brought about by the
       unwinding of the tape
   (b) an electric current initiated by specific programming at a defi-
       nite point on the tape
   (c) the silent unwinding of the tape puts the electromagnetic head
       into a generating phase

F. *Communication of action*
   —by the electric conductors of output
   —accessory circuits with effective or selective feedback simulating the
   choice according to relays and conditional probability
   —external manifestations
   —by the vibrating membranes of electromagnetic loud speakers
   —or by television, that is to say photoelectric reconstruction producing a picture or music or speech according to the quality of the incoming electrical impulses and the choice of the equipment for retransmission (scanning)
G. *Varieties of trouble in functioning*
   —accidental confusion of the input with the output. The reproduction
   is taken for an original production: the representation for a presentation
   —the tape unwinds, the current flows, but it is not transmitted to the
   loud-speaker

tism or the electromagnetic field or the record of the electric impulse.

TABLE III: Theoretical Classification to be Used in the Temporo-Electrical Functional Study of the Processes of Information, of Communication, of Action, and of Reaction of the Human Brain

A. *Disturbance of reception* (or of input of current):
   Deficit or alteration of information

Syndromes or distortions in the receptive area: because of "redundancy," that is to say, multiplicity of systems of information, these symptoms often must be very advanced before being perceived.

(a) of exogenous origin
Difficulties in perception and in sense organs—exteroceptive.
(b) of endogenous origin:
Difficulties with interoceptive or proprioceptive information, leading to irregularities of functioning of the central sympathetic system and of the hypothalamus

B. *Disturbances in afferent communication*
   (a) Syndromes or distortions of transmission: common characteristic or rather common consequence is disorientation in time and space, leading to "alienation" in them (Time, space)
   (b) Syndromes or disturbances in the programming of information: Diseases of recording
   —insufficiency of codes for the constitution of language (syntactical aphasia)
   —difficulties in conceptualization
   —difficulties in symbolization,
   —difficulties in *constituent* "memory"

C. *Disturbances in conservation* (or *of feedback*) (*faulty hysteresis*) (or of residual magnetism),
   (a) *Insufficiency* or *absence of polarization:* distortions in learning
   (b) Difficulties in the circuits of association: distortions in recognition (impossibility of establishing relationships leading to an alteration of intelligence)
   (c) Difficulties with the obstruction of circuits: anxiety, obsession, mania
   (d) Distortions in the recording (of the feedback or of the feed ahead): Difficulty of recall, distortions in *constituted* "memory" (forgetfulness, repression, suppression)

D. *Disturbances in efferent communication* (or *of output of current*)
   (a) Insufficiency or absence of depolarization: distortions of will or motivation
   (b) Absence of efferent electric nerve impulses: illnesses in the sphere of activity
   External consequences: paralysis, catatonia

TABLE III (*cont.*)

Internal consequences: loss of critical observation, hebephrenia, loss of ego, and *of the idea of internal time*

Mixed consequences: the "aphasias"

(c) Abnormal deviations of the current: visceral conversions, gastric and sexual conversions, etc.

All of these difficulties can exist separately or in various combinations and associations, creating clinical diversity.

(*Cf.* Table IV, Chapter 12 and Table VII, Chapter 20.)

TABLE IV: Plan to be Used in the Physiopathologic,
Functional, and Temporal Study of a Patient Suffering a
Neuropsychiatric Disorder

(*Confrontation of each individual patient with the following syndromes
will enable the clinician to evaluate the interrelation between the patient's ego, duration, and reality.*)

I. *Disorientation of External Space-Time*
   The subject's disorientation may be:
   —of exogenous origin: exteroceptive (disorders of information)
   —of endogenous origin: interoceptive or proprioceptive (disorders
                               of communication and its registration)

II. *Disorientation of Interior Times = Temporal "Alienations"*
   A. Due to Deficiency
      1. Extrinsic to the personality
         —sensory agnosias: information not coded
         —motor apraxias: loss of initiative of gestures
      2. Intrinsic to the personality
         —global disorders of information, of coding, of programming
           (*i.e.*, of symbolization, of registration, of recall), therefore
           also of secondary execution, from which come:
           amnesias of memorization
           disorders of integration
           amnesias of recall
           disorders of establishment (of information)
           disorders of expression (language)
   B. Due to Excess
      1. Hallucinations of the *present* and *false recognition* (the regis-
         tered idea is mistaken for one already registered)
      2. Hallucinations of the *past* and of *false new ideas* (the old reg-
         istration is not recognized)
      3. Temporal falsification and *old errors* (absence of code or error in
         the program)
      4. Artistic equivalents: *false reminiscences*
      5. Experimental reproductions: infectious, toxic

III. *Alteration of the Code and Program*
   Language Disorders (the Aphasias)
   —primary and isolated: rare
   —secondary and associated—the rule: language disorder is only an in-
     cidental phenomenon

IV. *Association of the Circuits with the Ideas*
   —coherence = correlation: greater or lesser degree
   —incoherence = simultaneous loss of contact of ego with reality and
     duration
         therefore, loss of critical power and plan
   —consequences: in the command: lack of initiative: impaired will
                     in the execution: no action ensues

TABLE IV (*cont.*)

V. *Activities of Behavior, i.e.,* Study of Action in Time and Reality
  A. Isolated Temporal Functional Disorders
    —hypersensitivity, indifference, anxiety, negativism
    —disorders of sleep, of dreams, of sexual life
    —disorders of imagination and emotivity, of attention
    —disorders of moral consciousness—appreciation of good and evil
  B. Associated Functional Disorders, Systematized and More Lasting
    1. *depressive* reactions: melancholia, cenesthopathies, depersonalization, asthenias and obsessions, psychosomatic phenomena, and stress
    2. reactions of *excitation:* mania, hypomania, aggressions, hates
    3. *cyclic* reactions: alternations of excitement and depression
    4. *obstructive* reactions
      (a) mental confusion, delusions, hallucinations
      (b) psychosensory disorders: delusions, aggressions, persecutions, plus feared loss of object
      (c) anxieties: phenomenon of withdrawal, conversion, dissociation, phobias (*cf.* when object is the ego = the subject himself)
    5. reactions of *escape:* hysteria, pithiatism, repressions, suppressions, compulsions (escape through activity), sublimations
    6. reactions of dissociation and disintegration (internal times are isolated and disconnected)
    —hebephrenia, schizophrenia, catatonia, catalepsy, paranoid psychoses = disintegration
VI. *Study of the Primary Functional Character—Pure or Secondary*
    (a) tumors: radiographic and electroencephalographic study
    (b) acute or chronic infections; infestations
    (c) acute or chronic intoxications
    (d) cortical and subcortical epilepsies
    (e) studies of associated conditions
        neurologic (meningitic, hemiplegic)
        vascular (hypertension)
        general (cardiac, glandular)
    (f) age and heredity
    (g) remote neoplasms (*i.e.,* not originally intracranial)
    (h) pharmacologic tests
    (i) question of the opportunity of shock treatment
    (j) problem of the opportunity of neurosurgery
    (k) prognostic functional evaluation and therapeutic conclusion

TABLE V: Classification of Automatisms and of Their Progressive Improvement

Apparent Structure	Real Nature	Causal Determinism (at least apparent)	Resultant Effect (provocative interaction in view of the effects)	Feedback	Consequences	Temporal Function
Parts adjusted in view of the action	Machine tools	External in view of determined actions	Coordination of actions	0	Manufacture	External to the system
Simple organization in view of the action	*Semi-automatic machine, i.e.,* sprinkler system, sensitive to rise in temperature	External, conditioning a reaction or a system of predetermined reactions	Limited by intentional specialization	0	Autoregulation of the cause	External to the system
Complex organization established in view of a system of reactions	Simple cybernetic models (James Watt's ball regulator)	External, but stabilized by its own interior effects	Automatism	+	Autoregulation of the effects	External to the system

		Internal to the system	Equilibration, often of several effectors (appearance of finality)	++	Interior equilibrium	Covariant to the reactive system
Autoregulatory organization	(a) Ashby's homeostat (b) Cannon's homeostasis (sympathetic)	*Internal* to the system (a) established by man (b) established by nature	Equilibration, often of several effectors (appearance of finality)	++	Interior equilibrium	Covariant to the reactive system
Pseudo-organic machine	General electronic computer, digital and analog-complex cybernetic models (Uttley H. Blum)	External programming secondarily interiorized and registered	Appearance of adaptation	Feedback constructed by man +++ addition of anticipator feed aheads	Equilibrium in view of stable action; appearance of the intelligence and will	Invariable
True organism	Nervous system of man, electro-chemical computer of the human brain	Programming from exterior and interior; code self-formed and conserved in memory	Reality of adaptation acting on the internal and external causes	Feedback self-formed +++ added regulating systems (either procrastinating or anticipatory)	*Mobile* equilibrium of *life* Reality of intelligence and free conceptual choice	Covariant, *inherent* to the system, is blended with reality of the ego

TABLE VI: Scheme of the Four Functional "Dimensions" of the Mind

Circumstantial Variety	First Dimension	Second Dimension	Third Dimension	Fourth Dimension
Degree	Unconscious and instinctive	Conscious and informative	Conscious and voluntary	Consciousness itself acting
Origin	Inborn, congenital	Acquired, informative	Acquired, progressive	Acquired, pragmatic
Principal anatomic localization	Peripheral sympathetic and central—hypothalamic region and basal gray nuclei	Sense organs, inputs and afferent pathways, cortex with its reticular, thalamic, cerebellar, etc., connections	Cortex: -interhemispheric association pathways -recurrent connections with hypothalamic and glandular regions -the entire diencephalon and mesencephalon -efferent output fibers	Cortex and its vast system of connection with feedback and feed ahead

Original essential functions	Homeostasis and maintenance of the constancy of the internal milieu for vital essential functions	Perception Selection Symbolization Definition Code Image—plan Idea Registration Memory Internal language	Association of ideas, of code words, computation by matching, i.e., comparison or contrast, establishment of relationships, intelligence, judgment, choice, free will Initiative of the motor act External language	Constituted mind: Internal temporal function in full exercise and activity -knowledge of the virtual has become real -behavior: former potential has become actual -the "ego" is included in the actual -consciousness is this double recognition of the ego in the present
Action of sleep	Liberated in the dream	Inhibited in sleep	Liberal inhibition in the dream	Notion of time disappears; that of space persists
External spatio-temporal relationships	Indirect, adaptive through vasomotor, respiratory, sympathetic, systems, etc.	Adaptive adjustment	Tentative action on this external space	Internal psychological time is dissociated from it
Derived functions	Automatisms of adaptation and survival	Constitution of subjectivity	Constitution of objectivity in view of the action	Junction of subjective and objective; the potential has become actual in view of the mental creation

TABLE VII: Temporal Patterns in Behavioral Psychoses

Reaction Types	Mental Disorders	Plans	Symbols and Language	Ego	Behavior Towards the Object	4th Dimension of the Mind and Variations in Temporal Function
1. Depressive Reactions	Melancholia Cenesthopathies Depersonalizations	Conceived but limited because they appear useless and doomed to failure	Paucity of symbols. Diminution of internal language. Tendency to mutism and self-accusation	Impoverishment of ego. Loss of security and self-esteem, probably an initial phenomenon	Loss of significance of the object. Asocial or antisocial attitude; in any case negative, eventually becoming aggressive	Attempt to justify refuge in the past. Present hopeless because dissociated from continuity of duration
2. Reactions of Excitation	Mania Hypomania	Impractical due to total lack of a scale of values. Vain repetition of plans	False exaggeration of certain symbols, false depreciation of others. Repetitive verbosity	Uncoordinated stimulation centered upon itself	Object seems out of reach. Object is blamed, is made responsible and, for this reason, hated	Patient makes plans for the future rendered impossible by refusal to construct a present

3. Cyclic Reactions	Cyclothymic constitution, with alternations and "swings" between excitation and depression	Alternation between 1 and 2. Suppression of plans that never materialize	Alternation between 1 and 2 in various combinations	Progressive weakening in course of the alternations	Patient regards excitation as an inspiration of "genius," depression as a "living death." Objects lose their significance. Patient retires from all participation in society	Progressive loss of time function with each alternation
4. Obstructive Reactions	(a) Confusion	Incoherent, consequently no plans	Symbolic chaos. Verbosity alternating with mutism	Impoverishment. Stupidity. Range from torpor to dreamlike agitation	Irritation or indifference towards objects	Temporal chaos. Confusion of the potential and the actual
	(b) Anxiety	Fear of unknown prevents making of new plans and forces abandonment of plans of proven worth	Fixed upon an old symbolic framework that cannot accommodate the present situation. Patient cannot verbalize and thus reduce pressure	Loss of identity and of confidence. Narrowing and restriction of ego	Loss or threat of loss of object, aggravated by loss of significance of object and ensuing inaction	Blocking of time function which nothing can stop gives patient the impression that time has turned back in a vicious circle without escape

TABLE VII (Cont'd)

Reaction Types	Mental Disorders	Plans	Symbols and Language	Ego	Behavior Towards the Object	4th Dimension of the Mind and Variations in Temporal Function
5. Escape Reactions	Hysteria Pithiatism	Altered perceptions and absence of normal communication deprive patient of the formative elements of a plan	Symbolism impaired and chaotic, absence of a code; conversion phenomena, substituted for language, are inappropriate but are often abundant	Enfeeblement of ego. Neither means nor aims. Alterations of judgment and critical ability. Split personality	Object is without significance. Patient is incapable of action worthy of the name	Loss of contact with temporal reality, which falls apart through the impossibility of living in the present. Emotional traumata are slow in taking effect
6. Reactions of Dissociation and Disintegration	Schizophrenia Dementia praecox Hebephrenia	Plans impossible despite a sense of omnipotence and transcendence. Religious and political megalomania alternating with depression, hebetude and negativism	Internal symbolization bears no resemblance to action; it constitutes a protective shelter. Safety-valve language that no longer has meaning as a code and	Ego disconnected and enfeebled, without emotional response, therefore without identity, therefore with no capacity for criticism or self-criticism	Object without significance; complete incapacity for behavior and thus for action. Conscience disconnected from objects. Total absence of	Complete disconnection of internal and external continuous time. Patient's only present is his feeling of immortality, superiority, transcendency,

	is drained of ideas, is stereo-typed. All action is symbolic, theo-retic, and fantas-mic, but barren		initiative to act. Catalepsy with or without cata-tonia	eternity, thus displaying the destruction of the temporal function
Paranoid psychoses	Apparently logi-cal reasoning based on false assumptions, from which plans are often detailed but ridiculous and delusional	Increased sym-bolization detached from reality. "Reason-ing 'folly'"—delusion existing only in thought. Profuse language associated with debased, ridicu-lous, incoherent ideas	Ego disorganized without self-criti-cal power; val-uation of ego is often exagger-ated, always overrated. Often violent, due to frustration of aims	Chaotic behavior. Incapacity for ac-tion. No appre-ciation of or con-tact with object; everything takes place in thought; no possible con-centration on the object	Temporal dis-connection always marked; often appears as the initial phenomenon